Addison-Wesley

Biology

Tests

Addison-Wesley Publishing Company

Menlo Park, California • Reading, Massachusetts • New York
Don Mills, Ontario • Wokingham, England • Amsterdam
Bonn • Paris • Milan • Madrid • Sydney • Singapore
Tokyo • Seoul • Taipei • Mexico City • San Juan

Cover photograph: Michael Fogden/DRK PHOTO

Addison-Wesley Publishing Company grants permission to classroom teachers
to reproduce the student materials in this booklet.

Copyright © by Addison-Wesley Publishing Company, Inc.
Printed in the United States of America. Published simultaneously in Canada.

ISBN 0-201-81184-7

5 6 7 8 9 10 - ML - 98 97 96 95

Contents

To the Teacher

The *Tests* are a component of the *Addison-Wesley Biology* assessment program. This component contains both chapter tests and unit tests. For each chapter in *Addison-Wesley Biology,* there are two types of tests that you can use to assess your students. Test A has 25 multiple choice questions that test students' understanding of key terms, content, and concepts. Test B offers questions that challenge students to explain, describe, compare, interpret, and apply higher order thinking skills. The unit tests each contain 50 multiple choice questions that assess the students' understanding of content and concepts from each of the chapters in the unit.

Chapter 1 Test A

Choose the best answer for each question and write its letter in the blank.

_____ 1. The approximately 30 million types of living things on Earth are known as
    a. factors.   **c.** phyla.
    b. species.   **d.** biospheres.

_____ 2. The land, water, and air on Earth that sustain life are known as the
    a. species.   **c.** biosphere.
    b. ecosystem.   **d.** environment.

_____ 3. Organisms are disappearing today at the fastest rate in the last
    a. 200 years.   **c.** 65 million years.
    b. 100 years.   **d.** 10 years.

_____ 4. Which of the following is *not* causing the extinction of life forms?
    a. pollution   **c.** replanting
    b. hunting   **d.** clearing forests

_____ 5. A species is a group of organisms in the same area that can
    a. interbreed.   **c.** become extinct.
    b. form prey-predator relations.   **d.** coexist.

_____ 6. The once-endangered American alligator has been protected by
    a. halting alligator hunting.   **c.** feeding the alligators.
    b. killing the predators of alligators.   **d.** keeping alligators in zoos.

_____ 7. The use of organisms to produce things people need is called
    a. bioengineering.   **c.** biotechnology.
    b. animal technology.   **d.** biomanufacturing.

_____ 8. Which molecule is normally found only in living things?
    a. SO_2 **c.** CO_2
    b. CO   **d.** DNA

_____ 9. Wool, silk, and leather clothing are all made from
    a. cowhide.   **c.** animal products.
    b. forest materials.   **d.** plant products.

_____ 10. The petroleum from which polyester and nylon are made is a
    a. totally synthetic product.   **c.** product of the silk worm.
    b. fossil fuel.   **d.** renewable resource.

_____ 11. The spotted owl and the Kirtland's warbler are endangered because of
    a. acid rain.   **c.** predation.
    b. destruction of forest habitat.   **d.** hunting.

_____ 12. Which of these organisms undergoes the most dramatic changes as it grows and develops?
    a. cheetah   **c.** caterpillar
    b. human   **d.** sparrow

_____ 13. Several different types of tissues that function together for a specific purpose make up a(n)
    a. organ.   **c.** cellular tissue.
    b. cell.   **d.** adaptation.

_____ 14. A plant responds to sunlight by
    a. turning away from it.   **c.** lengthening its roots.
    b. growing toward it.   **d.** losing its leaves.

_____ 15. Ultimately, almost all living organisms get their energy from
    a. water.   **c.** the sun.
    b. wind.   **d.** eating other organisms.

_____ **16.** Reproduction results either in a duplication of the parent or in
    a. a duplication with variation   **c.** duplication of previous generations.
    b. an unrelated organism.   **d.** none of the above.

_____ **17.** Adaptations are features of organisms that allow them to
    a. survive in changing environments.   **c.** keep the same characteristics.
    b. keep from changing environments.   **d.** remain one-celled.

_____ **18.** Which of the following conditions is necessary for a species to survive?
    a. All its organisms must reproduce.
    b. Some of its organisms must reproduce.
    c. All of its organisms must live in the same place.
    d. All of its organisms must live to old age.

_____ **19.** Which of the following is most closely associated with life on a molecular level?
    a. cells   **c.** DNA
    b. inorganic compounds   **d.** tissues

_____ **20.** What benefit does a water buffalo obtain from grass?
    a. energy   **c.** migration
    b. camouflage   **d.** protection from winter

_____ **21.** A group of cells that performs a specific function in an organism is called
    a. a tissue.   **c.** an energy system.
    b. a population.   **d.** an organ system.

_____ **22.** What is the smallest unit of life capable of carrying out all life functions ?
    a. organ   **c.** molecule
    b. cell   **d.** tissue

_____ **23.** Populations of different species living in the same place make up a(n)
    a. population level.   **c.** community.
    b. ecosystem.   **d.** organ system.

_____ **24.** The community of organisms in an area plus its nonliving factors make up the
    a. ecosystem.   **c.** organ system level.
    b. tissue level.   **d.** population.

_____ **25.** What is the study of heredity in living things?
    a. genetics   **c.** taxonomy
    b. molecular biology   **d.** cytology

Name _____ Class _____ Date _____

Chapter 1 Test B

Read each question or statement and respond in the space provided

1. Suppose that lions, zebras, vultures, and grasses are some of the organisms that live in a certain environment in Africa. Describe five important interactions that take place among these organisms. (15 points)

_____

_____

_____

_____

2. The extinction of individual species poses dangers for the biosphere. What are some of the dangers? Why is this an especially big problem now? What can be done about it? (15 points)

_____

_____

_____

_____

3. Describe how biological processes and an understanding of biology are important in the production of food, clothing, shelter, and fuel, and in promoting health. (15 points)

_____

_____

_____

_____

4. Use what you know about the anatomy and behavior of a horse to show how a horse illustrates the seven characteristics common to all organisms. (15 points)

_____

_____

_____

_____

5. The eight levels of organization of living things are as follows: molecular, cellular, tissue, organ, organ system, population, community, and ecosystem. For each of the following, state the level of organization that is illustrated, and explain your answer. (16 points)

    a. an oak leaf

_____

    b. a flock of crows

_____

    c. a protein in a seed

_____

    d. a red blood cell

_____

e. goldfish, guppies, and water plants in an aquarium

_____

f. a human biceps muscle

_____

g. the animals, plants, water, and climate on the coast of Massachusetts

_____

h. the mouth, esophagus, stomach, and intestines of a cow

_____

6. The twelve major areas of study in biology are: anatomy, botany, cytology, ecology, ethology, genetics, immunology, microbiology, molecular biology, physiology, taxonomy, and zoology. The table below lists the subject of each area of study and an example of each. For each example, identify the area of biology that best applies to it. Use each area once as an answer. (24 points)

SUBJECT OF AREA OF STUDY	EXAMPLE	AREA OF BIOLOGY
a. Heredity	Characteristics of offspring from a crossing of chickens	
b. Classification of organisms	Classification of a newly discovered insect	
c. Animal behavior	Behavior of wildcats	
d. Structure and function of cells	Examination of function of human skin cells	
e. Structure and function of plants	Structure and function of mosses, grasses, and trees	
f. Functions of organs and organ systems	Functioning of the circulatory system of a dog	
g. Defenses against disease and foreign substances	Protection of the human body against influenza	
h. Relationships among organisms and their environments	Relationships among birds, lizards, and coyotes in a desert environment	
i. Chemical processes within cells	Chemical changes in blood	
j. Structure and function of animals	Structure and function in bears and raccoons	
k. Microscopic organisms	Observation of bacteria	
l. Physical structure of organisms	Structure and parts of a lobster	

Name _____ Class _____ Date _____

Chapter 2 Test A

Choose the best answer for each question and write its letter in the blank.

_____ **1.** Which of the following technologies opened a new branch of science in the 1970s?
   a. the light microscope   **c.** the centrifuge
   b. altering the genes of bacteria   **d.** chromatography

_____ **2.** An attempt to explain an event or set of observations is called a(n)
   a. hypothesis.   **c.** solution.
   b. collaboration.   **d.** technology.

_____ **3.** Because scientists work together, the field of science is considered
   a. inaccurate.   **c.** uncertain.
   b. hypothetical.   **d.** collaborative.

_____ **4.** Uncertainty is characteristic of many scientific investigations partly because science
   a. does not always permit direct observation.
   b. is a collaborative effort.
   c. is always concerned with facts only.
   d. uses technology.

_____ **5.** Scientists use their senses, as well as instruments such as microscopes to
   a. create control setups.   **c.** communicate conclusions.
   b. make observations.   **d.** interpret data.

_____ **6.** Science can only study things that can be
   a. seen with the naked eye.   **c.** observed and tested.
   b. measured by instruments.   **d.** proven without a doubt.

_____ **7.** Carefully designed experiments are useful for testing
   a. hypotheses.   **c.** conclusions.
   b. skills.   **d.** reports.

_____ **8.** Any factor that can influence the outcome of an experiment is known as a
   a. setup.   **c.** prediction.
   b. variable.   **d.** hypothesis.

_____ **9.** An "If . . . then" statement is known as a
   a. variable.   **c.** conclusion.
   b. control.   **d.** prediction.

_____ **10.** Normally, how many variables should an experiment have?
   a. two   **c.** one
   b. none   **d.** as many as necessary

_____ **11.** An experiment has two parts: an experimental setup and a
   a. control setup.   **c.** prediction.
   b. conclusion.   **d.** control variable.

_____ **12.** Which is probably _not_ a way to find out more about biology?
   a. use the college library   **c.** read a scientific journal
   b. read a novel   **d.** interview a scientist

_____ **13.** What kind of an instrument is used to produce an enlarged image of a specimen?
   a. microscope   **c.** computer
   b. probe   **d.** variable

_____ **14.** As the resolution of a microscope gets better, the image gets
   a. larger.   **c.** clearer.
   b. smaller.   **d.** brighter.

_____ **15.** Light microscopes can magnify images up to
    a. 2 million times.
    b. 1500 times.
    c. twice their actual size.
    d. 10 times their actual size.

_____ **16.** Compared to a light microscope, the resolution of an electron microscope is
    a. about 1000 times better.
    b. about 1000 times worse.
    c. the same.
    d. sometimes the same and sometimes better.

_____ **17.** Chromatography is based on the different degrees to which parts of a mixture
    a. dissolve in other substances.
    b. can be used to produce tissues.
    c. can be recombined.
    d. can exist as organisms.

_____ **18.** The resolving power of the unaided human eye is about
    a. 1 mm.
    b. 0.1 mm.
    c. 1.5 mm.
    d. 10 mm.

_____ **19.** What are studies that take place in an organism's natural environment?
    a. field studies
    b. laboratory studies
    c. separation techniques
    d. cell fractionation

_____ **20.** Separating molecules according to shape, size, and charge is known as
    a. electrophoresis.
    b. molecular sorting.
    c. cell fractionation.
    d. isolation.

_____ **21.** To obtain a pure sample of an organelle, a biologist uses
    a. tissue culture.
    b. field study.
    c. cell fractionation.
    d. chromatography.

_____ **22.** What is one technique for separating the components of a gas?
    a. chromatography
    b. collaboration
    c. cell fractionation
    d. tissue culture

_____ **23.** A machine that separates mixtures by spinning them is known as a(n)
    a. cell fractioner.
    b. centrifuge.
    c. electron microscope.
    d. organelle.

_____ **24.** How are large amounts of a single kind of cell grown in the laboratory?
    a. by loading them onto a gel
    b. by making a tissue culture
    c. by using a centrifuge
    d. by using chromatography

_____ **25.** Which can eliminate the need for live animals in some experiments?
    a. tissue cultures
    b. dissection
    c. cell fractionation
    d. laboratory study

Chapter 2 Test B

Read each question or statement and respond in the space provided.

1. Explain what is wrong with each of the following statements about science: (20 points)

   a. Science is simply a body of knowledge.

   _____

   _____

   b. Science deals with absolute facts, not uncertainties.

   _____

   _____

   c. Scientific hypotheses are simply guesses. There is no way of ever knowing whether one is better than another.

   _____

   _____

   d. Important work in science can be done only by individuals working alone.

   _____

   _____

   e. Science is the business of scientists only.

   _____

   _____

2. Identify each of the following as an observation, hypothesis, experiment, or prediction, and explain your answer. (20 points)

   a. Changes in leaf color are caused by reducing the amount of daylight.

   _____

   _____

   b. If leaf color depends only on light, the leaves will have most color the week of October 10 because of the amount of daylight then.

   _____

   _____

   c. Half of the 10 trees in the sample are at maximum color this week.

   _____

   _____

d. Artificially reduce the amount of light received by trees to see whether the change produces a leaf color change.

_____

_____

3. A person is growing potted geraniums and wishes to find out whether giving the plants food and extra light will cause them to grow faster. (15 points)

a. Why is it not a good idea, scientifically speaking, to add food and increase light at the same time for all the plants? Why is it not necessarily a good idea in terms of raising plants?

_____

_____

_____

b. Describe two experiments that might be done to find out the effect of each added factor on growth. For each experiment, state which factors are being kept the same for both setups, what the control setup is, and what the variable setup is.

_____

_____

_____

_____

c. Why is it important to use controls in an experiment?

_____

_____

_____

4. A scientist wishes to observe fine details in a bacterium. She attempts to use a light microscope that magnifies about 1500 times, but that magnification turns out to be too low. She decides to use a special lens she has designed that can theoretically magnify 2000 times. That amount of magnification should be enough to make the structures visible. What problem is she likely to have? What should she do instead? (15 points)

_____

_____

_____

5. The behavior of a certain type of monkey is interesting to a zoologist. The zoologist considers doing both field studies and laboratory studies of the animal. Compare and contrast the two types of studies, in terms of advantages and disadvantages. (15 points)

_____

_____

_____

6. A scientist wants to separate some very large protein molecules from smaller ones. Explain how each of the following techniques might help in the process: electrophoresis, centrifuging, chromatography. (15 points)

_____

_____

_____

_____

Chapter 3 Test A

Choose the best answer for each question and write its letter in the blank.

_____ 1. Matter is defined as anything that occupies space and
    a. has mass.   **c.** is not living.
    b. is alive.   **d.** can be seen.

_____ 2. Which of the following is *not* matter?
    a. a leaf   **c.** heat
    b. a slice of pie   **d.** a stone

_____ 3. Physical properties are characteristics that
    a. allow matter to change into new substances.
    b. can be observed without changing chemical composition.
    c. allow something to burn.
    d. allow something to rust.

_____ 4. The amount of space occupied by matter is known as
    a. mass.   **c.** volume.
    b. density.   **d.** composition.

_____ 5. The words *solid, liquid,* and *gas* all refer to
    a. physical states.   **c.** mass.
    b. chemical properties.   **d.** density.

_____ 6. The ratio of matter's mass to its volume is called
    a. physical state.   **c.** mass.
    b. density.   **d.** prime volume.

_____ 7. Rusting, burning, and decomposing are all examples of matter's
    a. physical properties.   **c.** mass.
    b. volume.   **d.** chemical properties.

_____ 8. If an object sinks when placed in water, it's density is
    a. greater than 1.0.   **c.** either greater or lesser than 1.0.
    b. less than 1.0.   **d.** less than 3.0.

_____ 9. The smallest particle of an element that has the element's properties is a(n)
    a. compound.   **c.** molecule.
    b. atom.   **d.** nucleus.

_____ 10. Two elements linked chemically in definite proportions are called
    a. nucleized bonds.   **c.** a compound.
    b. molecules.   **d.** masses.

_____ 11. What are three particles that make up an atom?
    a. protons, neutrons, and isotopes   **c.** neutrons, isotopes, and electrons
    b. protons, neutrons, and electrons   **d.** positives, negatives, and electrons

_____ 12. The first energy level in an atom can hold
    a. a maximum of 2 electrons.   **c.** a maximum of 8 electrons.
    b. a minimum of 8 electrons.   **d.** one electron.

_____ 13. The atomic number is determined by the
    a. atomic mass of an element.   **c.** number of isotopes.
    b. density of an element.   **d.** number of protons in an element.

_____ 14. The number of protons and neutrons in an element determines its
    a. atomic mass.   **c.** energy levels.
    b. atomic number.   **d.** compounds.

_____ **15.** An atom that has an unstable nucleus is
    a. not radioactive.
    b. radioactive.
    c. not an element.
    d. likely to become stable in hydrogen solution.

_____ **16.** Isotopes are atoms of the same element with the same number of protons and
    a. different numbers of electrons.
    b. different numbers of neutrons.
    c. different numbers of molecules.
    d. the same numbers of neutrons.

_____ **17.** In a periodic table, elements are arranged
    a. according to their atomic numbers.
    b. alphabetically.
    c. according to when they were discovered.
    d. differently depending on the table.

_____ **18.** What are the horizontal rows in a periodic table?
    a. lines
    b. densities
    c. periods
    d. masses

_____ **19.** An ionic bond forms whenever ions with opposite charges
    a. repel each other.
    b. attract each other.
    c. form atoms.
    d. form elements.

_____ **20.** What happens when sodium chloride (NaCl) is put in water?
    a. an explosion
    b. an ionic bond
    c. the breaking of an ionic bond
    d. a nerve impulse

_____ **21.** Complete the following equation by balancing it
$HCl + NaOH \rightarrow NaCl + $ _____ .
    a. H_2O
    b. OH
    c. Na_2O
    d. ClO_2

_____ **22.** During a chemical reaction, substances become new substances by the
    a. appearance of new isotopes.
    b. breaking and forming of chemical bonds.
    c. elimination of isotopes.
    d. breaking apart of atoms.

_____ **23.** What is a solution?
    a. an uneven mixture of two substances
    b. a chemical reaction
    c. the breaking of a chemical bond
    d. a uniform mixture of two substances

_____ **24.** Which is the dissolving substance in a solution?
    a. the solvent
    b. the mixture
    c. the solute
    d. the isotope

_____ **25.** A measurement of the concentration of hydrogen ions in a solution is
    a. the pH scale.
    b. the base.
    c. the universal solvent.
    d. the polar molecule.

Name _____ Class _____ Date _____

Chapter 3 Test B

Read each question or statement and respond in the space provided.

1. Which properties of a transparent piece of glass tell you it is matter? Explain what each property is. Which properties tell you it is glass? (15 points)

_____

_____

_____

_____

2. In the drawings of the three bottles below, the white squares stand for one kind of atom, and the gray squares stand for another kind of atom. State whether each bottle contains an element, a compound, or a mixture, and explain your answers. (15 points)

   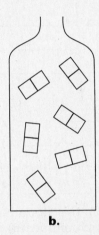   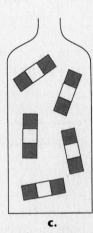

       a.   **b.**   **c.**

a. _____

_____

b. _____

_____

c. _____

_____

3. Study the drawing of the atom, and answer the questions that follow. (16 points)

    a. What is the number of protons? _____

    b. What is the number of electrons? _____

    c. What is the number of neutrons? _____

    d. What is the total number of negative

       charges in the atom?_____

    e. What is the total number of positive

       charges in the atom?_____

    f. What is the net charge of the atom?_____

    g. What is the atomic number?_____

    h. What is the atomic mass number? _____

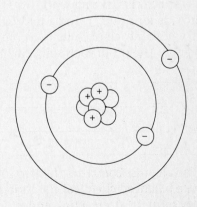

Chapter 3: Introduction to Chemistry **11**

4. Study the section of the periodic table, and answer the questions that follow. (18 points).

1							18
1 H 1.01	2	13	14	15	16	17	2 He 4.00
3 Li 6.9	4 Be 9.0	5 B 10.8	6 C 12.0	7 N 14.0	8 O 16.0	9 F 19.0	10 Ne 20.2
11 Na 23.0	12 Mg 24.3	13 Al 27.0	14 Si 28.1	15 P 31.0	16 S 32.1	17 Cl 35.5	18 Ar 39.9

a. Explain what the whole numbers in each box indicate.

_____

b. Give the symbol for an element with properties that are similar to those of element 2. Explain how you arrived at your answer.

_____

_____

c. How many periods are shown? _____

d. How many groups are shown?

_____

e. Which group contains noble gases? _____

f. What does the number 23.0 in the box for element Na indicate? _____

_____

5. a. Potassium bromide (KBr) is formed from two atoms: potassium (K), which originally has one electron in the outermost energy level, and bromine (Br), which originally has seven outermost electrons. What sort of bonding exists in KBr? Explain what happens during the formation of this compound. (9 points)

_____

_____

b. Hydrogen sulfide (H_2S) is formed from three atoms: S, which originally has six outermost electrons, and two H atoms, each of which originally has one outermost electron. What sort of bonding exists in H_2S? Explain what happens during the formation of this compound. (9 points)

_____

_____

6. a. A chemist is working with two solutions: a potassium hydroxide (KOH) solution, which produces hydroxide ions (OH^-), and a hydrogen bromide (HBr) solution, which produces hydrogen ions (H^+). State whether each of these two compounds is an acid, a base, or a salt. What would you expect to find about the pH of each solution? Explain your answers. (9 points)

_____

_____

_____

b. The chemist combines the two solutions, which produces a reaction that gives off heat energy. Write a balanced chemical equation for the change, including the formulas of the products and the energy term. Is this reaction endothermic or exothermic? (9 points)

_____

Chapter 4 Test A

Choose the best answer for each question and write its letter in the blank.

_____ 1. Why are most compounds that contain carbon called *organic compounds*?
  a. because they all have 7 electrons
  b. because they came from living organisms
  c. because they all can be eaten
  d. because they all came from plants

_____ 2. Which of these is an inorganic compound?
  a. sugar   c. fat
  b. protein   d. water

_____ 3. How many electrons does the element carbon have?
  a. 6   c. 8
  b. 2   d. 0

_____ 4. Groups of atoms that carry out chemical reactions are known as
  a. polymers.   c. organic compounds.
  b. functional groups.   d. monomers.

_____ 5. Molecules formed by linking two or more monomers are
  a. polymers.   c. inorganic compounds.
  b. functional groups.   d. reactives.

_____ 6. A monomer is a small, building block
  a. atom.   c. molecule.
  b. ion.   d. nucleus.

_____ 7. The removal of water when a compound is formed is called
  a. dehydration.   c. polymerization.
  b. hydrolysis.   d. amine formation.

_____ 8. What three elements make up all carbohydrates?
  a. nitrogen, hydrogen, and carbon   c. carbon, oxygen, and sulfur
  b. carbon, hydrogen, and oxygen   d. carbon, hydrogen, and sugar

_____ 9. Which of these is a fatty acid that has a bend in its carbon chain?
  a. citric acid   c. stearic acid
  b. oleic acid   d. palmitic acid

_____ 10. Table sugar is also known as sucrose. Surcose is a common
  a. disaccharide.   c. cellulose.
  b. monosaccharide.   d. carbonate.

_____ 11. Polysaccharides are giant polymers consisting of thousands of linked
  a. monosaccharides.   c. ethers.
  b. fat molecules.   d. proteins.

_____ 12. Which of the following use polysaccharide for support?
  a. humans   c. amebas
  b. plants   d. animals

_____ 13. The hard outer skeletons of certain animals, such as insects, are made of
  a. lipids.   c. chitin.
  b. cellulose.   d. phospholipids.

_____ 14. Fats, oils, waxes, and steroids are all
  a. lipids   c. human energy sources
  b. carbohydrates   d. foods

_____ **15.** A peptide is a compound consisting of two or more
    a. amino acids.   **c.** sugars.
    b. lipids.   **d.** steriods.

_____ **16.** When people wax their cars, they are using a compound of
    a. phosphate and lipids.   **c.** fatty acids and alcohols.
    b. steroids and hormones.   **d.** fatty acids and phospholipid.

_____ **17.** A polymer that consists of glycerol and three fatty acids is a
    a. fat.   **c.** carbohydrate.
    b. steroid.   **d.** hormone.

_____ **18.** A fatty acid is a compound made of a chain of carbon atoms plus
    a. an acid group at one end.   **c.** an amino group.
    b. acid groups at both ends.   **d.** amino groups at both ends.

_____ **19.** Saturated fats, such as butter and lard, are made of
    a. fatty acids containing several double bonds
    b. fatty acids containing no double bonds.
    c. lipids containing phosphorus.
    d. lipids containing certain alcohols.

_____ **20.** Compounds containing an amino group, a carboxyl group, and a side group are
    a. fatty acids.   **c.** peptide bonds.
    b. amino acids.   **d.** alanines.

_____ **21.** What is a peptide bond?
    a. an amino acid glycine group
    b. an amino acid hydrogen group
    c. a covalent bond between a polymer and lipid
    d. a covalent bond between an amino group and a carboxyl group

_____ **22.** Which is *not* a function of proteins in living things?
    a. duplicating themselves   **c.** making antibodies
    b. enabling movement   **d.** biochemical control

_____ **23.** Special proteins that speed up the chemical reactions in a cell are called
    a. acids.   **c.** sites.
    b. enzymes.   **d.** casein.

_____ **24.** Nucleic acids are composed of carbon, hydrogen, oxygen, nitrogen, and
    a. phosphorus.   **c.** sodium.
    b. iron.   **d.** salt.

_____ **25.** Which nucleic acid contains the sugar deoxyribose?
    a. DNA   **c.** mRNA
    b. tRNA   **d.** rRNA

Chapter 4 Test B

Read each question or statement and respond in the space provided.

1. a. Explain the difference between organic and inorganic compounds. (10 points)

_____

_____

_____

_____

b. Identify each of the following compounds as organic or inorganic: (8 points)

glucose _____

potassium chloride _____

carbon dioxide _____

chitin _____

2. A chemist working with small organic molecules causes a very large number of them to link together to form a very large molecule. This process is called dehydration synthesis.

a. What sort of general compound is formed by such a reaction? What are the individual parts that link together called? What is the other product of the reaction? (20 points)

_____

_____

b. What sort of compound would be formed if the monomers were amino acids? What sort of bond would be formed between the amino acids?

_____

3. Imagine that you are studying a newly discovered kind of plant. The plant bears sweet fruit and has a stiff stem and a tuberous underground structure like a potato's. What carbohydrate—cellulose, starch, or glucose—will probably be found in the largest quantities in each of these parts of the plant? Identify the carbohydrate as a monosaccharide, disaccharide, or polysaccharide, and tell what the carbohydrate does for the plant. (20 points)

a. fruit _____

b. stem _____

c. tuber _____

4. The types of lipids include fats, phospholipids, steroids, and waxes. Identify the type of lipid found in each of the following and state its functions. (18 points)

a. the coating of a feather _____

b. whale blubber _____

c. hormone produced by a deer ovary _____

d. cell membrane of a paramecium _____

e. oil produced by a walnut _____

f. cholesterol produced by a dog's liver _____

a.

```
    H              H              H
    |              |              |
H – C – H      H – C – H      H – C – H
    |              |              |
H – C – H      H – C – H      H – C – H
    |              |              |
H – C – H      H – C – H      H – C – H
    |              |              |
H – C – H      H – C – H      H – C – H
    |              |              |
H – C – H      H – C – H      H – C – H
    |              |              |
H – C – H      H – C – H      H – C – H
    |              |              |
H – C – H      H – C – H      H – C – H
    |              |              |
O = C – H      O = C – H      O = C – H
    |              |              |
    O              O              O
    |              |              |
H – C ————————— C ————————— C – H
    |              |              |
    H              H              H
```

b.

```
                CH₂OH
                 |
    H            C – O            H
     \          / OH  H \        /
      C ————— /          \ ————— C
   HO          C ——— C           OH
              / |     | \
             H  OH
                H   OH
```

CH$_2$OH

c.

```
                                    |
Phosphate                       Phosphate
    |                               |
Sugar — Nitrogen _ _ _ Nitrogen — Sugar
         base           base
    |                               |
Phosphate                       Phosphate
    |                               |
Sugar — Nitrogen _ _ _ Nitrogen — Sugar
         base           base
    |                               |
```

d.

```
        |
        C = O
        |
    H – N
        |
        H
        |
H – C – C – H
        |
        H
        |
        C = O
        |
    H – N
        |
        H
        |
H – C – C – H
        |
        H
```

5. Identify each of the four compounds (or segments of compounds) shown as a carbohydrate, a lipid, a protein, or a nucleic acid. Explain your answers. (24 points)

a. _____

_____

b. _____

_____

c. _____

_____

d. _____

_____

Chapter 5 Test A

Choose the best answer for each question and write its letter in the blank.

_____ **1.** Rudolf Virchow's hypotheses contradicted the idea of
    a. cells arising from preexisting cells.   **c.** the cell as the building block of life.
    b. life arising from nonliving matter.   **d.** organisms being made up of many cells.

_____ **2.** The first person to describe microscopic organisms and living cells was
    a. Theodor Schwann.   **c.** Matthias Schleiden.
    b. Rudolf Virchow.   **d.** Anton von Leeuwenhoek.

_____ **3.** Which is *not* a principle of cell theory?
    a. All matter consists of at least one cell. **c.** All cells arise from preexisting cells.
    b. Cells are the basic units of life.   **d.** All organisms are made of one or more cells.

_____ **4.** A cell membrane is a thin layer of lipid and
    a. monosaccharides.   **c.** chitin.
    b. protein.   **d.** water.

_____ **5.** Cell membranes are made of two phospholipid layers called a
    a. bilayer.   **c.** polarity.
    b. hydrophilic.   **c.** semilayer.

_____ **6.** Some ribosomes are free in the ectoplasm, while others line the membranes of the
    a. cell wall.   **c.** rough endoplasmic reticulum.
    b. mitochondria.   **d.** smooth endoplasmic reticulum.

_____ **7.** The fluid mosaic model presents the modern view of
    a. a membrane's structure.   **c.** aggregates of cells.
    b. chromosomes.   **d.** the nucleus.

_____ **8.** The "blueprints" in a cell that control all its activity are the
    a. eukaryotes.   **c.** chromosomes.
    b. vacuoles.   **d.** ribosomes.

_____ **9.** Prokaryotes are organisms whose cells contain no
    a. nucleus.   **c.** eukaryotes.
    b. cell membrane.   **d.** bilayers.

_____ **10.** What is the liquid between the cell membrane and the nucleus called?
    a. organelles   **c.** nucleoli
    b. cytoplasm   **d.** vacuoles

_____ **11.** What are organisms with cells that contain a nucleus or nuclei?
    a. eukaryotes   **c.** ribosomes
    b. prokaryotes   **d.** nucleoli

_____ **12.** Which is *not* an organelle?
    a. nucleus   **c.** prokaryote
    b. ribosome   **d.** mitochondria

_____ **13.** Where are poisons and wastes detoxified in a cell?
    a. ribosomes   **c.** lysosomes
    b. endoplasmic reticulum   **d.** Golgi apparatus

_____ **14.** A cell produces protein by using organelles called
    a. ribosomes.   **c.** flagella.
    b. mitochondria.   **d.** Golgi apparatus.

_____ **15.** The mitochondria of a cell contain an inner membrane that makes
    a. protein.   **c.** nuclei.
    b. ATP.   **d.** chloroplasts.

_____ **16.** What are membrane-bound sacs that package and secrete cell products?
    a. Golgi apparatus   **c.** mitochondria
    b. ATP   **d.** lysosomes

_____ **17.** Unlike animal cells, plant cells have
    a. cell membranes.   **c.** cell walls.
    b. mitochondria.   **d.** chromosomes.

_____ **18.** A chloroplast can convert light, carbon dioxide, and water into
    a. vacuoles.   **c.** protein.
    b. sugar.   **d.** cytoskeletons.

_____ **19.** What are flagella?
    a. long, whiplike projections   **c.** bundles of chloroplasts
    b. short, hairlike projections   **d.** central vacuoles

_____ **20.** In animal cells, the cytoskeleton maintains three-dimensional structure and
    a. stores the pigments.   **c.** contains the poisons.
    b. helps the cell move.   **d.** destroys the microfilaments.

_____ **21.** Diffusion is a term for the movement of molecules from
    a. an area of low concentration to an area of high concentration.
    b. an adjacent area to a gradient area.
    c. an area of high concentration to an area of low concentration.
    d. a nucleus to the mitochondria.

_____ **22.** Which molecules would diffuse faster?
    a. small molecules, low temperature   **c.** large molecules, high temperature
    b. small molecules, high temperature   **d.** large molecules, low temperature

_____ **23.** In a hypotonic solution, the concentration of solutes is lower than the
    a. concentration of solutes inside the cell.
    b. concentration of solutes outside the cell.
    c. concentration of osmosis in the membrane.
    d. concentration of diffusion in the membrane.

_____ **24.** Concentration of solutes inside and outside the cell are equal when
    a. the solution is isotonic.   **c.** the solution is hypertonic.
    b. the solution is hypotonic.   **d.** the solution is isometric.

_____ **25.** Molecules that are too large to cross a cell membrane are carried by
    a. hypotonic solution.   **c.** isotonic solution.
    b. bulk transport.   **d.** hypertonic solution.

Name _____ Class _____ Date _____

Chapter 5 Test B

Read each question or statement and respond in the space provided.

1. Using the modern cell theory, explain why each of the following claims must be false. (15 points)

   a. A cell has been developed from simple materials such as sugar water.

   _____

   b. A plant was grown from an animal cell.

   _____

   c. An organism that does not contain cells was discovered.

   _____

2. State the main functions of each of the following parts of cells. (16 points)

   a. nucleus _____

   b. nucleolus _____

   _____

   c. cytosol _____

   _____

   d. cell membrane _____

   _____

3. Identify each of the organelles and other parts of the cell shown in the drawing. Use the following terms: nucleus, mitochondrion, lysosome, ribosome, cell membrane, smooth endoplasmic reticulum, rough endoplasmic reticulum, nucleolus, Golgi apparatus, cytosol. (20 points)

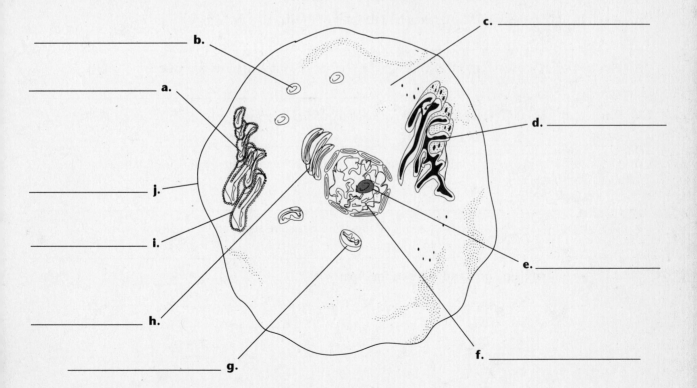

4. A biologist looking through a microscope observes cells that have the following sets of characteristics. On the basis of these characteristics, identify each cell as either a prokaryotic cell, an animal cell, or a plant cell. (15 points)

a. no cell wall, an endoplasmic reticulum, no chloroplasts

_____

b. one circular strand of DNA, flagella, no other cytoskeleton, no Golgi apparatus

_____

c. cell membrane, nucleus, many chromosomes, large ribosomes, mitochondria, no vacuoles

_____

d. Golgi apparatus, cell wall, chloroplasts, many chromosomes

_____

e. small ribosomes, no cell wall, no lysosomes

_____

5. Three potato slices are placed in hypertonic, hypotonic, and isotonic solutions. Compare the behavior of the cells in the three slices. Explain your answer on the basis of concentration gradients and diffusion. (16 points)

_____

_____

_____

_____

_____

6. For each of the following, identify the transport type as either osmosis, facilitated diffusion, active transport, pinocytosis, phagocytosis, or exocytosis. (18 points)

a. A cell membrane encloses and takes in a droplet of fluid.

_____

b. Carrier proteins use energy and act as a pump to move nutrients into a root cell.

_____

c. Carrier proteins take sugar into a cell without requiring energy input.

_____

d. Water diffuses across a membrane from a region of high water concentration to a region of low water concentration.

_____

e. Mucus and waste products packaged by Golgi apparatus are secreted by a cell.

_____

f. A cell membrane encloses and takes in food particles.

_____

Chapter 6 Test A

Choose the best answer for each question and write its letter in the blank.

_____ 1. What is the term for the ability to perform work?
   a. heterotrophy
   b. expenditure
   c. energy
   d. autotrophy

_____ 2. Animals that cannot make their own food are
   a. heterotrophs.
   b. autotrophs.
   c. photosynthesizers.
   d. grana.

_____ 3. Which are *not* autotrophs?
   a. animals
   b. plants
   c. algae
   d. some prokaryotes

_____ 4. Most organisms use an energy storage molecule called
   a. adenosine triphosphate.
   b. the vacuole.
   c. pigment.
   d. chlorophyll.

_____ 5. ATP molecules are composed of what three major parts?
   a. phosphate groups, adenine, and thykaloids
   b. stroma, grana, and pigment
   c. adenine, thykaloids, and stroma
   d. adenine, ribose, and phosphate groups

_____ 6. Energy from ATP is released when an enzyme called ATPase
   a. breaks the end phosphate off an ATP molecule.
   b. builds an ATP molecule.
   c. breaks the rechargeable prokaryotes apart.
   d. builds a new prokaryote.

_____ 7. During photosynthesis, a reduction reaction
   a. adds electrons to a molecule.
   b. subtracts electrons from a molecule.
   c. oxidizes a molecule.
   d. destroys a molecule.

_____ 8. Oxidation is a process that makes a molecule
   a. gain an electron.
   b. begin a reduction reaction.
   c. lose an electron.
   d. gain a nucleus.

_____ 9. Disk-shaped structures with photosynthetic pigments are known as
   a. Krebs cycles.
   b. thylakoids.
   c. carbohydrates.
   d. synthesizers.

_____ 10. The process by which autotrophs convert sunlight into energy is called
   a. photosynthesis.
   b. oxidation.
   c. pigmentation.
   d. photosystemizing.

_____ 11. A molecule that can absorb certain light wavelengths and reflect others is a
   a. photosystem.
   b. matrix.
   c. refraction structure.
   d. pigment.

_____ 12. What are the most common group of photosynthetic pigments in plants?
   a. chloroplasts
   b. stroma
   c. chlorophylls
   d. thykaloids

_____ 13. Stroma are a gel-like matrix that surround the
   a. thykaloids.
   b. chlorophylls.
   c. pathways.
   d. mitochondria.

_____ 14. The chemical equation $Mg + S \rightarrow Mg^{2+} + S^{2-}$ is an example of
   a. photosynthesis.
   b. a redox reaction.
   c. the Krebs cycle.
   d. deoxidation.

_____ **15.** Photosynthesis consists of two types of reactions: light-dependent and
  a. photosynthetic.
  b. photosystemic.
  c. carbon-fixing.
  d. environmental.

_____ **16.** Plants that use only the Calvin cycle for photosynthesis are called
  a. C_3 plants.
  b. algae.
  c. vacuole plants.
  d. pigmented plants.

_____ **17.** CAM plants can survive in dry, hot deserts because they can
  a. produce all their own oxygen.
  b. fix carbon dioxide at night.
  c. do photosynthesis without carbon dioxide.
  d. dry out at night.

_____ **18.** What is the process by which glucose is converted to pyruvate?
  a. electron transport
  b. aerobic respiration
  c. glycolysis
  d. photosynthesis

_____ **19.** In the first step of aerobic respiration, pyruvate binds to a molecule called
  a. acetyl-CoA.
  b. NADH.
  c. ATP.
  d. coenzyme A (CoA).

_____ **20.** The breakdown of pyruvate in the presence of oxygen is called
  a. glycolysis.
  b. NADH.
  c. aerobic respiration.
  d. energizing.

_____ **21.** With every completion of the Krebs cycle, how many electrons are freed?
  a. eight
  b. none
  c. four
  d. five

_____ **22.** What is the Krebs cycle?
  a. the second phase of anaerobic respiration
  b. the first phase of aerobic respiration
  c. the second phase of aerobic respiration
  d. the third phase of anaerobic respiration

_____ **23.** Which is *not* a step of the aerobic respiration of pyruvate after glycolysis?
  a. Electrons are reduced to form sulfur
  b. acetyl-CoA is converted into a series of intermediate molecules
  c. pyruvate is converted to acetyl-CoA
  d. some energy is lost as heat

_____ **24.** The conversion of pyruvate to carbon dioxide and ethanol is called
  a. lactic acid fermentation.
  b. alcoholic fermentation.
  c. gasohol conversion.
  d. glycolysis.

_____ **25.** The release of energy from food molecules in the absence of oxygen is
  a. lactic acid fermentation.
  b. alcoholic fermentation.
  c. aerobic respiration.
  d. anaerobic respiration.

Chapter 6 Test B

Read each question or statement and respond the space provided.

1. A caterpillar feeds on leaves from a bush that grows in a sunny place. The caterpillar is then eaten by a bird. Explain how each organism gets its energy, and classify each as an autotroph or heterotroph. (15 points)

_____

_____

_____

2. Explain what ATP is. Describe its importance for living things. (10 points)

_____

_____

_____

3. a. Compare oxidation and reduction. (10 points)

_____

_____

_____

b. In the reaction shown below, which molecule is being reduced and which is being oxidized? Explain your answer.

$$Cl_2 + H_2 \rightarrow 2H^+ + 2Cl^-$$

_____

_____

_____

_____

4. a. What role does photosynthesis play in the life of autotrophs? (15 points)

_____

_____

b. What substances are formed during photosynthesis? From what two substances are they formed?

_____

_____

c. Explain what the following parts of an autotrophic cell are, and what they do: chloroplast, thylakoid, stroma, grana, photosystem.

_____

_____

_____

_____

_____

5. Suppose that you wanted to do an experiment to find out how well plants would grow in green light rather than white light. Answer the following questions about the experiment you would design. (15 points)

    a. What materials or equipment would you use? _____

_____

    b. What sort of control setup and variable setup would you use? _____

_____

    c. What procedure would you carry out? _____

_____

    d. What sort of data would you collect? How would you organize the data in a table? _____

_____

    e. What is your prediction about what would happen? Explain the reason for your prediction.

_____

6. a. Briefly explain what cellular respiration is. (4 points)

_____

    b. What occurs during the glycolysis phase of respiration? (4 points)

_____

_____

    c. What occurs during the breakdown of pyruvate in aerobic respiration? (4 points)

_____

_____

    d. What occurs during the Krebs cycle of respiration? (4 points)

_____

_____

_____

    e. What occurs during the electron-transport phase of respiration? (4 points)

_____

_____

_____

7. a. How does anaerobic respiration differ from aerobic respiration? (5 points)

_____

_____

    b. What is alcoholic fermentation? What sorts of organisms can do it? (5 points)

_____

_____

    c. What is lactic acid fermentation? What sorts of organisms can do it? (5 points)

_____

_____

Name _____   Class _____   Date _____

Chapter 7 Test A

Choose the best answer for each question and write its letter in the blank.

_____   **1.** The phases in the life of a cell are called
    a. interphase.   **c.** the cell cycle.
    b. replication.   **d.** meiosis.

_____   **2.** The period of cell growth prior to division is
    a. replication.   **c.** reproduction.
    b. anaphase.   **d.** interphase.

_____   **3.** During the S phase of interphase, the chromosomes of the cell
    a. replicate.   **c.** condense.
    b. are destroyed.   **d.** triple.

_____   **4.** DNA replication in a cell results in
    a. brother chromatids.   **c.** sister chromatids.
    b. triple chromatids.   **d.** elimination of chromatids.

_____   **5.** Step 1 of cell division is called mitosis, and step 2 is called
    a. cytokinesis.   **c.** mitokinesis.
    b. replication.   **d.** centromere.

_____   **6.** Which is *not* a phase of mitosis?
    a. prophase.   **c.** metaphase.
    b. biphase.   **d.** telophase.

_____   **7.** In anaphase, the sister chromatids
    a. separate from each other.   **c.** condense and become thicker.
    b. join together.   **d.** become attached to spindle fibers.

_____   **8.** The cell is pinched in two and cytokinesis begins during
    a. prophase.   **c.** colored body continuation.
    b. telophase.   **d.** interphase.

_____   **9.** The assembling of microtubules that make up the spindle fibers occurs
    a. during telophase.   **c.** after mitosis.
    b. during prophase.   **d.** before mitosis.

_____   **10.** The term *cleavage furrow* refers to
    a. mitosis in plant cells.   **c.** cytokinesis in plant cells.
    b. mitosis in animal cells.   **d.** cytokinesis in animal cells.

_____   **11.** What is the term for the changes that take place in cells as they develop?
    a. differentiation   **c.** cytokinesis
    b. growth factors   **d.** cleavage

_____   **12.** Asexual reproduction is
    a. reproduction by two parents asexually.
    b. reproduction by one parent by cell division.
    c. reproduction by one parent by fertilization.
    d. reproduction by two parents by regeneration.

_____   **13.** During budding, a parent organism produces offspring by
    a. growing a tiny replica of itself.   **c.** spreading malignant cells.
    b. being torn into many pieces.   **d.** fragmenting.

_____   **14.** A lizard's ability to grow back its tail is an example of
    a. asexual reproduction.   **c.** tumor production.
    b. regeneration.   **d.** sexual reproduction.

_____ **15.** Cancer is an example of
     a. cells acquiring abnormal size, shape, and abilities.
     b. disorganized cell growth.
     c. vegetative reproduction.
     d. continual fragmentation.

_____ **16.** What are sexual reproductive cells called?
     a. homologous pairs   **c.** gametes
     b. buds   **d.** chromosomes

_____ **17.** Matching pairs of chromosomes in a diploid cell are
     a. homologous pairs.   **c.** diploids.
     b. gametes.   **d.** zygotes.

_____ **18.** In which of the following ways is meiosis similar to mitosis?
     a. One parent cell makes four daughter cells.
     b. It occurs in eukaryotic cells.
     c. Daughter cells are not alike.
     d. One parent cell makes two daughter cells.

_____ **19.** The single cell that results from sexual reproduction is the
     a. zygote.   **c.** bud.
     b. gamete.   **d.** daughter cell.

_____ **20.** Which happens during meiosis II?
     a. Telophase I stops.
     b. Chromosomes become thick and visible.
     c. Daughter cells divide for the second time.
     d. Anaphase I continues.

_____ **21.** The exchange of genes between pairs of homologous chromosomes is
     a. crossing over.   **c.** homologous pairing.
     b. meiosis I.   **d.** crossing back.

_____ **22.** Each protien in an organism is coded for by an individual
     a. gene.   **c.** gamete.
     b. chromosome.   **d.** chromatid.

_____ **23.** During meiosis I, homologous pairs
     a. join together.   **c.** cross over.
     b. separate.   **d.** undergo mitosis.

_____ **24.** Differences among members of a population are collectively called
     a. variation.   **c.** reproduction.
     b. evolution.   **d.** asexual meiosis.

_____ **25.** The reshuffling of genes in sexual reproduction increases
     a. survival chances for some.   **c.** the division of chromosomes.
     b. uniformity.   **d.** deaths in a population.

Name _____ Class _____ Date _____

Chapter 7 Test B

Read each question or statement and respond in the space provided.

1. Briefly describe what occurs during the following stages of the cell cycle. (20 points)

   a. G_1 phase of interphase _____

   _____

   _____

   b. S phase of interphase _____

   _____

   _____

   c. G_2 phase of interphase _____

   _____

   _____

   d. mitosis _____

   _____

   _____

   e. cytokinesis _____

   _____

   _____

2. The drawings below show the four phases of mitosis. Give the name of each phase and state what happens in each. (16 points)

   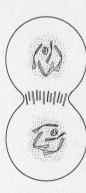

   a.   **b.**   **c.**   **d.**

   a. _____

   _____

   b. _____

   _____

   c. _____

   _____

   d. _____

   _____

3. Identify each of the changes below as one of the following cell growth processes: differentiation, regeneration, budding, fragmentation, vegetative reproduction, benign-tumor development, and cancer. (14 points)

    a. A yeast organism grows a small replica of itself on a part of its body. _____

    b. An abnormal growth of cells that lack binding surface proteins appears._____

    c. A runner is produced by a strawberry plant._____

    d. An amphibian grows back a new limb after losing one. _____

    e. An abnormal growth in which the cells remain together appears._____

    f. A flatworm divides in two and each part becomes another worm._____

    g. Cells in an unhatched chick take on different shapes and functions. _____

4. A certain kind of insect has 30 chromosomes in its body cells. It develops gametes and produces offspring. (18 points)

    a. What kind of cell—diploid or haploid—are the body cells of the insect? Through what process do these body cells reproduce as the insect grows?

_____

    b. What is the insect's diploid number? How is this number generally symbolized?

_____

    c. How many chromosomes do the gametes of the insect contain? Are these cells diploid or haploid?

_____

    d. Through what process are the gametes produced?

_____

    e. What is the haploid number? How is this number generally symbolized?

_____

    f. How many chromosomes are in the zygote that was formed when the insect reproduced? Is the zygote diploid or haploid?

_____

5. Describe what occurs in each of the following processes during meiosis. (18 points)

    a. prophase I _____

    b. metaphase I _____

    c. anaphase I _____

    d. telophase I _____

    e. meiosis II _____

    f. crossing over _____

6. An ameba is a one-celled organism that reproduces asexually. A trout is a many-celled organism that reproduces sexually. Suppose that amebas and trout are living in a lake environment to which they are well-adapted. Then, a drastic change occurs in the environment. Which type of organism is more likely to survive the change? Explain your answer in terms of evolution and gene reshuffling. (14 points)

_____

_____

_____

_____

Name _____ Class _____ Date _____

Unit 1 Test A

Choose the best answer for each question and write its letter in the blank.

_____ **1.** An ecosystem is the sum of a community of organisms and what?
  a. living factors in the area   **c.** those organisms outside the community
  b. nonliving factors in the area   **d.** all adaptations

_____ **2.** A cell can be defined as the smallest unit of life that can
  a. carry out all life functions.   **c.** undergo any chemical reaction.
  b. reproduce.   **d.** produce molecules.

_____ **3.** Because German shepherds and golden retrievers can interbreed, they are
  a. members of the same environment. **c.** members of different species.
  b. members of the same species.   **d.** genetically identical.

_____ **4.** Our sun is the source of all life on Earth because it provides
  a. heat.   **c.** energy.
  b. shelter.   **d.** protection against radiation.

_____ **5.** Which would *not* be considered a part of the biosphere?
  a. land   **c.** the mantle
  b. air   **d.** water

_____ **6.** When the environment changes, some organisms survive because of
  a. reproduction.   **c.** tissue levels.
  b. adaptations.   **d.** solar energy.

_____ **7.** Chromatography can be used in the laboratory to
  a. run centrifuges.   **c.** dissect cells.
  b. make tissue cultures.   **d.** separate components of gas.

_____ **8.** Tissue cultures are used to
  a. make large amounts of cells.   **c.** do field studies.
  b. produce electrophoresis.   **d.** magnify organisms.

_____ **9.** Observations are important to scientists because they
  a. raise questions leading to controlled experiments.
  b. replace the need for hypotheses.
  c. eliminate all uncertainty in science.
  d. can never be measured by technological devices.

_____ **10.** In control setups, the experimental variable is always
  a. predicted.   **c.** unnecessary.
  b. absent.   **d.** constant.

_____ **11.** Which would you use to study the internal structure of a cell?
  a. light microscope   **c.** scanning electron microscope
  b. transmission electron microscope **d.** dissecting tools

_____ **12.** The names for the functional groups —NH_2 and —PO_4 are
  a. amine and phosphate.   **c.** amino hydroxide and proteins.
  b. nitrate and phosphate.   **d.** none of the above.

_____ **13.** The number of protons in an element determines its
  a. atomic number.   **c.** isotopes.
  b. atomic mass.   **d.** neutrons.

_____ **14.** A covalent bond is the sharing of electrons between
  a. nuclei.   **c.** atoms.
  b. reactives.   **d.** radioactive substances.

_____ **15.** Dehydration synthesis is the removal of water during the forming of
   a. isotopes.
   b. a compound.
   c. a nucleus.
   d. atomic particles.

_____ **16.** The breaking and forming of chemical bonds takes place
   a. after a chemical reaction.
   b. during a mixture.
   c. during a chemical reaction.
   d. by means of solvents only.

_____ **17.** When two substances are completely and uniformly mixed together, they form a
   a. solution
   b. solvent
   c. reaction
   d. salt

_____ **18.** It is not possible to break an element down into a
   a. tracer.
   b. simpler substance.
   c. solution.
   d. more complex substance.

_____ **19.** Lactose is a disaccharide composed of galactose and
   a. sucrose.
   b. fructose.
   c. glucose.
   d. proteins.

_____ **20.** Protons, neutrons, and electrons are all
   a. atomic particles.
   b. atoms.
   c. mixtures.
   d. forms of energy.

_____ **21.** Which is *not* a typical characteristic of lipids?
   a. composed of carbon, hydrogen, and oxygen
   b. dissolve in water
   c. fewer oxygen atoms than carbohydrates
   d. organic compounds

_____ **22.** What are polymers made of thousands of linked monosaccharides called?
   a. liposomes
   b. steroids
   c. glycerides
   d. polysaccharides

_____ **23.** Enzymes are substances capable of speeding up
   a. radioactive processes.
   b. chemical reactions.
   c. nuclear disintegration.
   d. the forming of mixtures.

_____ **24.** Chemicals sent from one part of a body to control another part are called
   a. hormones.
   b. reactors.
   c. energizers.
   d. saturates.

_____ **25.** Amino acids contain an amino group, a carboxyl group, and
   a. a peptide group.
   b. a side group.
   c. a center group.
   d. an end group.

_____ **26.** Dehydration is the process of
   a. adding water.
   b. synthesizing water.
   c. breaking apart polymers.
   d. removing water.

_____ **27.** Which element is *not* part of carbohydrates?
   a. carbon
   b. nitrogen
   c. oxygen
   d. hydrogen

_____ **28.** Carbohydrates, proteins, and fats are all
   a. organic compounds.
   b. lipids.
   c. amino acids.
   d. sugars.

_____ **29.** The cytoplasm of a cell includes everything
   a. outside its cell membrane.
   b. inside its cell membrane.
   c. but the nucleus.
   d. between the cell membrane and the nucleus.

_____ **30.** When energy is used to move molecules across a cell membrane, the process is called
   a. active transport.
   b. passive transport.
   c. concentration gradient.
   d. isolation of solutes.

Unit 1 Test A

_____ **31.** Endocytosis brings substances into a cell, whereas exocytosis
    a. controls their reproduction.
    b. releases substances.
    c. encloses the particles in a pouch.
    d. brings in solutes.

_____ **32.** The nucleus of a cell is its
    a. control center.
    b. cytoplasm.
    c. only organelle.
    d. means of locomotion.

_____ **33.** The packaging and secreting of cell products is accomplished by the
    a. mitochondria.
    b. ribosomes.
    c. Golgi apparatus.
    d. nucleus.

_____ **34.** Chromosomes can be thought of as
    a. cell "blueprints."
    b. cell control centers.
    c. the "skin" of the cell.
    d. the digestive organs of cells.

_____ **35.** In isotonic solutions, concentrations of solutes from the inside to the outside of the cell are
    a. greater than equal.
    b. less than equal.
    c. equal.
    d. variable.

_____ **36.** Chloroplasts are organelles that contain which pigment?
    a. chlorophyll
    b. digestive enzymes
    c. cytoplasm
    d. chromosomes

_____ **37.** The complete name for ATP is
    a. adenosine trigger.
    b. amino triphosphate.
    c. adenosine triphosphate.
    d. alternative temperature pressure.

_____ **38.** What is the conversion of sunlight into a useable energy form by autotrophs called?
    a. digestion
    b. amino transfer
    c. respiration
    d. photosynthesis

_____ **39.** Anaerobic respiration releases enegy from food molecules in the absence of what?
    a. nitrogen
    b. oxygen
    c. sunlight
    d. photosynthesis

_____ **40.** The second phase of aerobic respiration is called the
    a. Krebs cycle.
    b. electron transport.
    c. glycolysis breakdown.
    d. carbon-fixing pathway.

_____ **41.** During glycolysis, glucose becomes pyruvate and
    a. proteins are made.
    b. energy is released.
    c. copper is converted to acetyl-CoA.
    d. fermentation always takes place.

_____ **42.** Pigments absorb certain light wavelengths and can
    a. reflect others.
    b. make proteins.
    c. make up the cell membrane.
    d. destroy chlorophyll.

_____ **43.** Organisms that make their own food are known as
    a. heterotrophs.
    b. reductionists.
    c. autotrophs.
    d. animals.

_____ **44.** During oxidation, a molecule will
    a. lose an electron.
    b. gain an electron.
    c. form a solution.
    d. not exchange energy.

_____ **45.** Budding is one form of
    a. sexual reproduction.
    b. asexual reproduction.
    c. evolution.
    d. photosynthesis.

_____ **46.** When cells acquire abnormal size, shape, and abilities, they are
    a. cancerous.
    b. undergoing respiration.
    c. becoming chloroplasts.
    d. repairing organelles.

_____ **47.** If a cell was created by asexual reproduction, it has
    a. two parents.
    b. one parent.
    c. hermaphroditic capabilities.
    d. two cell membranes.

_____ **48.** The longest phase in the cell cycle of most cells is
    a. mitosis.
    b. prophase.
    c. interphase.
    d. anaphase.

_____ **49.** Sexual reproduction can help a group of organisms survive by
    a. reshuffling genes.
    b. keeping organisms uniform.
    c. stopping meiosis.
    d. preventing fragmentation.

_____ **50.** The joining of egg and sperm cells is called
    a. asexual reproduction.
    b. fertilization.
    c. mitosis.
    d. crossing over.

Chapter 8 Test A

Choose the best answer for each question and write its letter in the blank.

_____ **1.** A trait is any characteristic that can be passed
    a. from plants to animals.
    b. from parent to offspring.
    c. from one species to another.
    d. through a cell membrane.

_____ **2.** A study of prehistoric genetics reveals that today's crops are
    a. descended from wild plants.
    b. from other planets.
    c. the parents of wild plants.
    d. exactly the same as wild plants.

_____ **3.** In the 1860s, Gregor Mendel conducted experiments that established
    a. bloodline theory.
    b. the blending hypothesis.
    c. codominance theory.
    d. modern genetics.

_____ **4.** A hybrid is an organism that receives different genetic information from
    a. each parent.
    b. different parts of its body.
    c. only one parent.
    d. changes in the environment.

_____ **5.** Each of the seven traits that Mendel studied occurred in
    a. one observable form.
    b. two distinct, observable forms.
    c. all plants.
    d. all plants and animals.

_____ **6.** When pure-bred plants are allowed to self-fertilize, they produce
    a. only genotypes.
    b. only phenotypes.
    c. only offspring with the parental trait.
    d. offspring with varying traits.

_____ **7.** Mendel called a trait that did not show in a hybrid a
    a. parental trait.
    b. codominant trait.
    c. dominant trait.
    d. recessive trait.

_____ **8.** Mendel hypothesized that each trait is controlled by a factor, now called a
    a. gene.
    b. mate.
    c. hybrid.
    d. dominance.

_____ **9.** What are different versions of a gene for the same trait?
    a. alleles
    b. phenotypes
    c. dihybrids
    d. pure-breds

_____ **10.** The law of segregation states that, during meiosis, each pair of alleles
    a. sticks together.
    b. is tripled.
    c. separates.
    d. becomes pure-bred.

_____ **11.** An allele that expresses itself in a hybrid is a(n)
    a. recessive allele.
    b. independent assortment.
    c. allele pair.
    d. dominant allele.

_____ **12.** The law of independent assortment states what?
    a. Gene pairs sort randomly and independently of each other.
    b. Gene pairs sort always in the same order.
    c. Half of an organism's gametes have one allele per pair.
    d. One allele is always dominant.

_____ **13.** The actual genetic makeup of an organism is called its
    a. phenotype.
    b. homozygous type.
    c. heterozygous type.
    d. genotype.

_____ **14.** An organism in which two alleles for a trait are different is
    a. heterozygous.
    b. homozygous.
    c. genotypic.
    d. phenotypic.

_____ **15.** Scientists can use probability to predict the results of
  a. any nonevent.
  b. a genetic cross.
  c. a future event of any kind.
  d. any past event.

_____ **16.** When you flip a coin, what is the probability of getting tails?
  a. 1/4
  b. 1
  c. 1/2
  d. 40 percent

_____ **17.** Punnett squares are grids that show
  a. the phenotypes of offspring.
  b. actual results of a genetic cross.
  c. all possible results of a genetic cross.
  d. only dihybrid crosses.

_____ **18.** A cross made to study a single trait is known as a
  a. monohybrid cross.
  b. dihybrid cross.
  c. Punnett square.
  d. gamete study.

_____ **19.** Crossing a pure-bred green-podded plant with a pure-bred yellow-podded plant is symbolized by
  a. Gg X gg
  b. GG X gg
  c. gG X Gg
  d. GG X GG

_____ **20.** The cross of GG plants with gg plants will produce what kind of offspring?
  a. all gg genotypes
  b. all GG genotypes
  c. all Gg genotypes
  d. all gGG genotypes

_____ **21.** A cross that is written RrGg X RrGg is an example of a
  a. monohybrid cross.
  b. dihybrid cross.
  c. phenotypic cross.
  d. genotypic cross.

_____ **22.** In incomplete dominance, there are no
  a. genetic crossings.
  b. homozygous phenotypes.
  c. dominant or recessive alleles.
  d. intermediate traits.

_____ **23.** Type AB blood is an example of
  a. codominance.
  b. incomplete dominance.
  c. blending of alleles.
  d. monogenic traits.

_____ **24.** Eye color involves many genetic factors and is an example of a
  a. synthetic trait.
  b. polygenic trait.
  c. simple hybrid.
  d. single-parent heredity.

_____ **25.** Multiple alleles for a trait are
  a. one individual with many different gene pairs.
  b. many different alleles within a whole population.
  c. incomplete dominance.
  d. environmental factors.

Name _____   Class _____   Date _____

Chapter 8 Test B

Read each question or statement and respond in the space provided.

1. You are experimenting with plants that are of the same basic type, but whose flowers differ in color. Some produce blue flowers and some produce white flowers. You make the following observations about these plants and their offspring:

I. When crossed with themselves only, the plants with blue flowers produced only blue-flowering plants.

II. When crossed with themselves only, the plants with white flowers produced only white-flowering plants.

III. When a pure-bred blue-flowering plant was crossed with a pure-bred white-flowering plant, only blue-flowering plants were produced in the F_1 generation.

Given these observations, answer each of the following questions. Explain your reasoning in each case. (20 points)

a. Were the original white plants and the original blue plants pure bred or hybrid?

_____

_____

b. Were the blue plants in the F_1 generation in III pure bred or hybrid, or were there some of each?

_____

_____

c. Is the gene for white color dominant or recessive? What about the gene for blue color?

_____

_____

d. If the blue-flowering plants produced in the F_1 generation in III were crossed with one another, what fraction of the F_2 generation would you expect to be blue-flowering? What fraction would you expect to be white-flowering?

_____

_____

_____

2. Identify which of Mendel's three laws is illustrated in each of the following. Include statements of the laws themselves. (15 points)

a. When a brown duck is crossed with a white duck, all the offspring are brown.

_____

_____

b. When tall, red-fruited berry plants are crossed with short, white-fruited berry plants, every possible combination of height and fruit color shows up in the F_2 generation.

_____

_____

_____

c. An insect produced from a black-eyed parent and a red-eyed parent produces some gametes that contain the gene for black eye color and some that contain the gene for red eye color.

_____

_____

_____

3. In the following genotypes, the gene for gray fur color is represented as G and the gene for white fur color is represented as g. In each case, state whether the organism is homozygous or heterozygous, and describe the phenotype color. (Remember that uppercase letters stand for dominant genes.) (12 points)

    a. gg _____

    b. GG _____

    c. Gg _____

4. Assuming that the probability of producing a male child is the same as the probability of producing a female, calculate the probability of each of the following. Show your work. (12 points)

    a. Producing two children, both of whom are female _____

    b. Producing two children: first, a male, and, second, a female _____

    c. Producing five children, all of whom are female _____

5. Two bean plants each have the genotype TtRr, in which T stands for tallness, t for shortness, R for red flower color, and r for yellow flower color. Suppose you want to cross the two plants. (25 points)

    a. What kind of cross would this be: monohybrid or dihybrid? Explain your answer.

    _____

    b. Fill in the Punnett square below to show the expected genotypes of the offspring from your cross.

Gametes of parent:

Gametes of parent:

    c. How many of each phenotype will be produced among the 16 offspring? Express this as a phenotype ratio.

    _____

6. Identify each of the following as incomplete dominance, codominance, polygenic traits, or multiple alleles. (16 points)

    a. A bird has inherited alleles for a certain blood type Q and a certain blood type R. The phenotype of the bird shows the full characteristics of both Q and R.

    _____

    b. The gene for the trait of nail color in a certain kind of bear can be any of three versions: one that produces white nails, one that produces brown nails, and one that produces black nails.

    _____

    c. All the offspring of a pure-bred black dog and a pure-bred white dog are gray.

    _____

    d. The pattern on the wings of a certain kind of butterfly depends on five different gene pairs.

    _____

Chapter 9 Test A

Choose the best answer for each question and write its letter in the blank.

_____ **1.** In 1903, Walter S. Sutton of Columbia University adapted Mendel's ideas into
    a. Aristotle's theories.
    b. the chromosome theory of heredity.
    c. Drosophila theory.
    d. microscope staining theory.

_____ **2.** The body color and wing shape of the fruit fly not assorting independently
    a. is proof of linked genes.
    b. disproves the theory of linked genes.
    c. makes Punnett squares useless.
    d. is the only exception to genetic theory.

_____ **3.** What is the shuffling of genes into new combinations by crossing over?
    a. chromosome shift
    b. gene linking
    c. gene mapping
    d. genetic recombination

_____ **4.** Locating genes on chromosomes is called
    a. gene mapping.
    b. gene recombining.
    c. gene linking.
    d. gene strategy.

_____ **5.** Recombination occurs more frequently between genes that are
    a. close together on a chromosome.
    b. far apart on a chromosome.
    c. genetically incompatible.
    d. genetically compatible.

_____ **6.** A chromosome is a cell structure that consists of
    a. many genes.
    b. one specific gene.
    c. no genes.
    d. only recessive genes.

_____ **7.** One reason that fruit flies are ideal for genetic studies is that they
    a. only produce a few young.
    b. produce new generations in two weeks.
    c. are all of one sex.
    d. live for a long time.

_____ **8.** Male fruit flies have the following gentic characteristic:
    a. two X chromosomes.
    b. two Y chromosomes.
    c. one X and one Y chromosome.
    d. two X and one Y chromosomes.

_____ **9.** What is a spontaneous change in a gene or a chromosome?
    a. sex-linked trait
    b. mutation
    c. gene map
    d. Y chromosome

_____ **10.** Genes found on the X chromosome are called
    a. mutant phenotypes.
    b. male-linked genes.
    c. sex-linked genes.
    d. mutations.

_____ **11.** White eye color in the *Drosophila* fruit fly is a(n)
    a. sex-linked trait.
    b. nondisjunction.
    c. inversion.
    d. mutation.

_____ **12.** A grouping by type and size of chromosomes from a cell is called a(n)
    a. autosome.
    b. karyotype.
    c. genotype.
    d. Punnett square.

_____ **13.** Sex-limited traits are autosomal traits that are expressed
    a. in either sex.
    b. only in embryos.
    c. only in one sex.
    d. only on sex chromosomes.

_____ **14.** All the chromosomes except the sex chromosomes are called
    a. Y chromosomes.
    b. autosomes.
    c. X chromosomes.
    d. gene pairs.

_____ **15.** X and Y chromosomes are largely nonhomologous, so most genes on one have
    a. no matching alleles on the other.   **c.** to do with the sex of the organism.
    b. a matching allele on the other.   **d.** exactly the same kind of genes as on the other.

_____ **16.** A sperm carrying a Y chromosome can produce a(n)
    a. female only.   **c.** male or female.
    b. male only.   **d.** autosome.

_____ **17.** About how many sperm produced by an organism carry an X chromosome?
    a. half   **c.** one-quarter
    b. most   **d.** 10 percent

_____ **18.** Beard growth in males and milk production in females are examples of
    a. sex-limited traits.   **c.** sex-free traits.
    b. sex determination.   **d.** chromosome addition.

_____ **19.** The sex of alligators is determined by
    a. sex chromosomes.   **c.** both parents.
    b. egg temperature.   **d.** heredity.

_____ **20.** Sex-influenced traits are expressed
    a. the same in both sexes.   **c.** in only one sex.
    b. differently in each sex.   **d.** only in females.

_____ **21.** When one or more genes is lost during division,
    a. deletion has taken place.   **c.** sex determination has taken place.
    b. duplication has taken place.   **d.** translocation has taken place.

_____ **22.** Having only one chromosome instead of two is called
    a. inversion.   **c.** translocation.
    b. monosomy.   **d.** duplication.

_____ **23.** The failure of one or more pairs of chromosomes to separate is called
    a. massive polyploidy.   **c.** cloning.
    b. nondisjunction.   **d.** translocation.

_____ **24.** Nondisjunction occurring in all chromosome pairs at once is known as
    a. polyploidy.   **c.** duplication.
    b. deletion.   **d.** monosomy.

_____ **25.** In inversion, a chromosome fragment breaks free and reattaches itself
    a. later.   **c.** in all chromosomes at once.
    b. in reverse order.   **d.** in translocation.

Chapter 9 Test B

Read each question or statement and respond in the space provided.

1. Explain what is meant by the chromosome theory of inheritance. How do Mendel's factors of inheritance relate to what you know about chromosomes? (17 points)

_____

_____

2. Fringed petals (genotype F) are dominant over nonfringed petals (f) in a certain kind of petunia. In the same kind of plant, orange stamens (O) are dominant over yellow stamens (o). (15 points)

    a. Suppose you cross a petunia of genotype FFOO with one of genotype ffoo. What phenotype(s) would you expect in the F_1 generation?

_____

_____

    b. Suppose that you then cross plants of the F_1 generation. Assuming that the chromosomes for the traits of fringing and stamen color are on separate chromosomes, what ratio of phenotypes would you expect in the F_2 generation? Why?

_____

_____

    c. Suppose the genes for these traits are on the same chromosome. What phenotype ratio would you expect in the F_2 generation, assuming that no genetic recombination had occurred? Explain your answer.

_____

_____

3. The gene for the trait of curved wings (C) versus flat wings (c) in a type of beetle is found only on the X chromosome. (15 points)

    a. What are genes such as this called?

_____

    b. How would you represent the genotype of a male beetle that has flat wings? Of a homozygous female beetle that has curved wings?

_____

_____

    c. Do a Punnett square to determine the genotypes of the offspring produced by crossing a male that has curved wings and a female that is heterozygous for wing type. Label the gametes to show if they came from the male or the female. What phenotype ratio would result?

4. State whether each of the following describes a sex-linked trait, a sex-limited trait, or a sex-influenced trait. (15 points)

a. The gene that produces a whitening of the coat in older deer is in both males and females. It can be expressed in both sexes, but differently, and is dominant only in the presence of male hormones. Females can develop this trait only when they have two genes for it.

_____

b. For a kind of bird, the gene that accounts for nest-building behavior occurs on an autosomal chromosome and is found in both males and females. It is expressed only in the females and is activated by female hormones.

_____

c. For a kind of insect, the gene that accounts for long antennae is found only on the X chromosome.

_____

5. A certain chromosome has the genes P_1, Q_1, and R_1. It is homologous with a chromosome that has the genes P_2, Q_2, and R_2. It is nonhomologous with a chromosome that has the genes S_3, T_3, and U_3. Look at the illustration below. It shows the results of four possible changes, during cell division, of the P_1 - Q_1 - R_1 chromosome. Identify each change as either normal crossover, deletion, duplication, translocation, or inversion. (20 points)

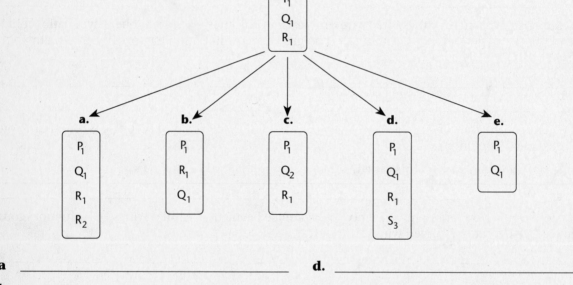

a _____   d. _____

b. _____   e. _____

c. _____

6. Each of the following changes involves a cell process in a kind of grain plant. The body cells of the plant contain 20 chromosomes. Identify each change as either normal meiosis, monosomy, trisomy, nondisjunction, normal fertilization, or polyploidy. (18 points)

a. A gamete that has 11 chromosomes is produced. _____

b. A gamete that has 10 chromosomes is produced. _____

c. A zygote that has 40 chromosomes is produced. _____

d. A zygote that has 19 chromosomes is produced. _____

e. A zygote that has 20 chromosomes is produced. _____

f. A zygote that has 21 chromosomes is produced. _____

Name _____ Class _____ Date _____

Chapter 10 Test A

_____

Choose the best answer for each question and write its letter in the blank.

_____ **1.** Transformation is the process by which bacteria are changed by absorbing
   a. genetic material from an outside source.
   b. mucous coats.
   c. heat-killed S bacteria.
   d. R cells.

_____ **2.** By 1944, scientists had proved that the transforming factor in heredity is
   a. bacteria.   **c.** protein.
   b. DNA.   **d.** bacteriophages.

_____ **3.** Griffith did an experiment in which live R bacteria was changed by dead S bacteria. Such a change is an example of
   a. fertilization.   **c.** repressive proteins.
   b. codon production.   **d.** transformation.

_____ **4.** Chargaff's rules state that in DNA, the amount of adenine equals
   a. the amount of cytosine.   **c.** the amount of thymine.
   b. the amount of guanine.   **d.** the amount of guanine and thymine.

_____ **5.** Rosalind Franklin helped reveal the structure of DNA by using
   a. X-ray crystallography.   **c.** centrifuge analysis.
   b. cytosine analysis.   **d.** bacteriophages.

_____ **6.** Which is *not* a characteristic of DNA?
   a. cytosine   **c.** a "backbone" of sugar and phosphates
   b. long strands of nucleotides   **d.** uracil

_____ **7.** The correct structure of DNA is a(n)
   a. double helix.   **c.** octagon.
   b. diamond.   **d.** triple ellipse.

_____ **8.** The term *replication* refers to DNA's ability to
   a. respond to X-ray photography.   **c.** make copies of itself.
   b. attack bacteriophages.   **d.** twist into a helix.

_____ **9.** Which is *not* a difference between DNA and RNA?
   a. presence of adenine   **c.** ribose
   b. number of strands   **d.** uracil

_____ **10.** A gene is a region of DNA that contains instructions for manufacture of
   a. adenine only.   **c.** *Neurospora* molds.
   b. a particular polypeptide chain.   **d.** cultures.

_____ **11.** The process of transferring information from DNA to RNA is called
   a. transcription.   **c.** messenger RNA.
   b. synthesis.   **d.** assembling.

_____ **12.** A three-base code for an amino acid is called a
   a. transcription.   **c.** codon.
   b. double genetic code.   **d.** base combination.

_____ **13.** After transcription, mRNA leaves the nucleus and moves to
   a. a complementary base.   **c.** a universal codon.
   b. a polysaccharide receptor.   **d.** a ribosome.

_____ **14.** Scientists have determined that the codes for the amino acids are
   a. universal.   **c.** never the same.
   b. different in humans and bacteria.   **d.** different in bacteria and viruses.

_____ **15.** If all the genes in a cell were expressed at the same time,
    a. hormones would lose molecules.   **c.** prokaryotes could control eukaryotes.
    b. metabolic disorder would occur.   **d.** DNA would coil.

_____ **16.** A group of genes with related functions is called a(n)
    a. operon.   **c.** promoter.
    b. regulator.   **d.** codon.

_____ **17.** It is probable that when chromatin is tightly coiled,
    a. DNA is transcribed.   **c.** prokaryotes can reproduce.
    b. the genes are active.   **d.** DNA cannot be transcribed.

_____ **18.** The part of a gene that continuously makes a repressor protein is the
    a. operon.   **c.** regulator.
    b. promoter gene.   **d.** coiler.

_____ **19.** The short sequences of DNA that code for a protein are called
    a. exons.   **c.** introns.
    b. point mutations.   **d.** operons.

_____ **20.** A methyl group is made up of one carbon atom bonded to
    a. two hydrogen atoms.   **c.** an exon.
    b. three hydrogen atoms.   **d.** a prokaryote.

_____ **21.** One difference in gene expression between prokaryotes and eukaryotes is that
    a. expression is more complex in eukaryotes.
    b. expression is more complex in prokaryotes.
    c. no DNA is involved in eukaryotes.
    d. there are no promoters in prokaryotes.

_____ **22.** A gene mutation can be thought of as a(n)
    a. absence of methyl groups.   **c.** change in nucleotide sequence.
    b. perfect copy during replication.   **d.** RNA splicing.

_____ **23.** Sickle-cell anemia is an example of
    a. point mutation.   **c.** regulatory protein.
    b. error-free DNA replication.   **d.** healthy hemoglobin.

_____ **24.** The loss of one or more bases from the DNA of a gene is called
    a. a mutagen.   **c.** deletion mutation.
    b. addition mutation.   **d.** protein synthesis.

_____ **25.** Factors in the environment that cause mutations are known as
    a. mutagens.   **c.** oncogenes.
    b. base pairs.   **d.** point mutations.

Chapter 10 Test B

Read each question or statement and respond in the space provided.

1. a. What was Griffith's contribution to our understanding of DNA? How did he arrive at his conclusions? (6 points)

_____

_____

_____

_____

b. What was the contribution of Chase and Hershey to our understanding of DNA? How did they arrive at their conclusions? (5 points)

_____

_____

2. Draw and label a simplified diagram of a DNA molecule. Show the location of these parts of the molecule: sugar, phosphate, nitrogen bases. (12 points)

3. What does the phrase "one gene—one polypeptide" mean in terms of genes and their relationship to proteins? (10 points)

_____

_____

4. Compare and contrast DNA and RNA in terms of structure and components. (12 points)

_____

_____

_____

5. a. Assume you are a scientist studying the cell process in which RNA is made from DNA. The segment of DNA with which you are working contains the following sequence of bases: A, G, G, C, A, T. What will the sequence of bases be for the RNA segment made from this DNA sequence? (15 points)

_____

b. What is this process of making long RNA molecules called? What type of RNA is made in this process?

_____

c. What are the other two types of RNA made in cells? What are their functions?

_____

6. The table below describes the role of various structures that control gene expression in prokaryotes and eukaryotes. Complete the table by filling in the name of the correct structure for each role described. Possible answers are: operon, structural gene, promoter gene, operator, regulator, intron, exon, methyl group, repressor protein, and regulatory protein. (20 points)

ROLE	STRUCTURE
a. Short gene sequence in eukaryotes that codes for protein	
b. Gene sequence in eukaryotes that does not code for protein	
c. Gene part that makes repressor protein	
d. Gene that causes movement of RNA polymerase	
e. Group of genes with related functions	
f. One-carbon structure that interferes with transcription	
g. Protein that turns off transcription in prokaryotes	
h. Protein that turns off transcription in eukaryotes	
i. DNA region that switches operons on and off	
j. Gene that codes for protein products of an operon	

7. Write the term that is best defined by each of the descriptions below. Use each of the following answers once: oncogene, mutagen, deletion, frameshift mutation, gene mutation, base-pair substitution, point mutation, carcinogen, addition, and base analog. (20 points)

a. Any change in the way bases are read resulting from a shifting of codons by one base

_____

b. Any environmental factor that causes a mutation _____

_____

c. Substance that causes cancer _____

d. DNA sequence that causes cancer _____

e. Replacement of nucleotides by different nucleotides_____

f. Loss of one or more bases from a sequence_____

g. Any change in the sequence of nucleotides in a gene sequence _____

h. Substance that is chemically similar to a part of the DNA molecule and may be incorporated into DNA

_____

i. Replacement of only one pair of bases_____

j. Gain of one or more bases to a sequence_____

Chapter 11 Test A

Choose the best answer for each question and write its letter in the blank.

_____ **1.** Selective breeding is the breeding of animals or plants to produce
    a. inbreeding.   **c.** outbreeding.
    b. biotechnology.   **d.** desired traits.

_____ **2.** The cause of deafness in some dalmatians is
    a. a recessive allele.   **c.** cross breeding.
    b. a dominant gene.   **d.** cloning.

_____ **3.** Scientists have discovered a way to make blood clotting protein by inserting purified genes into
    a. the human bloodstream.   **c.** lipids.
    b. cells from hamsters.   **d.** the DNA of human cells.

_____ **4.** Mules are an example of
    a. inbreeding.   **c.** polyploidy.
    b. outbreeding.   **d.** cloning.

_____ **5.** One way polyploidy can be incurred is by
    a. crossing distantly related organisms.   **c.** applying colchicine to a cell.
    b. culturing plasmids.   **d.** cloning.

_____ **6.** In genetic engineering, the carrier of genetic material is known as the
    a. vector.   **c.** recombinant DNA.
    b. plasmid.   **d.** DNA ligase.

_____ **7.** Small, circular pieces of DNA within bacteria are called what?
    a. vectors   **c.** plasmids
    b. genetic engineers   **d.** clones

_____ **8.** The use of special biochemical techniques to modify genes is called
    a. genetic engineering.   **c.** insulin insertion.
    b. cross breeding.   **d.** technical engineering.

_____ **9.** Recombinant DNA is a combination of DNA from
    a. bacteria.   **c.** different genes of the same organism.
    b. different organisms.   **d.** viral material.

_____ **10.** To cut DNA at a specific series of base pairs, genetic engineers use
    a. restriction enzymes.   **c.** ampicillin.
    b. insulin.   **d.** tetracycline.

_____ **11.** In the production of insulin, the enzyme DNA ligase is used to join
    a. insulin and tetracycline.   **c.** plasmid DNA and human insulin gene.
    b. bacteria and simple DNA.   **d.** insulin genes and diabetics.

_____ **12.** Another step in the genetic engineering of insulin is
    a. inserting plasmids into bacteria.
    b. bonding DNA and a restriction enzyme.
    c. constructing the eukaryote.
    d. making the bacteria resistant.

_____ **13.** Which is *not* an example of genetic engineering?
    a. charcoal briquets.   **c.** milk-stimulating hormone.
    b. certain laundry detergent enzymes.   **d.** interferon from bacterial plasmids.

_____ **14.** Genetically engineered frost-resistant bacteria could be used to
    a. keep bacteria from lowering the temperature of a host.
    b. protect a plant during a frost.
    c. prevent the temperature from falling below freezing.
    d. manufacture large quantities of insulin.

                Chapter 11: Applied Genetics   **45**

_____ **15.** Genetically engineered bacteria that consume oil might help to
  a. produce more oil.   **c.** destroy other harmful bacteria.
  b. clean the environment.   **d.** locate hidden oil reserves.

_____ **16.** Why would scientists want to clone the gene that causes hemophilia?
  a. to study the disease
  b. to increase the incidence of hemophilia
  c. to produce insulin
  d. to dissolve blood clots

_____ **17.** Mammalian cell culture is one way of
  a. improving yeast quality.   **c.** mapping genes on chromosomes.
  b. making large, complex proteins. **d.** eliminating DNA.

_____ **18.** The new test for Huntington's disease uses a DNA probe to
  a. simulate the symptoms of the disease.
  b. map all human genes.
  c. identify the marker for the disease.
  d. infect hamsters with the disease.

_____ **19.** A project underway to map every gene in the human population is called the
  a. DNA Project.   **c.** Human Genome Project.
  b. DNA Recombinant Project.   **d.** Genetic Engineering Project.

_____ **20.** Once a genetically engineered bacterium is released into the environment,
  a. it can be recalled at any time. **c.** it returns to the laboratory.
  b. it improves crop growth.   **d.** it cannot be recaptured.

_____ **21.** Genetically engineered proteins that bind only to certain types of cells may be useful
  in the treatment of
  a. Huntington's disease.   **c.** birth defects.
  b. hemophilia.   **d.** cancer.

_____ **22.** The first genetically engineered human vaccine, for hepatitis B, was
  a. engineered from yeast.   **c.** engineered from insulin.
  b. engineered from bacteria.   **d.** injected into corn cells.

_____ **23.** A. *tumefaciens* is a bacterium used to
  a. genetically modify plants.   **c.** cure crown gall disease in tobacco.
  b. clean up oil.   **d.** stimulate milk production.

_____ **24.** Unlike the insulin extracted from farm animals, genetically engineered insulin causes no
  a. change in human blood chemistry. **c.** allergic reaction.
  b. metabolism of sugar.   **d.** none of the above

_____ **25.** Trying to control human heredity by controlling mating is called
  a. eugenics.   **c.** genetics.
  b. gene alteration.   **d.** recombinant probing.

Chapter 11 Test B

Read each question or statement and respond in the space provided.

   1. Identify each of the following as biotechnology, gene transfer, genetic engineering, eugenics, or gene mapping. (15 points)

   a. the changing of human heredity through the control of mating

   _____

   b. the finding of the locations of specific DNA sequences on chromosomes

   _____

   c. any application of biological science to practical problems

   _____

   d. the use of biochemical techniques to study or modify DNA sequences

   _____

   e. the placement of DNA sequences from one kind of organism into another kind of organism

   _____

   2. The following descriptions are examples of controlled breeding. Identify each example as selective breeding, inbreeding, outbreeding, or induced polyploidy. (16 points)

   a. An orange is crossed with a type of grapefruit.

   _____

   b. Cows that mature quickly are permitted to reproduce, and the others are killed.

   _____

   c. Colchicine is applied to a tomato cell to produce a plant that produces larger fruit.

   _____

   d. Two closely related cats are bred to produce offspring with desirable traits.

   _____

   3. Explain what is meant by each of the following terms used in genetic engineering. (15 points)

   a. recombinant DNA _____

   b. vector _____

   c. plasmid _____

   d. restriction enzyme _____

   4. Suppose you are a scientist trying to help people who cannot produce an enzyme needed for proper digestion. Describe how you would use gene transfer processes to produce bacteria to make the enzyme. (20 points)

   _____

   _____

   _____

   _____

   _____

   _____

   _____

Name _____ Class _____ Date _____

5. Describe one example of an application of genetic engineering in each of the following areas. (18 points)

a. agriculture

_____

_____

_____

_____

b. industry

_____

_____

_____

_____

c. medicine

_____

_____

_____

_____

6. Many important ethical issues have been raised by genetic engineering. Suppose that a new kind of virus is being developed to attack and kill specific kinds of bacteria. (16 points)

a. Describe two possible benefits of such a development. _____

_____

_____

b. Name two potentially serious problems caused by this development._____

_____

_____

_____

_____

c. Describe steps that might be taken to control these problems. _____

_____

_____

_____

d. Explain why dangers might still remain despite safety precautions. _____

_____

_____

Chapter 12 Test A

Choose the best answer for each question and write its letter in the blank.

_____ **1.** Charts that show how a trait is inherited are called
    a. Punnett squares.
    b. pedigrees.
    c. karyotype charts.
    d. genetic charts.

_____ **2.** A photograph that shows chromosomes in homologous pairs is called a what?
    a. karyotype
    b. pedigree
    c. phenotype
    d. genotype

_____ **3.** In a pedigree, a shaded circle or square indicates a person who has
    a. an allele for a trait only.
    b. the trait as well as its allele.
    c. a male allele.
    d. a female allele.

_____ **4.** In a pedigree, which is numbered with Arabic numerals?
    a. generations
    b. visible traits
    c. alleles
    d. individuals

_____ **5.** Which of the following is shown in a karyotype?
    a. a pedigree chart
    b. DNA models
    c. chromosomal abnormalities
    d. ultrasound

_____ **6.** Some sickle-cell carriers are resistant to malaria. This occurs because when a red cell sickles, it loses
    a. potassium ions.
    b. sodium ions.
    c. insulin.
    d. nitrogen.

_____ **7.** The failure of chromosome pairs to separate during meiosis is
    a. defective chromosome structure.
    b. allele syndrome.
    c. nondisjunction.
    d. recessive genetic disorder.

_____ **8.** Turner syndrome is a disorder in which a person has one X chromosome and
    a. one Y chromosome.
    b. two Y chromosomes.
    c. no other sex chromosome.
    d. one other sex chromosome.

_____ **9.** An example of a disorder caused by defective chromosome structure is
    a. Klinefelter syndrome.
    b. Cri-du-chat syndrome.
    c. nondisjunction.
    d. Turner syndrome.

_____ **10.** People with Down syndrome are often prone to
    a. heart defects.
    b. sterility.
    c. loss of hair.
    d. a cry that sounds like a cat's.

_____ **11.** Males with Klinefelter syndrome may have
    a. excessively hairy bodies.
    b. no Y chromosome.
    c. large heads.
    d. breast development.

_____ **12.** Defective chromosome structure does *not* mean that chromosomes are
    a. inverted or deleted.
    b. of incorrect number.
    c. abnormal.
    d. translocated.

_____ **13.** A heterozygous carrier of a genetic disorder can
    a. become very ill from it.
    b. pass the disorder on to offspring.
    c. become homologous.
    d. infect others with it.

_____ **14.** A genetic disorder that causes secretion of mucus from some organs is
    a. cystic fibrosis.
    b. Tay-Sachs disease.
    c. Huntington's disease.
    d. sickle-cell disease.

_____ **15.** Sickle-cell disease is a disorder that involves
    a. only recessive alleles.
    b. codominant alleles.
    c. only dominant alleles.
    d. the nervous system.

_____ **16.** People with Huntington's disease develop deterioration of the
    a. circulatory system.   **c.** heart.
    b. reproductive organs.   **d.** nervous system.

_____ **17.** The allele for Tay-Sachs disease is found most often among
    a. Ashkenazi Jews.   **c.** Hispanic people.
    b. African Americans.   **d.** Sephardic Jews.

_____ **18.** Sickle-cell disease results in production of abnormal
    a. nerve cells.   **c.** color vision.
    b. hemoglobin.   **d.** muscle tissue.

_____ **19.** Two examples of sex-linked disorders are.
    a. hemophilia and color blindness.
    b. color blindness and sickle-cell anemia.
    c. hemophilia and cystic fibrosis.
    d. hemophilia and malaria.

_____ **20.** A color-blind man would have the genotype X^cY, and a color-blind woman would have which following genotype?
    a. X^cX^c **c.** XX^c
    b. X^cY^c **d.** XX

_____ **21.** Excessive bleeding can be caused by a disorder known as
    a. Tay-Sachs.   **c.** sickle-cell anemia.
    b. hemophilia.   **d.** cystic fibrosis.

_____ **22.** During a test known as chorionic villi sampling, a needle is inserted through the abdomen to remove
    a. fetal cells.   **c.** pieces of the zygote.
    b. bits of membrane around the fetus.   **d.** uterine hormones.

_____ **23.** Phenylketonuria is a disorder that causes inability to use
    a. hemoglobin.   **c.** a single amino acid.
    b. oxygen.   **d.** all proteins.

_____ **24.** Genetic counselors make use of pedigree analyses and
    a. genetic tests.   **c.** phenylalanine.
    b. skin grafts.   **d.** sex-linked traits.

_____ **25.** Amniocentesis is a test done during pregnancy that can
    a. cure genetic defects.   **c.** stimulate ultrasound.
    b. prevent chorionic villi.   **d.** detect genetic defects.

Chapter 12 Test B

Read each question or statement and respond in the space provided.

1. The following pedigree shows relationships for three generations of people. The trait being followed is a genetic disorder that leads to hearing problems. (18 points)

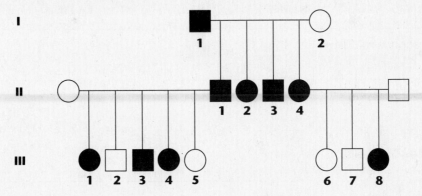

a. What do the circles represent? What do the squares represent? _____

b. What do the horizontal lines connecting circles and squares represent? The vertical lines?

_____

c. What do the darkened circles and squares represent? The undarkened ones?

_____

d. Does the II_2 person have the trait? Does the III_5 person have the trait? _____

_____

e. Is the trait dominant or recessive? How can you tell? _____

_____

f. Is person I_1 heterozygous or homozygous for the trait? How can you tell? How about person II_4?

_____

_____

2. Describe karyotyping, and tell why it is useful. (17 points) _____

_____

_____

_____

_____

3. What is the Human Genome Project? List two of its possible benefits and one drawback or possible abuse connected with it. (15 points)

_____

_____

_____

_____

_____

_____

_____

Name _____ Class _____ Date _____

4. The table below gives information on the symptoms of various chromosomal and single-allele disorders. Fill in the name of each disorder, choosing among the following: hemophilia, sickle-cell disease, Tay-Sach's disease, Down syndrome, Turner syndrome, Huntington's disease, cystic fibrosis, color blindness, cri-du-chat syndrome, and Klinefelter syndrome. Then state whether each is caused by monosomy, trisomy, defective chromosome structure, a recessive single allele, a dominant single allele, codominant alleles, or a sex-linked gene. (30 points)

SYMPTOMS	NAME	CAUSE
a. Brain deterioration in middle age		
b. Excessive bleeding		
c. Tangling of red blood cells		
d. Very small head, serious disabilities		
e. Almond-shaped eyes, enlarged tongue		
f. Lipid buildup in brain, seizures		
g. Males: underdeveloped testes, sterility		
h. Excessive mucus from organs		
i. Inability to distinguish hues		
j. Females: below-normal height, sterility		

5. a. What is genetic counseling? (20 points) _____

_____

b. Describe two general methods for genetically screening people who plan to have children.

_____

c. Describe two kinds of fetal testing. _____

_____

_____

d. Explain why genetic screening and fetal diagnosis during pregnancy can be important.

_____

_____

Unit 2 Test A

Choose the best answer for each question and write its letter in the blank.

_____ **1.** Alleles are different genes for the same
    a. cross-breeding.   **c.** genetic defect.
    b. trait.   **d.** dominance.

_____ **2.** A monohybrid cross is used to study
    a. two opposing traits.   **c.** a single trait.
    b. traits in humans only.   **d.** traits in animals only.

_____ **3.** A heterozygous organism is one in which alleles for a particular trait are
    a. identical.   **c.** pure-bred.
    b. different.   **d.** not dominant.

_____ **4.** Any characteristic that can be passed from parent to offspring is a
    a. phenotype.   **c.** monohybrid.
    b. dihybrid.   **d.** trait.

_____ **5.** If an organism receives different genetic information from each parent,
    a. it will have a genetic disorder.   **c.** it is a pure-bred.
    b. it is a hybrid.   **d.** it is a genotype.

_____ **6.** Mendel crossed a pure-bred tall plant (P) with a pure-bred short plant (p). Then he let the offspring self-fertilize to produce a second generation. What was the ratio of tall plants to short plants in the second generation? Use Punnett squares to find your answer.
    a. 2 : 1   **c.** 3 : 1
    b. 4 : 1   **d.** 1 : 1

_____ **7.** When neither allele expresses itself fully in a phenotype, the gene shows
    a. incomplete dominance.   **c.** recessive.
    b. a test cross.   **d.** homozygous.

_____ **8.** Scientists can predict the approximate results of cross-breeding by using
    a. intermediate inheritance.   **c.** hybridization.
    b. the laws of probability.   **d.** allele blending.

_____ **9.** An allele that is not expressed in a hybrid is
    a. dominant.   **c.** homozygous.
    b. pure-bred.   **d.** recessive.

_____ **10.** An example of a polygenic trait is
    a. eye color in humans.   **c.** seed shape in pea plants.
    b. seed color in pea plants.   **d.** tallness in pea plants.

_____ **11.** All sex-linked traits are controlled by genes found on
    a. sperm cells.   **c.** monohybrids.
    b. X or Y chromosomes.   **d.** dihybrids.

_____ **12.** Gene maps are used to locate genes on
    a. chromosomes.   **c.** DNA pairings.
    b. sex-linked traits.   **d.** Punnett squares.

_____ **13.** Nondisjunction in all pairs of chromosomes at once is called
    a. monosomy.   **c.** inversion.
    b. trisomy.   **d.** polyploidy.

_____ **14.** If a sperm carrying a Y chromosome fertilizes an egg, it will produce a what?
    a. male   **c.** autosome
    b. female   **d.** trisomy

_____ **15.** Genetic recombination is defined as the
  a. mapping of genes.
  b. shuffling of genes into new combinations by crossing over.
  c. grouping of genes on a chromosome.
  d. elimination of sex-linked traits by genetic engineering.

_____ **16.** A sex-limited trait is an autosomal trait that is expressed
  a. in both sexes.   **c.** only in one sex.
  b. in animals only.   **d.** only in females.

_____ **17.** When a zygote receives only one chromosome instead of two,
  a. monosomy has occurred.   **c.** the chromosome has inverted.
  b. polyploidy has occurred.   **d.** there are no sex-linked traits.

_____ **18.** When a piece of chromosome attaches to a chromosome in a different pair, what happens?
  a. Inversion has occurred.   **c.** There is no mutation.
  b. Duplication has occurred.   **d.** Translocation has occurred.

_____ **19.** Deletion is the loss of one or more genes from a chromosome during
  a. inversion.   **c.** polyploid disjunction.
  b. monosomy.   **d.** division.

_____ **20.** Traits that are expressed differently but occur in both sexes are
  a. sex-limited.   **c.** sex determined.
  b. autosomes.   **d.** sex-influenced.

_____ **21.** The amount of adenine always equals the amount of thymine in
  a. DNA.   **c.** hybrids.
  b. monohybrids.   **d.** sex-linked traits.

_____ **22.** An operon is a group of genes with
  a. the same chromosome number.   **c.** a codon.
  b. related functions.   **d.** a double helix.

_____ **23.** Intervening genes that are not part of a code for a protein are called
  a. exons.   **c.** introns.
  b. codons.   **d.** base-pair substitutions.

_____ **24.** The part of the gene that continuously makes a repressor protein is the
  a. regulator.   **c.** operon.
  b. eukaryote.   **d.** structural gene.

_____ **25.** The process of gene expression in prokaryotes is
  a. simpler than it is in eukaryotes.
  b. more complex than it is in eukaryotes.
  c. completely different than it is in eukaryotes.
  d. the same as it is in eukaryotes.

_____ **26.** The double-helix structure of DNA resembles a
  a. cone.   **c.** zig-zag pattern.
  b. spiralled ladder.   **d.** cell membrane.

_____ **27.** DNA and RNA differ in the composition of their
  a. purines.   **c.** sugars.
  b. proteins.   **d.** lipids.

_____ **28.** Point mutation involves the replacement of one pair of bases in a
  a. prokaryote.   **c.** mutagen.
  b. eukaryote.   **d.** gene.

_____ **29.** Transcription is the process of transferring information from
  a. DNA to RNA.   **c.** DNA to a chromosome.
  b. DNA to a gene.   **d.** RNA to a codon.

Unit 2 Test A

_____ **30.** A mutagen is a factor in the environment that can cause a
    a. transcription.
    b. mutation.
    c. DNA coiling.
    d. protein synthesis.

_____ **31.** Hybrid vigor results from
    a. outbreeding.
    b. inbreeding.
    c. vectoring.
    d. vaccine production.

_____ **32.** It is not always possible to control a genetically engineered bacterium that is
    a. a prokaryote.
    b. sexually produced.
    c. released into the environment.
    d. an insulin carrier.

_____ **33.** Hemophilia is a disorder that causes
    a. red blood cells to look like sickles.
    b. nervous system breakdown.
    c. monosomy 21.
    d. excessive bleeding.

_____ **34.** A pure-bred tall plant was crossed with a purebred short plant to produce all tall offspring. What was the *genotype* of the offspring?
    a. Tt
    b. tt
    c. ctt
    d. TT

_____ **35.** Plasmids are small, circular pieces of DNA found in
    a. plant cellulose.
    b. human skin.
    c. bacteria.
    d. African bees.

_____ **36.** In the genetic engineering of insulin, plasmid DNA and human DNA are cut by
    a. a tetracycline gene.
    b. an insulin harvest.
    c. a recombinant.
    d. a restriction enzyme.

_____ **37.** The application of biological science to practical problems is called
    a. biotechnology.
    b. genetic engineering.
    c. cytology.
    d. morphology.

_____ **38.** Mammalian cells can be engineered to make complex proteins such as
    a. yeast.
    b. blood-clotting protein.
    c. hemophilia.
    d. *Agrobacterium tumefaciens.*

_____ **39.** In genetic engineering, a vector is a
    a. recombinant DNA.
    b. gene splicer.
    c. carrier of genetic material.
    d. restriction enzyme.

_____ **40.** The probability that two separate events will both happen is calculated by multiplying their separate
    a. probabilities.
    b. combinations.
    c. outcomes.
    d. guesses.

_____ **41.** The trisomy condition in individuals with XXY chromosomes is
    a. Down syndrome.
    b. Klinefelter syndrome.
    c. Turner syndrome.
    d. hemophilia.

_____ **42.** Karyotypes are photographs that show an individual's
    a. chromosomes in homologous pairs.
    b. recombinant DNA.
    c. genome project.
    d. trisomy pairs.

_____ **43.** Color blindness is a genetic disorder that is
    a. related to Down syndrome.
    b. sex-linked.
    c. non-sex-linked.
    d. damaging to hemoglobin.

_____ **44.** A genetic disorder that prevents the use of an amino acid in milk is
    a. phenylketonuria.
    b. amniocentesis.
    c. Tay-Sachs disorder.
    d. sickle-cell disease.

_____ **45.** Cri-du-chat syndrome is a disorder caused by what?
    a. an incorrect number of chromosomes
    b. a trisomy condition
    c. inability to produce hemoglobin
    d. a defective chromosome structure

_____ **46.** Nondisjunction is the failure of chromosomes to separate
    a. during meiosis.   **c.** before meiosis.
    b. during mitosis.   **d.** during monosomy.

_____ **47.** Another word for Turner syndrome is
    a. Klinefelter syndrome.   **c.** monosomy X.
    b. cystic fibrosis.   **d.** single-allele disease.

_____ **48.** Cystic fibrosis is a genetic disorder that causes
    a. mucus secretion.   **c.** low hemoglobin.
    b. color blindedness.   **d.** genomes.

_____ **49.** In a pedigree, a square represents a(n)
    a. gene.   **c.** inherited disorder.
    b. male.   **d.** chromosome.

_____ **50.** Most genetic disorders are caused by
    a. double alleles.   **c.** mutant alleles.
    b. sickle-shaped cells.   **d.** lipid accumulation.

Chapter 13 Test A

Choose the best answer for each question and write its letter in the blank.

_____ 1. Spontaneous generation is a hypothesis that life can come from
     a. living matter.   **c.** nonliving matter.
     b. cells.   **d.** DNA.

_____ 2. Pasteur proved that no life can arise from
     a. nonliving matter.   **c.** bacteria.
     b. one parent.   **d.** curve-necked flasks.

_____ 3. Redi worked with maggots on meat in an attempt to prove the validity of
     a. nonliving things.   **c.** genetic theory.
     b. biogenesis.   **d.** Pasteur's experiment.

_____ 4. When Earth was first formed, it was probably
     a. gravityless.   **c.** quite cold.
     b. under an atmosphere.   **d.** very hot.

_____ 5. The primitive atmosphere lacked
     a. free oxygen.   **c.** carbon dioxide.
     b. methane.   **d.** nitrogen.

_____ 6. Many of the gases in Earth's primitive atmosphere probably came from what source?
     a. the sun   **c.** rain
     b. volcanoes   **d.** plant life

_____ 7. Which is *not* one of the four steps in which life probably originated?
     a. the beginning of mammals   **c.** the formation of polymers
     b. the beginning of heredity   **d.** the synthesis of organic molecules

_____ 8. Oparin, Miller, and Urey have performed experiments to test
     a. the hypothesis that polymers were caused by enzymes.
     b. the age of Earth.
     c. Crick's theory of membranes and droplets.
     d. hypotheses about the chemical reactions that produced organic molecules.

_____ 9. Two hypotheses about the polymerization of monomers involve
     a. clay and seawater.   **c.** seawater and microspheres.
     b. salts and clay.   **d.** eukaryotes.

_____ 10. Microspheres behave like cell membranes but are actually
     a. pure protein.   **c.** clay films.
     b. protein and water bubbles.   **d.** air bubbles.

_____ 11. The first molecule able to replicate itself was probably which of the following?
     a. RNA   **c.** enzyme
     b. DNA   **d.** water

_____ 12. The first cells were probably
     a. eukaryotes.   **c.** autotrophic.
     b. protists.   **d.** heterotrophic.

_____ 13. Which phrase does *not* pertain to stromatolites?
     a. extinct   **c.** layered mats
     b. fossils   **d.** bacteria and sediment

_____ 14. The first eukaryotic cells probably evolved about
     a. 3.5 million years ago.   **c.** 1.5 billion years ago.
     b. 3.5 billion years ago.   **d.** 10 million years ago.

                     Chapter 13: Origin of Life   **57**

_____ **15.** Of the following, which is the largest time period?
   a. period   **c.** era
   b. eon   **d.** decade

_____ **16.** When continents that were once joined split and drifted,
   a. rainfall and temperature changed.   **c.** fossils began to form for the first time.
   b. the first proteins evolved.   **d.** no significant changes took place.

_____ **17.** Scientists who study life through the fossil record are called what?
   a. anatomists   **c.** molecular biologists
   b. paleontologists   **d.** geneticists

_____ **18.** Which is *not* a reason for our fossil record being incomplete?
   a. erosion   **c.** soft bodies of some organisms
   b. rock burial of fossils   **d.** production of false fossils

_____ **19.** Potassium-argon dating can be used to determine the ages of some rock by
   a. comparing the amount of argon to the amount of ^{40}K.
   b. finding out the half-life.
   c. studying the fossil record.
   d. finding homologous structures.

_____ **20.** What is the time it takes for half an element's atoms to decay radioactively?
   a. radiocarbon life   **c.** period
   b. eon   **d.** half-life

_____ **21.** Which of the following is *not* a fossil?
   a. shell imprint   **c.** preserved bone
   b. leaf imprint   **d.** rock layer

_____ **22.** Suppose scientists had determined that a fossil had lost 1/2 of its ^{14}C. About how old would the fossil be?
   a. 5600 years old   **c.** 3000 years old
   b. 2400 years old   **d.** 6000 years old

_____ **23.** Structures similar in purpose but not inherited from common ancestors are
   a. homologous.   **c.** vestigial.
   b. analogous.   **d.** embryonic.

_____ **24.** The hip bone of a python is an example of a
   a. vestigial structure.   **c.** biochemical structure.
   b. fossil record.   **d.** homologous structure.

_____ **25.** Organisms that have the most similar genetic makeup would also have
   a. the least biochemical similarities.   **c.** the least vestigial structures.
   b. a recent common ancestor.   **d.** the most distant parents.

Chapter 13 Test B

Read each question or statement and respond in the space provided.

1. Explain what each of the following terms means. Give evidence in support of the ones that are still accepted. (15 points)

a. spontaneous generation _____

_____

b. biogenesis _____

_____

_____

c. Margulis' hypothesis of endosymbiosis _____

_____

_____

_____

2. a. Compare the composition of Earth's primitive atmosphere to Earth's modern atmosphere. Which had more oxygen? More nitrogen? More carbon dioxide? More methane, ammonia, and sulfur-containing substances? (7 points)

_____

_____

b. Explain how changes in the atmosphere and in living things led to the development and evolutionary success of aerobic organisms. (7 points)

_____

_____

_____

_____

_____

_____

3. a. What does the Oparin hypothesis claim? (10 points) _____

_____

_____

b. Describe an experiment you might perform to test this hypothesis. What sort of control set-up would you use? What sort of equipment? What kinds of data would you collect? What result would support the hypothesis? (10 points)

_____

_____

_____

_____

_____

_____

4. a. Name the three most recent geological eras. Roughly how many millions of years ago did each begin? (2 points)

_____

b. During which era did the first human beings appear? (2 pts.) _____

c. During which era did the first flowering plants appear? (2 pts.) _____

d. During which era did the first fishes and amphibians appear? (2 pts.) _____

e. During which era were dinosaurs the dominant animal? (2 pts.) _____

f. During which era did the first land-dwelling air breathers appear? (2 pts.) _____

5. A scientist decides to determine the age of a fairly recent fossil by means of radioactive carbon dating. Roughly how old is a fossil if its ratio of ^{14}C to ^{12}C is $\frac{1}{8}$ that in a living organism? Show your calculation. Assume that the half-life of ^{14}C is 5600 years. (12 points)

_____

6. Classify each of the following structures as either homologous, vestigial, or analogous. (12 points)

a. the flipper of a whale and the arm of a person _____

b. the flipper of a whale and the fin of a fish _____

c. the bones at the bottom of an ape's spine that are remnants of ancestral tail bones_____

d. the wings of a butterfly and the wings of a bat _____

e. the human appendix, which has no known function _____

f. the teeth of a bear and the teeth of a dog _____

7. Briefly explain how the idea of evolutionary relationships is influenced by each of the following areas of study. (15 points)

a. comparative anatomy_____

_____

_____

b. comparative embryology _____

_____

_____

c. comparative biochemistry _____

_____

_____

Chapter 14 Test A

Choose the best answer for each question and write its letter in the blank.

_____ **1.** Change in a population over a period of time is known as
   a. biogenesis.   **c.** evolution.
   b. periodic catastrophe.   **d.** extinction.

_____ **2.** According to the principle of use and disuse, modifications caused by an organism's life style are
   a. inherited.   **c.** not inherited.
   b. diseases.   **d.** disused.

_____ **3.** Lamarck's hypothesis was disproven by Weismann, who showed that mice with severed tails had
   a. offspring with severed tails.   **c.** no offspring.
   b. offspring with abnormal tails.   **d.** offspring with normal tails.

_____ **4.** As Darwin's voyage on the *Beagle* progressed, what gradual trend did he observe?
   a. differences among animals and plants along the coast
   b. changes in the depth of the sea
   c. changes in weather
   d. degrees of seasickness based on ocean tides

_____ **5.** The choice by farmers of animal parents with the most desirable characteristics is
   a. population resources.   **c.** natural selection.
   b. selective breeding.   **d.** population accumulation.

_____ **6.** Which is *not* part of the theory of natural selection?
   a. variation within populations
   b. favorable disasters
   c. favorable variations
   d. many die, few survive

_____ **7.** In the public press, Darwin's theory was referred to as
   a. survival of the fittest.   **c.** population selection.
   b. variation of the fittest.   **d.** natural breeding.

_____ **8.** Variations in a population come from mutation and
   a. niches.   **c.** recombination.
   b. the least fit.   **d.** prokaryotes.

_____ **9.** Mutated genes that can produce major structural changes are referred to as
   a. homeobox genes.   **c.** population genes.
   b. recombined genes.   **d.** recessive genes.

_____ **10.** A population's way of life and its use of the environment is called its
   a. directional selection.   **c.** variation.
   b. trait.   **d.** niche.

_____ **11.** Many characteristics of organisms can be drawn as graphs with the same bell-like shape due to
   a. normal distribution.   **c.** directional selection.
   b. stabilizing selection.   **d.** niche disruption.

_____ **12.** Whenever two populations try to occupy the same niche,
   a. they work together.   **c.** fierce competition arises.
   b. homeobox genes decrease.   **d.** natural selection does not take place.

_____ **13.** Selection against the most common variation is known as
   a. disruptive selection.   **c.** directional selection.
   b. variable selection.   **d.** nonvariable selection.

_____ **14.** When environmental conditions favor individuals at one extreme of the normal distribution,
   a. stabilizing selection takes place.
   b. there is no selection.
   c. directional selection takes place.
   d. distribution of characteristics do not change.

_____ **15.** During stabilizing selection, there is selection against
   a. extremes.
   b. similarities.
   c. the environment.
   d. dark colors.

_____ **16.** When England became industrialized, soot from factories helped which moths survive?
   a. light-colored moths
   b. neither light nor dark moths
   c. dark moths
   d. both light and dark moths

_____ **17.** The study of all the traits in a population is called
   a. genetic equilibrium.
   b. genetic drift.
   c. allele frequency.
   d. population genetics.

_____ **18.** What is the combined genetic makeup of all members of a population called?
   a. a gene pool
   b. divergent evolution
   c. stabilizing selection
   d. convergent evolution

_____ **19.** Modern science defines biological evolution as a change within a population of
   a. randomly mating organisms.
   b. migrating species.
   c. allele frequencies.
   d. predators.

_____ **20.** If a population is in equilibrium, then all its allele frequencies must be
   a. unequal.
   b. equally favorable.
   c. significant.
   d. selectively advantaged.

_____ **21.** Genetic drift is nonselective change in
   a. gene frequency.
   b. migration.
   c. stabilizing selection.
   d. paired mating.

_____ **22.** A constant state of allele frequency with no evolution is called
   a. genetic drift.
   b. genetic equilibrium.
   c. mutational equality.
   d. significant mutation.

_____ **23.** A population of organisms that can interbreed to produce healthy offspring is
   a. a species.
   b. an evolved population.
   c. a niche.
   d. an adaptive radiation.

_____ **24.** When different species of organisms evolve similar characteristics, how can their evolution be described?
   a. divergent
   b. adaptive
   c. restrictive
   d. convergent

_____ **25.** Multiple branching of a family tree is known as what?
   a. radioactive adaptation
   b. adaptive radiation
   c. convergent evolution
   d. genetic convergence

Name _____ Class _____ Date _____

Chapter 14 Test B

Read each question or statement and respond in the space provided.

1. a. State the main ideas of Lamarck's hypothesis on evolution. (18 points)_____
_____
_____

   b. What evidence seemed to support the hypothesis? _____
_____
_____

   c. How did the evidence of Weisman refute the hypothesis?_____
_____
_____

2. a. What idea of Lyell influenced Darwin's theory? (12 points) _____
_____
_____

   b. What idea of Malthus influenced Darwin's theory? _____
_____
_____

3. In his theory of natural selection, what did Darwin suggest about each of the following. (20 points)
   a. variation
_____
_____
_____

   b. the number of young typically produced in each generation
_____
_____
_____

   c. the reason why some offspring are able to survive and reproduce
_____
_____
_____

   d. the way in which changes in population occur and the time span over which they occur
_____
_____
_____

4. There are several different mechanisms of natural selection that involve changes in niches. These mechanisms include directional selection, disruptive selection, and stabilizing selection. State which of these is involved in each of the following examples. Also predict the change, if any, produced by each. (18 points)

a. Most giraffes and trees in an area are of about the same height. Adult giraffes much taller or much shorter than this height are unusual. The type and typical height of the vegetation does not change.

_____

_____

b. Most grasshoppers in an area are the medium-green color of the grass in a typical wet year. Smaller numbers of them are light green and some are dark and brownish. There is an especially dry year, however, and most of the grass dies off. The brown soil is exposed in many areas, and the only grass that will grow at all is pale green.

_____

_____

c. In an area, some chipmunks have light-colored fur and some have dark fur, but the largest number have medium-colored fur. The ground is usually a medium-brown color in winter. However, one year snow is unusually frequent and heavy.

_____

_____

5. State whether each of the following changes in a population does or does not violate one of the conditions of the Hardy-Weinberg principle of genetic equilibrium. Explain why. (20 points)

a. Natural selection for a certain population of birds operates in the usual way, with certain alleles favored over others.

_____

b. Squirrels in a population move about within an area without leaving the population.

_____

_____

c. A small number of individual coyotes move from the outside into a population of coyotes.

_____

d. Some chickens in a population prefer certain of the roosters to others for mating, but all mating takes place within the original population.

_____

6. Identify each of the following as an example of divergent evolution by isolation, adaptive radiation, or convergent evolution. (12 points)

a. A population of wolves divides into two groups because of the migration of some individuals to a new area in which conditions are different. Both groups continue to evolve.

_____

b. A kind of rodent and a kind of snake both become adapted to life underground. Eventually both types of organisms are sightless.

_____

c. Different lizards of the same type in a certain area begin to adapt differently to different niches within the area. A number of different varieties are developed from the original type.

_____

d. Populations of a type of dog and a type of bear both move northward to a colder area. A number of generations later, most individuals of both types of animal have thicker coats than their ancestors generally did.

_____

Chapter 15 Test A

Choose the best answer for each question and write its letter in the blank.

_____ 1. A group of mammals that includes monkeys, apes, and humans is the
    a. primates.   **c.** pongids.
    b. chordates.   **d.** hominids.

_____ 2. Which is the only primate that can walk upright for an extended time?
    a. humans.   **c.** gorillas
    b. apes.   **d.** monkeys

_____ 3. The thumbs of humans can grasp things because they are
    a. opposable.   **c.** unjointed.
    b. upright.   **d.** thin.

_____ 4. The oldest known primate fossil is about
    a. 10 million years old.   **c.** 170,000 years old.
    b. 250 million years old.   **d.** 65 million years old.

_____ 5. The tarsier and the loris are monkey-like animals known as
    a. prosimians.   **c.** lemurs.
    b. prehensiles.   **d.** shrews.

_____ 6. Anthropoids of the European-Asian-African landmass evolved into
    a. New World monkeys and apes.   **c.** New World prosimians.
    b. Old World monkeys and apes.   **d.** tarsiers.

_____ 7. Archaeologists study the lives and cultures of ancient peoples through
    a. live specimens.   **c.** fossils and artifacts.
    b. prehensile maps.   **d.** New World maps.

_____ 8. A flexible tail that allows a monkey to grip branches while climbing is called
    a. prehensile.   **c.** prosimian.
    b. hominid.   **d.** spiralled.

_____ 9. What is the only species of hominids still living?
    a. *Australopithecus*.   **c.** humans
    b. spider monkeys.   **d.** apes

_____ 10. When did the first human ancestor separate from the apes?
    a. 20 million years ago.   **c.** 10 to 15 million years ago
    b. 5 to 8 million years ago.   **d.** a million years ago

_____ 11. All the anthropoids that belong to the human family are called
    a. *Homo sapiens*.   **c.** hominids.
    b. *Anthropoid erectus*.   **d.** *Homo habilis*.

_____ 12. *Australopithecus* fossils were first discovered in
    a. southern Africa.   **c.** North America.
    b. Australia.   **d.** South America.

_____ 13. The oldest of all known *Australopithecus* species was discovered in 1974 and was nicknamed
    a. Afar.   **c.** Lucy.
    b. Robustus.   **d.** Africanus.

_____ 14. Archaeologists determined that *Australopithecus* could walk by studying which fossil structure?
    a. the bones of the feet   **c.** the hip bone
    b. the skull   **d.** the thigh bones

_____ **15.** *Australopithecus robustus* and *Australopithecus boisei* were probably side branches of the hominid family tree that
   a. survive to this day.
   b. became extinct about 1 million years ago.
   c. predated *Australopithecus africanus*.
   d. were ancestors of humans.

_____ **16.** The discovery of the first hominids to make tools and weapons was by
   a. the Leakeys.   **c.** Raymond Dart.
   b. Donald Johanson.   **d.** Lucy.

_____ **17.** A group of closely related species is known as a
   a. fossil.   **c.** population.
   b. genus.   **d.** primate.

_____ **18.** Because this species of hominids could make tools, it is known as
   a. *Homo erectus*.   **c.** *Homo sapiens*.
   b. *Homo habilis*.   **d.** Cro-Magnon man.

_____ **19.** Of the following, who had the largest brain?
   a. *Homo habilis*   **c.** *Homo sapiens*
   b. *Homo erectus*   **d.** *Australopithecus africanus*

_____ **20.** The word *Homo* refers to a
   a. species.   **c.** class.
   b. genus.   **d.** order.

_____ **21.** Which adaptation contributes to the ability of a species to make tools?
   a. ability to walk upright.   **c.** prehensile tails
   b. continental drift.   **d.** warm outer covering

_____ **22.** What does the name *Homo sapiens* mean?
   a. tool-maker   **c.** upright walker
   b. tree liver   **d.** wise man

_____ **23.** The earliest fully modern human fossils are about
   a. 1 million years old.   **c.** 100,000 years old.
   b. 30,000 years old.   **d.** 500,000 years old.

_____ **24.** We know something about Cro-Magnon culture because these people left behind
   a. Neanderthals.   **c.** furs.
   b. cave paintings.   **d.** brick houses.

_____ **25.** Some of the gaps in the fossil record are now being filled in by
   a. genetic information.   **c.** maps.
   b. bones.   **d.** interbreeding.

Chapter 15 Test B

Read each question or statement and respond in the space provided.

1. Identify the following characteristics as those of all primates or as those of humans only. (12 points)

   a. language and speech control areas in the brain _____

   b. eyes at the front of the face _____

   c. extended care of young _____

   d. fully upright posture _____

   e. opposable thumbs _____

   f. arms that can move freely around the shoulder joint _____

2. Identify each of the sets of characteristics in the table below as those of one of the following groups of primates: prosimians, New World monkeys, Old World monkeys, or apes. Also give an example of a member of each group. (12 points)

CHARACTERISTICS	GROUP	EXAMPLE
a. Long, prominent noses; nonprehensile tails		
b. Large size; very large brains; no tails		
c. Broad, flat noses; prehensile tails		
d. Small size; large eyes; nocturnal		

3. Compare and contrast *Australopithecus, Homo habilis,* and *Homo erectus* in terms of physical characteristics (including brain size), period when alive, and use of tools. Also explain how each got its name (20 points)

_____

_____

_____

_____

_____

_____

_____

_____

_____

_____

Name _____ Class _____ Date _____

4. a. Describe the physical characteristics of the Neanderthals. (20 points) _____
_____

b. Describe the behavior and skills of the Neanderthals. _____
_____

c. To what species did they belong? _____

d. Where were Neanderthal fossils first found? _____

e. What reasons are often given to explain why the Neanderthals died out? _____
_____
_____

5. a. Describe the physical characteristics of Cro-Magnons. (20 points)
_____

b. Describe their behavior and skills. _____
_____

c. To what species did they belong? _____

d. Where were Cro-Magnon fossils first found? _____
_____

6. Suppose you were an archaeologist studying and comparing hominid fossils. What problems would you have finding, classifying, and telling apart specimens? How might these problems cause you to make mistakes? (20 points)

_____

_____

_____

_____

_____

_____

_____

_____

_____

_____

_____

_____

_____

_____

_____

_____

_____

_____

_____

Chapter 16 Test A

Choose the best answer for each question and write its letter in the blank.

_____ **1.** The field of biology that deals with classifying organisms is called
    a. nomenclature.   **c.** hierarchy.
    b. classification.   **d.** taxonomy.

_____ **2.** To avoid confusion, scientific names for organisms are all
    a. according to country.   **c.** official and international.
    b. taxons.   **d.** in three languages.

_____ **3.** A category into which related organisms are placed is called a
    a. taxon.   **c.** binomial.
    b. systemization.   **d.** hierarchy.

_____ **4.** Linnaeus's system of classification was based upon
    a. German names for organisms.   **c.** structural similarities between organisms.
    b. colors.   **d.** human uses of organisms.

_____ **5.** A system that ranks categories from the broadest to the most specific can be thought of as a
    a. hierarchy.   **c.** nomenclature.
    b. homologous structure.   **d.** kingdom.

_____ **6.** How many groups are contained in Linnaeus's broadest division of all organisms?
    a. four   **c.** two
    b. three   **d.** one

_____ **7.** How many more levels did modern scientists add to Linnaeus's five levels of classification?
    a. one   **c.** three
    b. two   **d.** four

_____ **8.** In modern classification, the animal kingdom is divided into phyla, whereas the plant kingdom is divided into
    a. strains.   **c.** hierarchies.
    b. categories.   **d.** divisions.

_____ **9.** Identifying organisms by their genus and species names is called
    a. binomial nomenclature.   **c.** trinomial nomenclature.
    b. ancestral nomenclature.   **d.** "one-name naming".

_____ **10.** In the scientific name *Homo sapiens, sapiens* is the name of the
    a. species.   **c.** kingdom.
    b. genus.   **d.** order.

_____ **11.** Which is *not* a consideration when grouping organisms into a particular kingdom?
    a. food value   **c.** cellular structure
    b. metabolism   **d.** methods of obtaining nutrients

_____ **12.** The kingdom Protista includes many unicellular and
    a. no multicellular eukaryotes.   **c.** many multicellular prokaryotes.
    b. a few multicellular eukaryotes.   **d.** some multicellular plants.

_____ **13.** All fungi are either decomposers or
    a. parasites.   **c.** prokaryotes.
    b. protists.   **d.** producers.

_____ **14.** The organisms having no nuclear membrane and no membrane-bound organelles are the
    a. Animalia.   **c.** Protista.
    b. Monera.   **d.** Plantae.

_____ **15.** Plantlike protists are usually called
    a. decomposers.   **c.** monerans.
    b. amebas and paramecia.   **d.** algae.

_____ **16.** Molds, mildews, and yeasts all belong to which kingdom?
    a. Fungi   **c.** Animalia
    b. Protista   **d.** Prokaryote

_____ **17.** The cells of organisms belonging to the Kingdom Animalia have
    a. cellulose.   **c.** no cell walls.
    b. chitin.   **d.** protozoa.

_____ **18.** Which organisms belong to the kingdom Plantae?
    a. sea stars   **c.** algae
    b. mushrooms   **d.** mosses

_____ **19.** The more differences there are between the DNA sequences of two organisms,
    a. the more distant their common ancestor.
    b. the more recent their common ancestor.
    c. the farther apart they now live.
    d. the closer their homologous structures.

_____ **20.** New evidence suggests that crocodiles are more closely related to birds than they are to
    a. each other.   **c.** other living reptiles.
    b. their ancestors.   **d.** parakeets.

_____ **21.** Which is *not* a basis for classification?
    a. DNA similarities   **c.** physical structure
    b. protein similarities   **d.** predator relationships

_____ **22.** In a phylogenetic tree, the tips of the branches represent
    a. the most modern organisms.   **c.** the strongest organisms.
    b. the most ancient organisms.   **d.** the least divergent organisms.

_____ **23.** Each time the branch of a phylogenetic tree divides, it shows the emergence of a new
    a. kingdom.   **c.** ancestral species.
    b. single allele.   **d.** classification system.

_____ **24.** A dichotomous key is a tool used for identifying
    a. birds only.   **c.** familiar organisms.
    b. unfamiliar organisms.   **d.** family trees.

_____ **25.** Another name for a dichotomous key is a
    a. family tree.   **c.** classification key.
    b. binomial nomenclature.   **d.** taxon.

Name _____ Class _____ Date _____

Chapter 16 Test B

Read each question or statement and respond in the space provided.

1. a. What does *taxonomy* mean? (12 points)_____
_____

b. Describe Linnaeus's system of taxonomy. _____
_____
_____

c. What were two advantages of Linnaeus's system compared to the methods used until then?
_____
_____

d. What is one disadvantage of Linnaeus's system compared to the system used today?
_____

2. Suppose you were interested in the scientific classification of wolves. You looked up the scientific name for a wolf and discovered that it is *Canis lupus*.

a. How does this name illustrate binomial nomenclature? (15 points) _____

b. What taxonomic category does each part of the name represent? _____

c. If you looked up the scientific names for a dog and for a red fox, you would find that the names are *Canis familiaris* and *Vulpus fulva*, respectively. What do the names show about how closely related each of these animals is to the other and to a wolf?
_____
_____
_____

3. The seven levels of classification are, in alphabetical order: class, family, genus, kingdom, order, phylum, and species. List these seven levels in the correct taxonomic order, from highest (most general) to lowest (most specific). (10 points)
_____

4. Complete the table below by filling in the missing information on the organisms in the five kingdoms generally used in classification. (20 points)

KINGDOM	EUKARYOTIC OR PROKARYOTIC	UNICELLULAR, MULTICELLULAR, OR EITHER	AUTOTROPHIC, HETEROTROPHIC, OR EITHER
a. Monerans			
b. Protists			
c. Fungi			
d. Plants			
e. Animals			

5. Consider the following information on physical characteristics and on a corresponding protein sequence for three kinds of animals, X, Y, and Z. On the basis of the information, decide whether X is more closely related to Y or to Z. Explain your answer. (12 points)

X: legless, coldblooded, four-chambered heart, sequence QVEGKKIDEF

Y: four legs, coldblooded, two-chambered heart, sequence QVEQKKITEF

Z: legless, warmblooded, four-chambered heart, sequence QVTAKKTAEF

_____

_____

_____

_____

6. Look at the following family tree for six orders of mammals. Answer the questions below. Explain your answers on the basis of the tree and the idea of common ancestry. (16 points)

a. Which of the orders shown is most closely related to Rodentia?

_____

b. Which two of the orders are most distantly related to Rodentia?

_____

_____

c. Which of the orders most recently became a separate order?

_____

d. Which of the orders has been a separate order for the longest time?

_____

Insectivora   Lagomorpha   Rodentia   Primates   Carnivora

7. How might you use a dichotomous key to identify a kind of plant you have never seen before? (15 points)

_____

_____

_____

_____

_____

_____

_____

_____

_____

_____

_____

_____

Unit 3 Test A

Choose the best answer for each question and write its letter in the blank.

_____ **1.** Analogous structures are similar in purpose, but have evolved from
      a. the same structures.   **c.** different structures.
      b. each other.   **d.** legs and arms.

_____ **2.** People who study fossil remains often determine the age of a rock by
      a. DNA analysis.   **c.** protein analysis.
      b. potassium-argon dating.   **d.** lipid studies.

_____ **3.** The hypothesis that life can arise from nonliving matter is called
      a. spontaneous generation.   **c.** genetics.
      b. biogenesis.   **d.** natural selection.

_____ **4.** Membranes may have originally developed from
      a. electrode sparks.   **c.** microspheres.
      b. methane gas.   **d.** volcanoes.

_____ **5.** Before life appeared on the earth, there was little or no free
      a. methane.   **c.** carbon dioxide.
      b. oxygen.   **d.** sulfur dioxide.

_____ **6.** One hypothesis about the origin of inner membranes is that they formed from the infolding of the what?
      a. cell membrane   **c.** nucleus
      b. mitochondria   **d.** nitrogen envelope

_____ **7.** Paleontologists are scientists who study life through
      a. biochemical reactions.   **c.** the fossil record.
      b. soft bodies of organisms.   **d.** planetary debris.

_____ **8.** Inherited but unused body structures are known as
      a. vestigial structures.   **c.** fossil structures.
      b. homologous structures.   **d.** phylogenetic structures.

_____ **9.** Who was the person who used curved-neck flasks to prove that life cannot arise from nonliving matter?
      a. Redi   **c.** Crick
      b. Miller   **d.** Pasteur

_____ **10.** Convergent evolution is the evolution of what by different types of organisms?
      a. similar traits   **c.** adaptive radiations
      b. dissimilar traits   **d.** isolations

_____ **11.** According to the theory of natural selection,
      a. all variations are favorable.
      b. some variations are favorable.
      c. organisms never over-reproduce.
      d. there is no variation in a given population.

_____ **12.** Directional selection is the favoring of individuals at one extreme of a
      a. stability.   **c.** normal distribution.
      b. genetic drift.   **d.** paired mating.

_____ **13.** Disruptive selection is selection against what?
      a. the most unusual variation   **c.** the most common variation
      b. the environment   **d.** predators

_____ **14.** When all the allele frequencies in a population are stable, it is in
      a. disruption.   **c.** genetic drift.
      b. directional equilibrium.   **d.** genetic equilibrium.

_____ **15.** When members of the same species interbreed, the offspring are
  a. normal and healthy.   **c.** mutants.
  b. genetically undesirable.   **d.** always exactly alike.

_____ **16.** A nonselective change in gene frequency is called
  a. genetic drift.   **c.** a niche.
  b. selective inbreeding.   **d.** stabilization.

_____ **17.** Adaptive radiation leads to
  a. multiple branching of a family tree.   **c.** no change in traits.
  b. stabilization.   **d.** spontaneous generation.

_____ **18.** Individuals with average phenotypes are favored by
  a. directional selection.   **c.** stabilizing selection.
  b. paleontologists.   **d.** dark genotypes.

_____ **19.** A gene pool is the combined genetic makeup of all members of a
  a. kingdom.   **c.** specific mutation.
  b. migration.   **d.** population.

_____ **20.** A change within a population of allele frequencies is defined as
  a. biological evolution.   **c.** dramatic, immediate mutation.
  b. destruction of a niche.   **d.** endangered species.

_____ **21.** What effect can a mutation in a homeobox gene produce?
  a. stabilize a population   **c.** major structural changes
  b. prevent variation   **d.** decrease competition

_____ **22.** According to the theory of natural selection, variations are
  a. sometimes favorable.   **c.** never favorable.
  b. unimportant to evolution. **d.** always extreme.

_____ **23.** Fierce competition can arise when two populations try to occupy the same
  a. species.   **c.** niche.
  b. ecosystem.   **d.** allele.

_____ **24.** The ability to walk upright helped free hominids to
  a. swing from branches.   **c.** eliminate opposable thumbs.
  b. make tools.   **d.** run faster.

_____ **25.** When did the earliest *Homo sapiens* probably evolve?
  a. 500,000 to 300,000 years ago   **c.** 5 million to 3 million years ago
  b. 20,000 years ago   **d.** 1 million years ago

_____ **26.** The New World monkeys of South America evolved from
  a. anthropoids in Africa.   **c.** anthropoids on the American continents.
  b. *Australopithecus*.   **d.** *Homo habilis*.

_____ **27.** *Australopithecus* is a species of
  a. prosimian.   **c.** spider monkey.
  b. Old World monkey.   **d.** hominid.

_____ **28.** Prehensile tails are used like an extra arm by monkeys to
  a. hold food.   **c.** swing from tree branches.
  b. walk upright.   **d.** warn Neanderthals.

_____ **29.** Which was the first hominid to make tools and weapons?
  a. *Homo sapiens*   **c.** *Australopithecus africanus*
  b. *Homo erectus*   **d.** *Homo habilis*

_____ **30.** The people who first discovered the remains of *Homo habilis* were
  a. Louis and Mary Leaky.   **c.** Lamarck and Darwin.
  b. Johanson and his team.   **d.** Lucy and Raymond Dart.

_____ **31.** *Homo habilis* means "handy man." *Homo erectus* means what?
    a. "wise man"   **c.** "upright man"
    b. "tall man"   **d.** "builder man"

_____ **32.** The skeleton called "Lucy" is thought to be a member of which species?
    a. *Homo habilis*   **c.** *Australopithecus afarensis*
    b. *Australopithecus africanus*   **d.** *Homo erectus*

_____ **33.** Early humans who left behind cave paintings in an area of France are known as
    a. Cro-Magnons.   **c.** Prosimians.
    b. *Homo habilis*.   **d.** Prometheans.

_____ **34.** The human family of anthropoids are all called the
    a. Neanderthals.   **c.** Cro-Magnons.
    b. *Homo sapiens*.   **d.** hominids.

_____ **35.** Genetic information has allowed researchers to discover a very close relationship between humans and
    a. chimpanzees.   **c.** Cro-Magnons.
    b. *Homo sapiens*.   **d.** non-primates.

_____ **36.** Two prosimians are the loris and the
    a. apes.   **c.** *Australopithecus africani.*
    b. spider monkey.   **d.** tarsier.

_____ **37.** When did the Neanderthals live in Europe and Asia?
    a. 1 and 2 million years ago   **c.** 10 and 20 million years ago
    b. 70,000 and 80,000 years ago   **d.** 130,000 and 30,000 years ago

_____ **38.** Which body part would you expect *not* to be preserved in a fossil?
    a. leg bone   **c.** skin
    b. tooth   **d.** ankle bone

_____ **39.** Another name for a ranking system is a
    a. nomenclature.   **c.** protist.
    b. hierarchy.   **d.** taxonomist.

_____ **40.** To which kingdom do animals belong?
    a. Monera   **c.** Fungi
    b. Plantae   **d.** Animalia

_____ **41.** New evidence has placed crocodiles close on the evolutionary tree to
    a. reptiles.   **c.** protists.
    b. birds.   **d.** mammals.

_____ **42.** Scientists can classify unfamiliar organisms by using a
    a. Linnaean system.   **c.** trinomial nomenclature.
    b. nonhierarchical key.   **d.** dichotomous key.

_____ **43.** Which is *not* a fungus?
    a. moss   **c.** mildew
    b. mushroom   **d.** mold

_____ **44.** Binomial nomenclature uses two words to identify organisms by their genus and their
    a. hierarchy.   **c.** heterotrophy.
    b. species.   **d.** cellular structure.

_____ **45.** In Linnaeus's system, related organisms are placed in a category called a
    a. taxon.   **c.** phylogene.
    b. cytochrome.   **d.** homology.

_____ **46.** All prokaryotes belong to the kingdom
    a. Animalia.   **c.** Insectivora.
    b. Protozoa.   **d.** Monera.

        Unit 3: Change and Diversity **75**

_____ **47.** Monera have no membrane-bound organelles and no
  a. bacteria.
  b. prokaryote.
  c. cellular membrane.
  d. nucleus.

_____ **48.** Multicellular eukaryotes that perform photosynthesis are known as
  a. plants.
  b. bacteria.
  c. protists.
  d. animalia.

_____ **49.** Which is an example of an animal-like protist?
  a. algae
  b. the worm
  c. mildew
  d. the Paramecium

_____ **50.** All organisms, living or extinct, descended from
  a. fungi.
  b. plants.
  c. prokaryotes.
  d. eukaryotes.

Chapter 17 Test A

Choose the best answer for each question and write its letter in the blank.

_____ **1.** Who was the first person to isolate the tobacco mosaic virus?
    a. Adolf Mayer
    b. Dmitri Ivanovsky
    c. Martinus Beijerinck
    d. Wendell Stanley

_____ **2.** A virus is a particle that consists of a core of nucleic acid and a
    a. protein coat.
    b. poison.
    c. bacterium.
    d. crystal.

_____ **3.** Viruses were only seen after the invention of the
    a. particle accelerator.
    b. light microscope.
    c. transmission electron microscope.
    d. bacteria filter.

_____ **4.** The core of a virus contains either RNA or
    a. a capsid.
    b. DNA.
    c. bacteriophage.
    d. mosaic.

_____ **5.** The capsid of a virus protects its
    a. nucleic acid.
    b. protein coat.
    c. membrane.
    d. envelope.

_____ **6.** The spikes covering the envelopes of some viruses allow them to do what?
    a. burst capsids
    b. filter bacteria
    c. attach to cells they infect
    d. stop protein streams

_____ **7.** Because viruses are so small, they have to be measured in
    a. millimeters.
    b. phages.
    c. angstroms.
    d. nanometers.

_____ **8.** One hypothesis about the origin of viruses is that they evolved from
    a. fungi.
    b. cells of host organisms.
    c. minerals.
    d. parasites.

_____ **9.** Viruses that infect and kill bacteria are known as
    a. bacteriophages.
    b. nanometers.
    c. chromosomal invaders.
    d. site-specific bacteria.

_____ **10.** What is responsible for the specificity of viruses?
    a. receptor proteins on the cell membranes of their host cells
    b. their incredibly small size
    c. their similarity to plants
    d. their polyhedral shape

_____ **11.** Viruses are more likely to have genes like their host's than like other
    a. chromosomes.
    b. viruses.
    c. bacteria.
    d. parasites.

_____ **12.** Which characteristic of living things do viruses lack?
    a. independent growth
    b. DNA
    c. RNA
    d. protein

_____ **13.** A parasite requires host cells to reproduce and always
    a. defends the host cells.
    b. harms the host cells.
    c. breeds with the host cells.
    d. neither harms nor hurts the host cells.

_____ **14.** The process of reproduction in viruses is called
    a. viral replication.
    b. prophage.
    c. viral reproduction.
    d. reproductive specificity.

_____ **15.** Two different cycles in which a virus can infect a host cell are the lysogenic cycle and the
  a. prophage cycle.　　　　　　　　　　**c.** lytic cycle.
  b. bacteriophage cycle.　　　　　　　　**d.** prion cycle.

_____ **16.** The nucleic acid of a bacterial virus that attaches to the host's chromosome is called a
  a. lytic acid.　　　　　　　　　　　　**c.** prophage.
  b. bacteriophage.　　　　　　　　　　**d.** lysogenic acid.

_____ **17.** When a host cell is rapidly killed by a virus, what type of viral replication cycle has occurred?
  a. lytic cycle　　　　　　　　　　　　**c.** retrocycle
  b. lysogenic cycle　　　　　　　　　　**d.** nucleic acid cycle

_____ **18.** Which is *not* a stage in the lysogenic cycle?
  a. attachment of bacteriophage to cell　　**c.** DNA injected
  b. invasion of virus by cell　　　　　　**d.** prophage cut off from host chromosome

_____ **19.** Tiny particles of pure RNA that cause diseases in plants are known as
  a. viroids.　　　　　　　　　　　　　**c.** bacteriophages.
  b. prions.　　　　　　　　　　　　　**d.** retroviruses.

_____ **20.** Which disease is caused by a virus?
  a. diabetes mellitus　　　　　　　　　**c.** influenza
  b. malaria　　　　　　　　　　　　　**d.** sickle-cell anemia

_____ **21.** Infecting a person with the weakened form of a virus to prevent disease is called what?
  a. transference　　　　　　　　　　　**c.** vaccination
  b. genetic engineering　　　　　　　　**d.** replication

_____ **22.** Using viruses to transfer genes from one host cell to another is an example of
  a. genetic engineering.　　　　　　　　**c.** vaccination.
  b. parasitism.　　　　　　　　　　　　**d.** retrovision.

_____ **23.** Viruses that replicate nucleic acid in the reverse of the standard way are known as
  a. prions.　　　　　　　　　　　　　**c.** retroviruses.
  b. genetic engineers.　　　　　　　　　**d.** bacteriophages.

_____ **24.** Prions are particles of protein that cause diseases in what kind of organism?
  a. animals　　　　　　　　　　　　　**c.** bacteria
  b. plants　　　　　　　　　　　　　　**d.** other viruses

_____ **25.** One way viroids and prions differ from viruses is that they have no
  a. RNA.　　　　　　　　　　　　　　**c.** capsids.
  b. chemistry.　　　　　　　　　　　　**d.** power to cause disease.

Chapter 17 Test B

Read each question or statement and respond in the space provided.

1. Explain how study of tobacco mosaic disease by Mayer, Ivanovsky, Beijerinck, and Stanley contributed to current understanding of viruses. (12 points)

_____
_____
_____
_____
_____
_____
_____
_____

2. Describe the structure, shape, size, and specificity of viruses. (15 points)

_____
_____
_____
_____

3. Some scientists consider viruses to be living things. Others consider viruses to be nonliving. Suppose you were given the task of deciding between these two views. What evidence could you use to support each? (15 points)

_____
_____
_____

4. Describe the process by which viruses may have evolved from cells of host organisms they now infect. What evidence supports this view? (15 points)

_____
_____
_____
_____
_____
_____
_____

5. What occurs during each of the following processes of viral infection of a host bacterium? (16 points)

a. lytic cycle

_____

_____

_____

_____

b. lysogenic cycle

_____

_____

_____

_____

6. An organism has been infected with a virus. Suppose you observed the structure and operation of the virus. How could you tell whether it is a standard virus or a retrovirus? (12 points)

_____

_____

_____

_____

_____

7. Complete the following table, which illustrates the differences between viruses, viroids, and prions. (15 points)

AGENT	AFFECT PLANTS OR ANIMALS	NUCLEIC ACID PRESENT (DNA, RNA, EITHER, OR NEITHER)	PROTEIN PRESENT? (YES/NO)
a. virus			
b. viroid			
c. prion			

Chapter 18 Test A

Choose the best answer for each question and write its letter in the blank.

_____ 1. The most numerous organisms on the earth are the
  a. eukaryotes.   **c.** endospores.
  b. monerans.   **d.** fungi.

_____ 2. Prokaryotes do have a cell membrane but do not have a
  a. nucleus.   **c.** ribosome.
  b. single cell.   **d.** cell wall.

_____ 3. What are all of the 5,000 known species of monerans?
  a. eukaryotes   **c.** viruses
  b. prokaryotes   **d.** multicellular

_____ 4. Which field has been the most useful in the study of monerans?
  a. molecular biology   **c.** taxonomy
  b. paleontology   **d.** archaeology

_____ 5. The kingdom Monera can be divided into two groups: eubacteria and
  a. methanogens.   **c.** archaebacteria.
  b. cyanobacteria.   **d.** gram-negative bacteria.

_____ 6. Archaebacteria called chemosynthesizers use inorganic compounds as a(n)
  a. energy source.   **c.** sulfur-storing site.
  b. habitat.   **d.** host.

_____ 7. The archaebacteria that produce methane are called
  a. thermoacidophiles.   **c.** extreme halophiles.
  b. eubacteria.   **d.** methanogens.

_____ 8. Archaebacteria that thrive in very salty conditions, such as the Dead Sea, are called
  a. thermoacidophiles.   **c.** extreme halophiles.
  b. cyanobacteria.   **d.** gram-negative bacteria.

_____ 9. Which of the following is an important tool for classifying eubacteria?
  a. gram stain   **c.** chromatium stain
  b. methanogen stain   **d.** chemosynthesis stain

_____ 10. Gram-negative monerans that can perform plantlike photosynthesis and release oxygen
  are called
  a. peptidoglycan layers.   **c.** methanogens.
  b. cyanobacteria.   **d.** actinomycetes.

_____ 11. Which of the following is a gram-positive bacterium?
  a. *Oscillatorium*   **c.** *Lactobacillus*
  b. rhizobacterium   **d.** cyanobacterium

_____ 12. One group of gram-positive bacteria, used to make antibiotics, is called the
  a. actinomycetes.   **c.** *Clostridia.*
  b. rhizobacteria.   **d.** sulfur-producing bacteria.

_____ 13. In the root nodules of such plants as clover and alfalfa grow bacteria called
  a. Clostridium botulinum.   **c.** rhizobacteria.
  b. cyanobacteria.   **d.** blue-green algae.

_____ 14. Gram-negative bacteria are distinguished by an extra layer of
  a. lipids.   **c.** proteins.
  b. nodules.   **d.** sulfur.

_____ 15. How do Rhizobacteria help plants?
  a. through parasitism   **c.** by producing toxin
  b. by fixing nitrogen   **d.** by fixing oxygen

_____ **16.** Which bacteria were the first living organisms discovered in the volcanic vents of Mount St. Helens?
  a. rhizobacteria
  b. *Chromatia*
  c. actinomycetes
  d. cyanobacteria

_____ **17.** Organisms that obtain energy from inorganic substances instead of sunlight are called
  a. chemoautotrophs.
  b. photoheterotrophs.
  c. flagella.
  d. photoautotrophs.

_____ **18.** Whiplike structures used by monerans for movement are called
  a. spheres.
  b. spirilla.
  c. flagella.
  d. pili.

_____ **19.** Photoheterotrophs need two things to produce energy: carbon compounds and
  a. sunlight.
  b. aerobes.
  c. gram-negative bacteria.
  d. tetani.

_____ **20.** Individual cells of monerans can be spheres, spirals, or
  a. cubes.
  b. rods.
  c. flagella.
  d. plasmids.

_____ **21.** Bacterial cells pick up and incorporate DNA from dead bacterial cells in a process called
  a. transformation.
  b. symbiosis.
  c. conjugation.
  d. binary fission.

_____ **22.** What is the term for using a virus to transfer DNA from one bacteria cell to another?
  a. mutualism
  b. transduction
  c. conjugation
  d. plasmid reduction

_____ **23.** The process in which the chromosome of a moneran replicates and the cell divides is called
  a. transduction.
  b. symbiosis.
  c. decomposition.
  d. binary fission.

_____ **24.** Which of the following is *not* true of mutualism?
  a. two organisms involved
  b. a symbiotic relationship
  c. not a symbiotic relationship
  d. both organisms benefit

_____ **25.** The bacterial process of exchanging genetic material through cell-to-cell contact is
  a. conjugation.
  b. transformation.
  c. symbiosis.
  d. binary fission.

Chapter 18 Test B

Read each question or statement and respond in the space provided.

1. In what ways are monerans different from other organisms? (15 points)

_____

_____

_____

_____

2. Imagine that you are a biologist studying archaebacteria. You find such organisms that have each of the following characteristics. Classify each as either a methanogen, thermoacidophile, chemosynthesizer, or extreme halophile. (12 points)

    a. uses H_2S as an energy source, is found near a hot volcanic vent on the ocean floor

_____

    b. is found in the Dead Sea

_____

    c. is found in hot water that has a pH of 3

_____

    d. survives without oxygen, produces CH_4

_____

3. a. What are eubacteria? (4 points)

_____

    b. What are three common subgroups of eubacteria? (4 points)

_____

    c. How can you tell these subgroups apart? (4 points)

_____

_____

_____

_____

4. What are the three basic shapes of monerans? What are the technical terms for monerans with each of these shapes? (10 points)

_____

5. State the source of energy for each of the following types of monerans. (12 points)

    a. standard autotrophs

_____

    b. chemoautotrophs

_____

    c. standard heterotrophs

_____

    d. photoheterotrophs

_____

Name _____ Class _____ Date _____

6. Imagine that you have observed monerans that function in each of the following ways in the presence and the absence of oxygen. Identify each as either an obligate aerobe, an obligate anaerobe, or a facultative anaerobe. Also give an example of a moneran that fits each category. (12 points)

    a. can live in the presence or in the absence of oxygen

_____

    b. dies in the absence of oxygen

_____

    c. dies in the presence of oxygen

_____

7. Identify each of the following as either binary fission, conjugation, transformation, transduction, or endospore formation. Also state whether the process is an example of genetic exchange, asexual cell reproduction, or cell survival strategy. (15 points)

    a. A chromosome replicates and a cell divides.

_____

    b. A cell becomes dehydrated, thick-walled, and inactive.

_____

    c. A cell picks up and incorporates DNA from a dead cell.

_____

    d. A cell obtains new DNA from another cell through viral infection.

_____

    e. A cell exchanges genetic material through cell-to-cell contact.

_____

8. State four beneficial uses of bacteria. (12 points)

_____

_____

_____

_____

_____

_____

_____

_____

Chapter 19 Test A

Choose the best answer for each question and write its letter in the blank.

_____ **1.** Two things that all protists have in common are being eukaryotes and having
   a. cilia.
   b. membrane-bound organelles.
   c. flagella.
   d. chlorophyll.

_____ **2.** One way to classify protists is to divide them into
   a. heterotrophs, autotrophs, and decomposers.
   b. plant-like, animal-like, and algae-like.
   c. unicellular, multicellular, and noncellular.
   d. protozoans, ameba, and paramecia.

_____ **3.** What is the term for all protists with animal-like characteristics?
   a. sarcodinians.   **c.** zooflagellates.
   b. protozoans.   **d.** amebas.

_____ **4.** Many amebas can survive harsh conditions by forming
   a. flagellates.   **c.** cysts.
   b. spores.   **d.** pseudopods.

_____ **5.** A zooflagellate that eats cellulose and lives in termites is
   a. *Entameba histolytica*.   **c.** *Trypanosoma*.
   b. *Paramecium*.   **d.** *Trichonympha*.

_____ **6.** Sarcodinians are protozoans that move by extending lobes of
   a. nuclei.   **c.** flagella.
   b. membrane.   **d.** cytoplasm.

_____ **7.** An example of a sarcodinian is the protozoan
   a. *Plasmodium*.   **c.** *Entameba histolytica*.
   b. *Trichonympha*.   **d.** Pseudopod.

_____ **8.** Two kinds of sarcodinians that have hard shells are the radiolarians and the
   a. foraminiferans.   **c.** ciliates.
   b. amebas.   **d.** *Trypanosoma*.

_____ **9.** Which parasite causes african sleeping sickness in humans?
   a. *Trichonympha*   **c.** *Entameba histolytica*
   b. *Trypanosoma*   **d.** Sporozoan

_____ **10.** When a paramecium reproduces sexually, it exchanges genetic information by using its
   a. micronucleus.   **c.** pellicles.
   b. macronucleus.   **d.** spores.

_____ **11.** Ciliaphorans can propel themselves through water using their
   a. vacuoles.   **c.** macronucleus.
   b. cilia.   **d.** sporozites.

___✗___ **12.** Which groups of protozoans has no means of movement and lives as an animal parasite?
   a. *Paramecium*   **c.** dinoflagellates
   b. sarcodinians   **d.** sporozoans

_____ **13.** Protozoans are a part of a group of floating, microscopic ocean organisms known as
   a. protocysts.   **c.** plankton.
   b. parasites.   **d.** cysts.

_____ **14.** The protozoan that causes malaria is named
   a. *Trypanosoma*.   **c.** *Plasmodium*.
   b. Tsetse fly.   **d.** *Giardia*.

_____ **15.** What are the plant-like protists that can perform photosynthesis?
    a. dinoflagellates   **c.** plankton
    b. ciliates   **d.** algae

_____ **16.** Euglenoids, dinoflagellates, and diatoms are all
    a. multicellular algae.   **c.** green algae.
    b. brown algae.   **d.** unicellular algae.

_____ **17.** The dinoflagellates are a group of algae that
    a. grow holdfasts.   **c.** spin through water.
    b. eat small animals.   **d.** make glass cell walls.

_____ **18.** The extra pigments in red algae allow them to trap sunlight in what situation?
    a. in deep water   **c.** in forests
    b. from other organisms   **d.** at night

_____ **19.** The air bladders of brown algae keep them near the water's surface so that they can perform
    a. conjugation.   **c.** spinning.
    b. photosynthesis.   **d.** polishing.

_____ **20.** Algae that lack both cilia and flagella but that have silica are called
    a. multicellular thalli.   **c.** diatoms.
    b. euglenoids.   **d.** brown algae.

_____ **21.** Alternation of generations implies a diploid, spore-producing phase alternating with a(n)
    a. haploid, gamete-producing phase.
    b. triploid, gamete-producing phase.
    c. sperm-producing phase.
    d. asexual phase.

_____ **22.** Instead of a rigid cell wall, a *Euglena* has a flexible protein covering called a what?
    a. thallus   **c.** pellicle
    b. hydra   **d.** coralline coat

_____ **23.** Organisms that extract their nutrients from dead organisms or their remains are called
    a. decomposers.   **c.** phytoplankton.
    b. haploids.   **d.** euglenoids.

_____ **24.** The water mold known for damaging Irish potato crops in the nineteenth century is
    a. *Plasmodium.*   **c.** *Phytophthora infestans.*
    b. white rust.   **d.** *Pseudoplasmodium.*

_____ **25.** What is the name of the feeding stage in the life cycle of a plasmodial slime mold?
    a. plasmoid   **c.** zygote
    b. fungi   **d.** plasmodium

Name _____ Class _____ Date _____

Chapter 19 Test B

Read each question or statement and respond in the space provided.

1. a. What characteristic do *all* protists have in common? (5 points)

_____

b. What characteristic do *most* protists have in common? (5 points)

_____

c. What classification problem do protists present? (5 points)

_____

_____

2. The following table provides information on the three groups into which protists are generally divided. Complete the table. (15 points)

GROUP	RESEMBLE FUNGI, ANIMALS, OR PLANTS	AUTOTROPHIC, HETEROTROPHIC, OR DECOMPOSERS
a. protozoans		
b. algae		
c. slime molds		

3. Into what four groups are protozoans divided? How do the organisms in these groups differ from each other in terms of the way they move? Give an example of an organism in each group. (16 points)

_____

_____

_____

_____

4. Identify each of the labeled parts in the drawing of the Paramecium below. Choose among the following: cilia, macronucleus, oral groove, trichocysts, contractile vacuole, micronucleus, pellicle, anal pore, food vacuole. (9 points)

a. _____

b. _____

c. _____

d. _____

e. _____

f. _____

g. _____

h. _____

i. _____

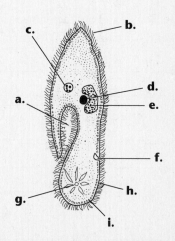

5. What disease does *Plasmodium* cause? Describe the life cycle of this organism. (12 points)

_____

_____

_____

_____

_____

_____

6. Suppose you are on a scientific expedition to classify algae. Read the following descriptions of specimens, and state in which group you would classify each. Choose from among the following: dinoflagellate, diatom, euglenoid, Chlorophyta, Rhodophyta, Phaeophyta. (18 points)

a. has a pellicle, two flagellas, and no cell wall. When placed in darkness, it functions as a heterotroph.

_____

b. has thalli with branching filaments, is 50 cm long, was collected in deep ocean water in the tropics

_____

c. was found floating on the ocean, has no cilia or flagella, has a glasslike cell wall

_____

d. is 50 m long, was found in cool ocean water, has air bladders

_____

e. has two flagellas and a cell wall, was found in salt water

_____

f. was found in a pond, is multicellular and green, has flagella, becomes dormant when water is unavailable

_____

7. a. What characteristics do fungus-like protists have in common? (5 points)

_____

_____

b. Into what three groups are these protists divided? (5 points)

_____

_____

c. State two of the characteristics of the organisms in each of these groups. (5 points)

_____

_____

_____

_____

_____

_____

_____

_____

Chapter 20 Test A

Choose the best answer for each question and write its letter in the blank.

_____ **1.** Which of the following does *not* depend on the action of fungi?
    a. bread   **c.** mushrooms
    b. abrasive polishers   **d.** antibiotics

_____ **2.** Fungi differ from plants in that they do not reproduce by seeds and lack
    a. chlorophyll.   **c.** mobility.
    b. many cells.   **d.** chitin.

_____ **3.** Most fungi have nuclei and
    a. cellulose.   **c.** mitochondria.
    b. nematodes.   **d.** ringworms.

_____ **4.** An organism that digests dead organisms and absorbs their nutrients is called a
    a. septa.   **c.** fruiting body.
    b. mycelium.   **d.** saprophyte.

_____ **5.** One of the largest organisms in the world is probably a Michigan mushroom. How much does that mushroom weigh?
    a. 9 tons   **c.** 90 metric tons
    b. 500 pounds   **d.** 500 tons

_____ **6.** Tiny tubes filled with cytoplasm and nuclei that form the body of a fungus are called
    a. hyphae.   **c.** mycelia.
    b. rhizoids.   **d.** fruiting bodies.

_____ **7.** Septa are the cross-walls that divide
    a. mycorrhizae.   **c.** hyphae.
    b. stolon basidia.   **d.** mycelia.

_____ **8.** The spore-producing structures of fungi are called what?
    a. mycelia   **c.** septa
    b. fruiting bodies   **d.** lichen

_____ **9.** Hyphae tangle and interweave to form a mass known as a
    a. mycelium.   **c.** rhizoid.
    b. basidium.   **d.** fruiting body.

_____ **10.** By fusing their nuclei and through meiosis, spores of sac fungi form a(n)
    a. basidium.   **c.** ascus.
    b. stolon.   **d.** septum.

_____ **11.** One common mold found on bread is called black bread mold, or
    a. *Rhizopus stolonifera.*   **c.** *Aspergillus flavans.*
    b. sac fungi.   **d.** club fungi.

_____ **12.** A zygospore of a fungus is a resting stage that contains many
    a. molds.   **c.** nuclei.
    b. parasites.   **d.** clubs.

_____ **13.** Stolons are hyphae that connect clumps of
    a. spores.   **c.** rhizoids.
    b. bracket fungi.   **d.** mycelia.

_____ **14.** What are the most familiar club fungi to most people?
    a. rhizoids   **c.** molds
    b. *Arthrobotrys*   **d.** mushrooms

_____ **15.** Which of the following are *not* sac fungi?
    a. lacy stinkhorn   **c.** cup fungi
    b. truffles   **d.** unicellular yeasts

_____ **16.** The process in which a smaller cell breaks away from a larger cell in some yeasts is called
 a. conjugation. **c.** budding.
 b. fusion. **d.** basidiospore.

_____ **17.** Fungi that do not undergo sexual reproduction are known as
 a. sac fungi. **c.** haploid nuclei.
 b. imperfect fungi. **d.** common molds.

_____ **18.** Fungi help return nutrients to the ecosystem by acting as
 a. predators. **c.** molds.
 b. packed mycelia. **d.** decomposers.

_____ **19.** Mycorrhizae are mutualistic associations between a fungus and what?
 a. the roots of a plant **c.** an animal
 b. protozoa **d.** plant leaves

_____ **20.** American elm trees are now rare in this country due to a sac fungus that acts both as a parasite and as a(n)
 a. imperfect fungus. **c.** decomposer.
 b. yeast. **d.** photosynthesizer.

_____ **21.** A lichen is a symbiotic association between a fungus and which organism?
 a. photosynthetic organism **c.** mycorrhizae
 b. ringworm **d.** button mushroom

_____ **22.** Lichens can grow on almost any surface because they
 a. produce their own oxygen. **c.** absorb chemical nutrients from the air.
 b. grow slimy roots. **d.** cause fungal infections.

_____ **23.** A plant can benefit from a fungus because the fungus
 a. keeps organic matter from breaking down.
 b. acts as a parasite.
 c. prevents secretion of digestive enzymes.
 d. breaks down organic matter in the soil.

_____ **24.** Which fungus is used in making soy sauce and citric acid?
 a. ringworm **c.** *Aspergillus*
 b. *Candida* **d.** *E. coli*

_____ **25.** Fungal infections are especially dangerous to
 a. people with AIDS. **c.** inorganic matter.
 b. genetic engineers. **d.** dry areas of the body.

Name _____ Class _____ Date _____

Chapter 20 Test B

Read each question or statement and respond in the space provided.

1. State the main characteristics of fungi. (18 points)

_____

_____

_____

_____

2. Identify each of the following as either hypha, septum, mycelium, fruiting body, rhizoid, stolon, basidium, or ascus. (16 points)

    a. rootlike structure that anchors a fungus to its nutrient source _____

    b. cross-wall that divides a fungal filament into sections_____

    c. structure in which sac fungus spores form _____

    d. reproductive stalk and sac in which most types of fungi reproduce_____

    e. one of the tubelike filaments that together make up most of a fungus _____

    f. structure in which club fungi form spores_____

    g. mass of filaments that form the body of a fungus_____

    h. filament that connects clumps of rootlike structures in a fungus _____

3. Complete the following table, which illustrates the characteristics of the four divisions of fungi. In each case, give the common name of the division (club fungi, common molds, imperfect fungi, or sac fungi). Then state how the fungi in that division typically reproduce. Finally, name an example of a fungus in the division. (16 points)

DIVISION	COMMON NAME	MAIN FORM OF REPRODUCTION (ASEXUAL, SEXUAL, OR BOTH)	EXAMPLE OF ORGANISM
a. Ascomycota			
b. Deuteromycota			
c. Zygomycota			
d. Basidiomycota			

4. Describe reproduction in mushrooms. (17 points)

_____

_____

_____

_____

_____

5. Suppose you were involved in a debate over whether fungi should be considered beneficial or harmful. Take one of the positions and give five pieces of supporting evidence for it. (15 points)

_____

_____

_____

_____

_____

_____

_____

_____

_____

_____

6. a. Describe the symbiosis that occurs in lichens. What type of symbiosis is this, and why? (9 points)

_____

_____

_____

_____

b. Describe the symbiosis that occurs in mycorrhizae. What type of symbiosis is this, and why? (9 points)

_____

_____

_____

_____

Unit 4 Test A

Choose the best answer for each question and write its letter in the blank.

_____ **1.** Receptor proteins on the cell membranes of viruses give them
    a. independent growth.   **c.** specificity.
    b. chromosomes.   **d.** motility.

_____ **2.** An organism that uses host cells to reproduce and harms them is a(n)
    a. parasite.   **c.** ameba.
    b. algae.   **d.** sarcodinian.

_____ **3.** The nucleic acid of a virus is contained and protected by its
    a. DNA.   **c.** cell wall.
    b. capsid.   **d.** flagella.

_____ **4.** Vaccination is the practice of preventing disease by inoculating an individual with which agent?
    a. defensive protozoa   **c.** a weakened form of the disease
    b. strong doses of viruses   **d.** antiviral drugs

_____ **5.** Tiny particles of pure RNA that cause disease in plants are known as
    a. bacteria.   **c.** retroviruses.
    b. bacteriophages.   **d.** viroids.

_____ **6.** Inside the protein coat of a virus is a core of
    a. lipids.   **c.** proteins.
    b. nucleic acid.   **d.** fatty acids.

_____ **7.** Genetic engineering techniques have been used to transfer genes from
    a. one cell to another.   **c.** inorganic matter to organic matter.
    b. cell membranes to sap.   **d.** vaccinia to halophiles.

_____ **8.** The replication process in which a virus does not immediately kill a host is called the
    a. lysogenic cycle.   **c.** vaccination.
    b. lytic cycle.   **d.** transformation cycle.

_____ **9.** How does a virus make copies of itself?
    a. by injecting chlorophyll into fungi
    b. by injecting its DNA into a host cell
    c. by blocking most of the enzymes in protists
    d. by filtering bacteria

_____ **10.** The nucleic acid of a bacterial virus attached to the host's chromosome is the
    a. prophage.   **c.** prophase.
    b. bacteriophage.   **d.** capsid.

_____ **11.** Viruses initially attach to cells using the
    a. lysosomes in their cytoplasm
    b. lysogenic host cells they carry
    c. protein spikes that cover their envelope
    d. prions in their nuclei

_____ **12.** Bacteriophages are viruses that infect which kind of organism?
    a. bacteria   **c.** plants
    b. humans   **d.** other viruses

_____ **13.** Retroviruses are viruses that replicate nucleic acid in
    a. the standard way.
    b. the genes of monerans only.
    c. three different ways.
    d. the reverse of the standard way.

_____ **14.** Of all the organisms on Earth, the most numerous are the
    a. protists.   **c.** plants.
    b. fungi.   **d.** monerans.

_____ **15.** Transformation is the process in which bacterial cells pick up DNA from
    a. viruses.   **c.** aerobes.
    b. dead bacterial cells.   **d.** fungi.

_____ **16.** A symbiotic relationship in which both organisms benefit could be termed
    a. degenerative.   **c.** mutualistic.
    b. parasitic.   **d.** competitive.

_____ **17.** Extreme halophiles live in environments with a lot of which substance?
    a. sand   **c.** sugar
    b. salt   **d.** methane

_____ **18.** The group of bacteria used in the production of antibiotics are
    a. gram-positive.   **c.** the amebas.
    b. gram-negative.   **d.** rhizobacteria.

_____ **19.** Bacteria that take on a purple color during Gram staining are
    a. gram negative.   **c.** gram positive.
    b. sulfur-producing.   **d.** cyanobacteria.

_____ **20.** Methanogens belong to the group of bacteria called
    a. eubacteria.   **c.** true bacteria.
    b. *Clostridium.*   **d.** archaebacteria.

_____ **21.** Cyanobacteria can perform photosynthesis, and release which gas?
    a. carbon dioxide   **c.** methane
    b. oxygen   **d.** sulfur gases

_____ **22.** Bacteria that can withstand hot, acidic water are known as
    a. thermoacidophiles.   **c.** extreme halophiles.
    b. heat synthesizers.   **d.** extreme chemosynthesizers.

_____ **23.** Rhizobacteria live on the roots of plants in structures called
    a. plasmids.   **c.** root nodules.
    b. ribosomes.   **d.** sporozoans.

_____ **24.** Moneran chromosomes replicate and divide by a process called
    a. conjugation.   **c.** lactobacillus.
    b. parasitism.   **d.** binary fission.

_____ **25.** During conjugation, bacteria come together to exchange
    a. transduction coats.   **c.** endospores.
    b. genetic material.   **d.** food.

_____ **26.** Radiolarians are sarcodinians with hard
    a. outer shells.   **c.** stems.
    b. nuclei.   **d.** air bladders.

_____ **27.** *Plasmodium* is a protozoan that causes which disease?
    a. African sleeping sickness   **c.** yeast infections
    b. malaria   **d.** AIDS

_____ **28.** The classification of protists is controversial because
    a. they may not be living organisms.
    b. they are changed by viruses.
    c. they are all multicellular.
    d. they share so few common characteristics.

_____ **29.** Huge deposits of limestone called chalk were made by the buildup of
    a. foraminiferans.   **c.** paramecia.
    b. plankton.   **d.** algae.

_____ **30.** Many *Euglenas* have both chloroplasts and
    a. silica.   **c.** diatoms.
    b. flagella.   **d.** decomposers.

_____ **31.** Red algae can live where there is little light because they
    a. do not perform photosynthesis.
    b. need no light for photosynthesis.
    c. can survive high temperatures.
    d. have other pigments besides chlorophyll.

_____ **32.** Clusters of green algae cells with flagella living together in a ball-shaped colony are called
    a. diatoms.   **c.** thalli.
    b. *Volvox.*   **d.** sea lettuce.

_____ **33.** If a plasmodial slime mold cannot find food, it will form a
    a. fruiting body.   **c.** water mold.
    b. plasmodium.   **d.** cellular slime.

_____ **34.** Decomposers extract the nutrients they need from
    a. metals.   **c.** dead organisms.
    b. viruses.   **d.** soil.

_____ **35.** When there is little food available to cellular slime molds, they clump together into which structure?
    a. pseudoplasmodium   **c.** phytophthora infestans
    b. plasmodium   **d.** euglenoid

_____ **36.** Algae are protists that can perform
    a. invasion of host cells.   **c.** spontaneous generation.
    b. phagocytosis.   **d.** photosynthesis.

_____ **37.** In a paramecium, the macronucleus controls
    a. sexual reproduction.   **c.** asexual reproduction.
    b. genetic exchange.   **d.** conjugation.

_____ **38.** Protozoans in soil usually emerge from their cysts when
    a. the soil becomes wet.   **c.** the temperature is very high.
    b. the soil dries out.   **d.** the temperature drops below freezing.

_____ **39.** What are tiny fungal tubes filled with cytoplasm and nuclei called?
    a. septa   **c.** rhizoids
    b. hyphae   **d.** euglena

_____ **40.** The fruiting bodies of fungi are able to produce
    a. spores.   **c.** mycelia.
    b. roots.   **d.** mushrooms.

_____ **41.** All the asexual fungi have been placed in one division called
    a. sac fungi.   **c.** budding fungi.
    b. perfect fungi.   **d.** imperfect fungi.

_____ **42.** Fungi's ability to break down organic matter in the soil is
    a. dangerous for most other life forms.
    b. helpful to many plants.
    c. harmful to the ecosystem.
    d. a vestigial adaptation.

_____ **43.** Sexual reproduction in sac fungi occurs when haploid mycelia fuse to form the
    a. ascogonium.   **c.** flagella.
    b. bud.   **d.** gram negative.

_____ **44.** Saprophytes can obtain nutrients by digesting
    a. living organisms.   **c.** dead organisms.
    b. their own chitin.   **d.** viruses.

_____ **45.** Which is *not* true of fungi?
  a. most are multicellular   **c.** most move by themselves
  b. heterotrophic   **d.** eukaryotic

_____ **46.** The hyphae that connect groups of rhizoids are called
  a. stolons.   **c.** zygospores.
  b. sacs.   **d.** basidia.

_____ **47.** A mycelium is a tangled, interwoven mass of
  a. fruiting bodies.   **c.** leaves.
  b. hyphae.   **d.** spores.

_____ **48.** Which is *not* true of most fungi?
  a. can reproduce by spores
  b. can grow from mycelium fragment
  c. can make their own chlorophyll
  d. are heterotrophs

_____ **49.** An association between a fungus and a photosynthetic organism is called a
  a. lichen.   **c.** cyanobacterium.
  b. mushroom.   **d.** euglena.

_____ **50.** Two fungi that are often beneficial to humans are *Agaricus campestris* and
  a. Dutch elm.   **c.** *Penicillium*.
  b. *Candida*.   **d.** plankton.

Chapter 21 Test A

Choose the best answer for each question and write its letter in the blank.

_____ **1.** About how many species of plants are there?
   a. 4 million
   b. half a million
   c. 100,000
   d. 10,000

_____ **2.** All plants are photosynthetic, multicellular, and
   a. asexual.
   b. nonreproductive.
   c. prokaryotic.
   d. sexually reproducing.

_____ **3.** All plants probably evolved from
   a. a multicellular green alga.
   b. animal cells.
   c. a fungus.
   d. a species of monerans.

_____ **4.** One of the greatest problems encountered by the first land plants was the need for
   a. sunlight.
   b. nitrogen.
   c. water.
   d. fertilization.

_____ **5.** Which of the following structures is lacking in green algae?
   a. chloroplasts.
   b. cellulose.
   c. starch.
   d. stems.

_____ **6.** How does water aid the fertilization of some organisms?
   a. provides a medium for sperm to move
   b. discourages predators
   c. holds cells together
   d. slows meiosis

_____ **7.** How many phases are there in the life cycle of plants?
   a. three
   b. two
   c. one
   d. five

_____ **8.** One adaptation that helped land plants to slow the evaporation of water was
   a. a cuticle.
   b. lack of roots.
   c. porous cell walls.
   d. chloroplasts.

_____ **9.** The earliest plants probably had no
   a. cell walls.
   b. cell division.
   c. leaves.
   d. water.

_____ **10.** Over 90 percent of today's plant species are
   a. vascular.
   b. nonvascular.
   c. heterotrophic.
   d. algae.

_____ **11.** What controls the size of pores on leaves?
   a. guard cells
   b. rhizoids
   c. gymnosperms
   d. angiosperms

_____ **12.** In order to reproduce, a nonvascular plant must have
   a. rhizoids.
   b. a lot of sunlight.
   c. liquid water.
   d. cold temperatures.

_____ **13.** Rhizoids are long, thin strands of cells that resemble
   a. roots.
   b. leaves.
   c. spores.
   d. guard cells.

_____ **14.** The roots of vascular plants absorb water and
   a. ward off bacteria.
   b. aid in reproduction.
   c. perform photosynthesis.
   d. provide support.

_____ **15.** The cell walls of plants are strengthened by a compound called
   a. lignin.   **c.** cycad.
   b. ginkgo.   **d.** chlorophyll.

_____ **16.** Which is *not* a way that some plants cope with cold temperatures?
   a. bud scales   **c.** producing a compound like antifreeze
   b. becoming dormant   **d.** producing metabolic heat

_____ **17.** What often happens to seeds when animals eat fruit?
   a. They are carried far from the parent plant.
   b. They are destroyed.
   c. They begin to grow inside the animal.
   d. They mutate into a different species.

_____ **18.** Which of the following is a seedless plant?
   a. pine tree   **c.** fern
   b. rose   **d.** daisy

_____ **19.** How many divisions are contained within the plant kingdom?
   a. 10   **c.** 4
   b. 5   **d.** 3

_____ **20.** Bryophytes lack true seeds, leaves, and
   a. chlorophyll.   **c.** roots.
   b. photosynthetic tissues.   **d.** rhizoids.

_____ **21.** Plants that produce seeds protected by a fruit are called
   a. gymnosperms.   **c.** liverworts.
   b. angiosperms.   **d.** Pterophyta.

_____ **22.** A dicot is an angiosperm whose embryo has two
   a. pollen grains.   **c.** cotyledons.
   b. leaves.   **d.** parallel veins.

_____ **23.** Plants remove carbon dioxide from the air by the process of
   a. photosynthesis.   **c.** nitrogenation.
   b. respiration.   **d.** division.

_____ **24.** A series of organisms through which energy moves in the form of food is called a
   a. sample population.   **c.** symbiotic community.
   b. food chain.   **d.** energy chain.

_____ **25.** The majority of humans get most of their food from what source?
   a. wild plants   **c.** cultivated plants
   b. synthetic compounds   **d.** animals

Chapter 21 Test B

Read each question or statement and respond in the space provided.

1. State the general characteristics of plants. (12 points)

_____

_____

_____

_____

2. a. What is the evolutionary connection between green algae and plants? (6 points)

_____

_____

_____

b. What evidence is there for this connection? (6 points)

_____

_____

_____

c. What special adaptations did plants develop for success on land? (6 points)

_____

_____

_____

3. What are the two main categories of plants? What are the differences between them? (12 points)

_____

_____

_____

_____

4. The table below illustrates the characteristics of the major types of plants. Complete the table by filling in the missing information. (24 points)

GROUP	VASCULAR OR NONVASCULAR?	PRODUCE SEEDS IN CONES, SEEDS IN FRUIT, OR NEITHER?	HAVE TRUE ROOTS, STEMS, AND LEAVES?	EXAMPLE
a. bryophytes				
b. pterophytes				
c. gymnosperms				
d. angiosperms				

5. Suppose you were walking in a forest and found an interesting-looking seed. You brought it home, sprouted it, and observed the resulting plant. How could you classify it as being a monocot or a dicot? (16 points)

_____

_____

_____

_____

_____

6. a. Explain why plants are so important in the biosphere. (6 points)

_____

_____

_____

_____

_____

b. State five ways in which people use plants. (6 points)

_____

_____

_____

_____

c. State three problems that different plants can cause. (6 points)

_____

_____

_____

_____

Chapter 22 Test A

Choose the best answer for each question and write its letter in the blank.

_____ **1.** In mosses, water moves through the plant by passing
   a. through a complicated vascular system.
   b. from cell to cell by osmosis.
   c. through liquid medium only.
   d. through a special symbiotic fungus.

_____ **2.** About how many kinds of mosses are there?
   a. ten   **c.** 14,000
   b. 100,000   **d.** 1 million

_____ **3.** The reproduction of most mosses alternates between a haploid gametophyte and
   a. a diploid sporophyte.   **c.** a haploid sporophyte.
   b. vascular tissue.   **d.** a haploid antheridium.

_____ **4.** A moss reproduces asexually by growing tiny pieces of tissue called
   a. gemmae.   **c.** hornworts.
   b. rhizomes.   **d.** capsules.

_____ **5.** The egg-producing organ of a moss is known as the
   a. antheridium.   **c.** gametophyte.
   b. archegonium.   **d.** petiole.

_____ **6.** Most mosses can only undergo fertilization
   a. in very dry climates.   **c.** during or after rain or flooding.
   b. in the winter.   **d.** in the presence of club ferns.

_____ **7.** A wet ecosystem formed by large mats of sphagnum is called a(n)
   a. peat bog.   **c.** swamp.
   b. bryophyte pond. **d.** marsh.

_____ **8.** The structure of a moss that forms haploid spores is known as a
   a. gemmae.   **c.** sphagnum.
   b. capsule.   **d.** cyanobacterium.

_____ **9.** Survival of new branches in liverworts functions as a kind of
   a. rhizome.   **c.** blade.
   b. photosynthesis. **d.** asexual reproduction.

_____ **10.** Where do the archegonia and antheridia of hornworts grow?
   a. inside the plant   **c.** on the trunks of trees
   b. outside the plant   **d.** only underwater

_____ **11.** Humans use peat moss for fuel and for
   a. diapers.   **c.** glass-making.
   b. gelatin.   **d.** insecticides.

_____ **12.** In *Marchantia,* which is a liverwort, where do the gemmae grow?
   a. in the stem   **c.** in tiny cups
   b. only near flowering plants **d.** in the zygotes of hornworts

_____ **13.** The gametophytes of vascular plants are usually smaller than the
   a. sporophytes.   **c.** rhizomes.
   b. peat bogs.   **d.** horsetails.

_____ **14.** For fertilization, liverworts need which of the following?
   a. acid conditions   **c.** petioles
   b. abundant water   **d.** dry conditions

_____ **15.** One of the few vascular plants that lacks true leaves and roots is the
        a. liverwort.   **c.** conifer.
        b. peat moss.   **d.** whisk fern.

_____ **16.** Rhizomes are underground stems that function as
        a. roots.   **c.** embryos.
        b. leaves.   **d.** gametes.

_____ **17.** Club mosses are low-growing
        a. bryophytes.   **c.** ferns.
        b. vascular plants.   **d.** fungi.

_____ **18.** The stems of horsetails are tough and scratchy because they contain which of the following?
        a. cellulose   **c.** silica
        b. diatoms   **d.** spicules

_____ **19.** Before flashbulbs, photographers made flash powder out of
        a. dried fronds.   **c.** dried spores of club mosses.
        b. whisk fern stems.   **d.** horsetails.

_____ **20.** Inside the rhizoids of the gametophyte of a whisk fern lives a
        a. vascular body.   **c.** *Nostoc.*
        b. fungus.   **d.** liverwort.

_____ **21.** After it rains, a resurrection plant
        a. starts to grow again.   **c.** reproduces.
        b. dies.   **d.** becomes a parasite.

_____ **22.** Ferns are the largest group of living seedless
        a. nonvascular plants.   **c.** fungi.
        b. gymnosperms.   **d.** vascular plants.

_____ **23.** The life cycle of a fern alternates between a sporophyte and a
        a. gametophyte.   **c.** rhizome.
        b. petiole.   **d.** photosynthetic frond.

_____ **24.** What is the leaf of a fern called?
        a. petiole   **c.** frond
        b. blade   **d.** spore case

_____ **25.** A sorus is a spore-containing structure on the
        a. underside of the fern leaf.   **c.** fern stem.
        b. blade of the frond.   **d.** top of the fern leaf.

Name _____ Class _____ Date _____

Chapter 22 Test B

Read each question or statement and respond in the space provided.

1. a. In what division of the Plant Kingdom are mosses classified? (7 points)

_____

b. Describe the vascular system and transport in mosses. (7 points)

_____

_____

_____

2. A moss is shown below at different stages of its life. Identify each of the labeled structures in the illustration. (10 points)

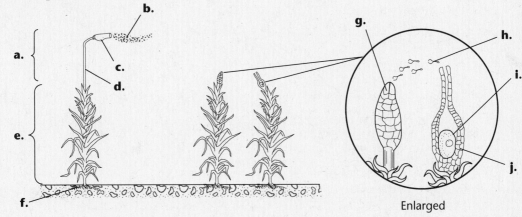

Enlarged

a. _____ f. _____

b. _____ g. _____

c. _____ h. _____

d. _____ i. _____

e. _____ j. _____

3. Describe what happens during the life cycle of a moss. (15 points)

_____

_____

_____

_____

4. What are liverworts and hornworts? How can you tell them apart? (15 points)

_____

_____

_____

_____

_____

_____

_____

5. a. State the characteristics of seedless vascular plants. (9 points)

_____

_____

_____

_____

b. What are the four groups of seedless vascular plants? (9 points)

_____

_____

_____

6. The drawing below shows a fern at different stages of its life. Identify each of the labeled structures. (13 points)

a.	_____	h.	_____
b.	_____	i.	_____
c.	_____	j.	_____
d.	_____	k.	_____
e.	_____	l.	_____
f.	_____	m.	_____
g.	_____		

7. Describe what happens during the life cycle of a fern. (15 points)

_____

_____

_____

_____

_____

_____

_____

Chapter 23 Test A

Choose the best answer for each question and write its letter in the blank.

_____ **1.** Cells that support the nongrowing parts of plants are called
  a. collenchyma cells.   **c.** sclerenchyma cells.
  b. parenchyma cells.   **d.** meristematic cells.

_____ **2.** Sugars are transported in vascular plants through which of these structures?
  a. phloem   **c.** epidermis
  b. tracheids   **d.** sclereids

_____ **3.** Xylem is a tissue in a vascular plant that is used to transport
  a. fats.   **c.** water and minerals.
  b. sugars.   **d.** cellulose.

_____ **4.** Which plant cells are the most abundant and least structurally specialized?
  a. parenchyma cells   **c.** vascular cells
  b. collenchyma cells   **d.** phloem cells

_____ **5.** Long, narrow cells of xylem with thin separations between them are known as
  a. ground tissue.   **c.** meristems.
  b. tracheids.   **d.** vessel elements.

_____ **6.** Short, wide cells of xylem with no end walls function in water transport when
  a. the cells are dead.   **c.** the cells are alive.
  b. an end wall forms.   **d.** water is scarce.

_____ **7.** Cells of phloem that help the sieve tube elements to function are called
  a. tracheids.   **c.** primary growth cells.
  b. dermal tissue.   **d.** companion cells.

_____ **8.** Growth that makes a plant stem thicker is known as
  a. secondary growth.   **c.** epidermal growth.
  b. primary growth.   **d.** tracheid growth.

_____ **9.** In the meristem regions of plants you would expect to find
  a. companion cells.   **c.** inactive cells.
  b. dividing cells.   **d.** gametes.

_____ **10.** Collenchyma cells would help support which parts of a celery plant?
  a. growing stems   **c.** dormant roots
  b. photosynthesizing leaves   **d.** dormant seeds

_____ **11.** The epidermis on the stems and leaves of young plants prevents
  a. photosynthesis.   **c.** reproduction.
  b. premature aging.   **d.** drying out.

_____ **12.** The vascular cylinder of a root is surrounded by
  a. cortex.   **c.** phloem.
  b. epidermis.   **d.** endodermis.

_____ **13.** A plant absorbs water and minerals through
  a. a smooth epidermis.   **c.** root hairs.
  b. stomata.   **d.** the cortex.

_____ **14.** What cell layer of the root can be compared to a row of bricks?
  a. monocot   **c.** epidermis
  b. endodermis   **d.** dicot

_____ **15.** Grasses usually have which type of roots?
  a. taproots   **c.** fibrous roots
  b. horizontal roots   **d.** aerial roots

Chapter 23: Plant Structures

_____ **16.** In stems, vascular tissue is arranged to form
  a. a central cylinder.   **c.** taproots.
  b. veins.   **d.** vascular bundles.

_____ **17.** What are the pores in the epidermis of leaves that control water evaporation called?
  a. vascular bundles   **c.** veins
  b. stomata   **d.** lobes

_____ **18.** In C_4 plants, the Calvin cycle occurs in the
  a. bundle sheath cells. **c.** roots.
  b. endodermal cells.   **d.** meristematic cells.

_____ **19.** What is the process of the evaporation of water from the leaves of a plant called?
  a. transport   **c.** pumping
  b. absorption   **d.** transpiration

_____ **20.** The movement of sugars in a plant can be explained by
  a. transpiration.   **c.** the pressure-flow hypothesis.
  b. reverse transport.   **d.** evaporation.

_____ **21.** What causes water molecules to stick together and pull each other up a plant stem?
  a. cohesion   **c.** saturation
  b. sugar tapping   **d.** aphid stylets

_____ **22.** Sugar made in photosynthesis is transported by being pumped into the
  a. roots.   **c.** cortex.
  b. pores.   **d.** sieve tubes.

_____ **23.** Adaptations allow some plants to get oxygen to
  a. water-soaked roots. **c.** the soil.
  b. the cohesion chambers. **d.** minerals.

_____ **24.** Which of these is *not* an adaptation of plants?
  a. trap insects for nitrogen **c.** use methane instead of CO_2
  b. withstand heat   **d.** live in symbiosis with animals

_____ **25.** In plant cells, an increase in osmotic pressure causes an increase in
  a. turgor.   **c.** transpiration.
  b. carnivorousness.   **d.** primary growth.

Chapter 23 Test B

Read each question or statement and respond in the space provided.

1. Identify each of the plant cell types described below. Choose from among the following possible answers: sclereids, parenchyma, fibers, collenchyma, sclerenchyma. (15 points)

a. cells that support the growing parts of plants _____

b. any cells that support the nongrowing parts of plants_____

c. long, strandlike cells, such as those in the strings in celery, that support the nongrowing parts of plants

_____

d. thick-walled cells, such as those in pears and in peach pits, that support the nongrowing parts of plants

_____

e. cells that are least structurally specialized and that are used for functions such as photosynthesis, food storage, and general metabolism

_____

2. Describe the transpiration-cohesion theory of water movement in plants. (12 points)

_____

_____

_____

3. Suppose you were trying to identify the following types of tissues in a plant. What structure or function would identify each type? (18 points)

a. xylem in general_____

b. tracheids_____

_____

c. vessel elements _____

_____

d. phloem in general _____

_____

e. sieve tube elements _____

_____

f. companion cells_____

_____

4. State the main functions of each of the following. (15 points)

a. roots _____

b. stems _____

c. leaves_____

Name _____ Class _____ Date _____

5. Identify each of the labeled structures in the cross-sections of the dicot root, stem, and leaf below. (20 points)

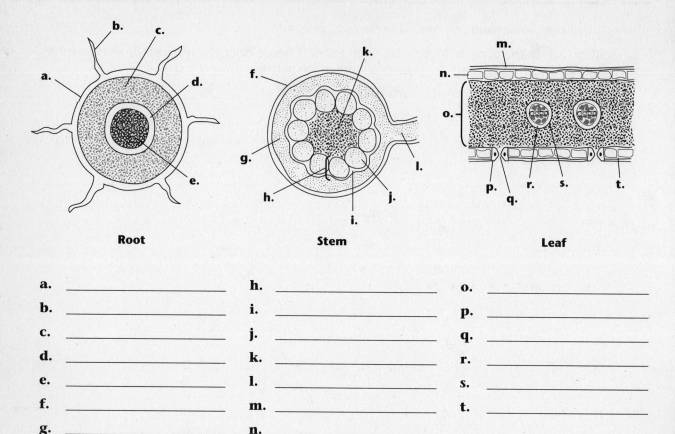

Root   Stem   Leaf

a. _____   h. _____   o. _____
b. _____   i. _____   p. _____
c. _____   j. _____   q. _____
d. _____   k. _____   r. _____
e. _____   l. _____   s. _____
f. _____   m. _____   t. _____
g. _____   n. _____

6. Identify each kind of leaf below as either a monocot, pinnate, palmate, pinnately compound, or palmately compound. (20 points)

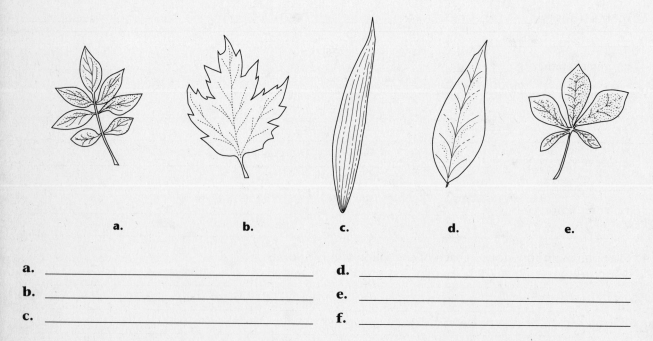

a.   b.   c.   d.   e.

a. _____   d. _____
b. _____   e. _____
c. _____   f. _____

Chapter 24 Test A

Choose the best answer for each question and write its letter in the blank.

_____ **1.** One advantage that seeds have over spores is the ability to
    a. perform photosynthesis.   **c.** carry nutrients.
    b. transfer pollen.   **d.** graft branches.

_____ **2.** What are the oldest surviving seed plants on Earth?
    a. angiosperms   **c.** grasses
    b. gymnosperms   **d.** bryophytes

_____ **3.** An angiosperm's stems and leaves develop from a part of the embryo known as the
    a. epicotyl.   **c.** pollinator.
    b. filament.   **d.** hypocotyl.

_____ **4.** Monocots are angiosperms whose seeds contain only one
    a. cotyledon.   **c.** cone.
    b. fruit.   **d.** gymnosperm.

_____ **5.** Which kind of plant would you expect to find if you were mountain climbing in an extremely cold, dry area?
    a. apple tree   **c.** fir tree
    b. rice plant   **d.** rose bush

_____ **6.** Below the cotyledon of an angiosperm embryo is tissue that will produce roots for the plant. This tissue is called the
    a. hypocotyl.   **c.** epicotyl.
    b. anther.   **d.** corolla.

_____ **7.** What characteristic of resin helps female gymnosperm cones capture pollen grains released by male cones?
    a. a prickly exterior   **c.** stickiness
    b. ability to dissolve the pollen   **d.** wide cracks

_____ **8.** In gymnosperms, an egg surrounded by protective cells that will develop into a seed is known as a(n)
    a. ovule.   **c.** cotyledon.
    b. bristlecone.   **d.** anther.

_____ **9.** Gymnosperms have extremely light pollen grains. This works as an advantage in reproduction by allowing the pollen to be
    a. vaporized by heat.   **c.** absorbed by soil.
    b. carried by the wind.   **d.** fertilized by female cones.

_____ **10.** During the life cycle of a pine tree, where do the seeds develop?
    a. on the winglike structures of pollen   **c.** on the male cones
    b. on the scales of female cones   **d.** at the base of male and female cones

_____ **11.** Sperm cells of angiosperms reach the egg through which structure?
    a. pistil   **c.** scale
    b. sperm tube   **d.** pollen tube

_____ **12.** Flowers have three basic components: male parts, female parts, and sterile parts. Which of these components helps attract bees?
    a. female parts   **c.** sterile parts
    b. male parts   **d.** all of the above

_____ **13.** The female, or egg-producing, part of a flower is known as the
    a. filament.   **c.** corolla.
    b. anther.   **d.** pistil.

_____ **14.** Pollen grains containing sperm cells are produced by a structure called the
    a. anther.   **c.** pistil.
    b. ovule.   **d.** stigma.

_____ **15.** Which parts of a flower are sterile?
    a. pistil and sepal   **c.** sepal and style
    b. anther and petal   **d.** sepal and petal

_____ **16.** The corolla of a flower is
    a. a single petal.   **c.** all the petals collectively.
    b. the base of the petal.   **d.** the crown of a petal.

_____ **17.** The anther of a flower is supported by a structure known as the
    a. calyx   **c.** stigma.
    b. filament.   **d.** style.

_____ **18.** A flower with five petals would be the flower of a
    a. monocot plant.   **c.** corolla plant.
    b. dicot plant.   **d.** gymnosperm.

_____ **19.** Which of these organisms could help ensure the hybridization of angiosperms?
    a. a ladybug   **c.** a pine tree
    b. a worm   **d.** an ameba

_____ **20.** Unlike sexual reproduction, asexual reproduction always produces
    a. hybrids.   **c.** pollen.
    b. clones.   **d.** sepals.

_____ **21.** The kind of asexual reproduction that occurs naturally in plants is known as
    a. grafting.   **c.** pollination.
    b. tissue propagation.   **d.** vegetative reproduction.

_____ **22.** Producing new plants from cuttings is made possible by a plant's ability to
    a. reproduce sexually.   **c.** produce culture tissues.
    b. regenerate lost parts.   **d.** form hybrids.

_____ **23.** Sexual reproduction in angiosperms begins when microspores form by meiosis in
    a. anthers   **c.** stigma.
    b. ovules.   **d.** cones.

_____ **24.** What is the method by which an entire plant can be grown from a few individual cells?
    a. grafting   **c.** cross-breeding
    b. tissue culture   **d.** vegetative propagation

_____ **25.** Which of the following is *not* a form of asexual reproduction in plants?
    a. tissue culturing   **c.** grafting
    b. cutting   **d.** pollinating

Chapter 24 Test B

Read each question or statement and respond in the space provided.

1. a. What structures are present in all seeds? (8 points)

_____

b. How do the seeds of gymnosperms, monocots, and dicots differ from one another? (8 points)

_____

_____

_____

_____

_____

_____

2. Summarize the life cycle of gymnosperms. (16 points)

_____

_____

_____

_____

_____

_____

_____

_____

_____

_____

3. Look at the drawing of the flower below. Identify each of the labeled structures. Write the name of the structure in the spaces provided on the next page. (22 points)

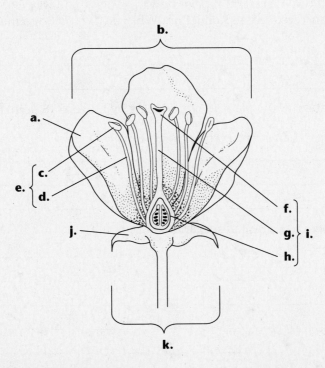

Name _____ Class _____ Date _____

a. _____   g. _____
b. _____   h. _____
c. _____   i. _____
d. _____   j. _____
e. _____   k. _____
f. _____   l. _____

4. Summarize the life cycle of angiosperms. (16 points)

_____

_____

_____

_____

_____

_____

_____

_____

_____

_____

_____

_____

_____

_____

5. a. Suppose you are growing a certain type of flowering plant and want flowering and seed production rather than vegetative reproduction. What might you do to make the plant reproduce in this way? (8 points)

_____

_____

b. What is the advantage to the plant in reproducing by flowers? (8 points)

_____

_____

_____

6. Describe three methods of artificial propagation. (15 points)

_____

_____

_____

_____

_____

Chapter 25 Test A

Choose the best answer for each question and write its letter in the blank.

_____ **1.** A period of decreased activity caused by structural and biochemical changes in a plant is called
   a. germination.   **c.** primary root.
   b. auxin.   **d.** dormancy.

_____ **2.** The part of the embryo that forms the primary root of a plant is called the
   a. coleoptile.   **c.** radicle.
   b. meristem.   **d.** axillary bud.

_____ **3.** Which region of a primary root contains cells that can develop into phloem?
   a. the zone of elongation   **c.** the zone of differentiation
   b. the apical meristem   **d.** the monocot shoot

_____ **4.** If the main tip of a primary shoot is damaged,
   a. the plant can no longer grow.
   b. axillary buds can still form branches or flowers.
   c. root hairs develop in the stem.
   d. flowers will be unable to reproduce.

_____ **5.** What causes the split bark seen on white birch trees?
   a. several layers of cork cambium   **c.** release of ethylene
   b. sugar transport by phloem   **d.** release of abscisic acid

_____ **6.** In a typical dicot, the shoot that breaks the soil first has the shape of a(n)
   a. hook.   **c.** meristem.
   b. oval.   **d.** blade.

_____ **7.** Which kind of plant is best adapted to growing tall?
   a. one that undergoes primary growth only
   b. one that undergoes both primary and secondary growth
   c. one that has no lateral meristems
   d. none of the above

_____ **8.** The clogged, dark-colored layers of xylem at the center of a tree are called
   a. heartwood.   **c.** vascular cambium.
   b. sapwood.   **d.** cork cambium.

_____ **9.** The cross-section of a tree trunk showed nine rings. How old was the tree?
   a. nine months old   **c.** 36 months old
   b. 90 years old   **d.** 9 years old

_____ **10.** What kind of meristem causes plants to thicken?
   a. cambium   **c.** auxin
   b. xylem   **d.** phytochrome

_____ **11.** Sapwood is the name for the outer, light-colored layers of secondary
   a. phloem.   **c.** xylem.
   b. resin.   **d.** ethylene.

_____ **12.** Cork cambium is the meristem located between the phloem and the
   a. epidermis.   **c.** heartwood.
   b. xylem.   **d.** root hairs.

_____ **13.** Wood that is difficult to drive a nail through probably came from a tree that
   a. is a dicot.   **c.** is a gymnosperm.
   b. lacks fibers.   **d.** is a softwood.

_____ **14.** Plants can respond to changing environmental conditions by the use of what kinds of chemicals?
  a. vascular cambium   **c.** hormones
  b. tropisms   **d.** kudzus

_____ **15.** When botanist Frits Went applied agar blocks to coleoptiles with cut-off tips, the coleoptiles curved away from the agar. This is because the agar also contained
  a. auxin.   **c.** abscisic acid.
  b. ethylene.   **d.** sugar.

_____ **16.** A plant hormone that stimulates the growth of stems and leaves is
  a. abscisic acid.   **c.** phytochrome.
  b. ethylene.   **d.** gibberellin.

_____ **17.** Which two hormones work together to control the falling of leaves from some trees in the fall?
  a. gibberellin and cytokinin   **c.** abscisic acid and ethylene
  b. ethylene and IAA   **d.** cytokinin and auxin

_____ **18.** How do heavy rains in the desert cause some plants to germinate?
  a. by washing abscisic acid from seeds
  b. by stimulating production of ethylene
  c. by causing apical dominance
  d. by washing cytokinins from seeds

_____ **19.** The ability of a shoot's apical meristem to inhibit the growth of nearby axillary buds is called
  a. apical inhibition.   **c.** apical dominance.
  b. axillary inhibition.   **d.** axillary dominance.

_____ **20.** Why are wrapped fruits likely to ripen more quickly than unwrapped fruits?
  a. Ethylene gas is trapped.   **c.** Ethylene gas is kept out.
  b. More NAA is produced.   **d.** There is a build-up of abscisic acid.

_____ **21.** Positive gravitropism insures that a plant will
  a. be anchored in soil by its roots.   **c.** lose its leaves in winter.
  b. make pigments.   **d.** have tips that grow upward.

_____ **22.** Which kind of plant movement most resembles the change in the shape of a balloon as it is inflated?
  a. thigmotropism   **c.** nastic movement
  b. photoperiodism   **d.** flowering

_____ **23.** Phytochrome is a blue pigment that controls
  a. photoperiodism.   **c.** nastic movements.
  b. photosynthesis.   **d.** bud scaling.

_____ **24.** Which of the following plant blooms are *not* affected by the length of the day?
  a. roses and snapdragons   **c.** asters and chrysanthemums
  b. corn and radishes   **d.** ragweed and wheat

_____ **25.** When would you be most likely to find bud scales on a tree?
  a. in May   **c.** in July
  b. in November   **d.** in June

Chapter 25 Test B

Read each question or statement and respond in the space provided.

1. **a.** Describe the process of seed germination. (5 points)

    _____
    _____
    _____

    b. What two environmental conditions affect germination, and in what way? (5 points)

    _____
    _____
    _____

    c. How do the shoots of monocots and dicots differ in their growth out of the soil? (5 points)

    _____
    _____

2. Give the location of each of the following structures. State whether primary or secondary growth is associated with each. Finally, state which plant parts may grow from each. (15 points)

    a. radicle _____
    b. vascular cambium _____
    c. cork cambium _____
    d. apical meristem _____
    e. axillary bud _____

3. Suppose you were to examine the wood in a cross-section of a tree that had been cut down. Explain what each of the following types of wood is, and what it would look like. Where would you find each in the cross-section? (12 points)

    a. sapwood _____
    _____

    b. heartwood _____
    _____

    c. spring wood _____
    _____

    d. summer wood _____
    _____

4. **a.** What are the differences between hardwoods and softwoods, in terms of properties and structure? (6 points)

    _____
    _____

    b. From what kinds of trees do hardwoods and softwoods come? (6 points)

    _____
    _____

5. Identify each of the following plant hormones. Choose from among the answers: auxin, gibberellin, cytokinin, ethlyene, abscisic acid. (15 points)

    a. promotes cell division and the growth of axillary buds_____

    b. controls the opening and closing of leaf stomata and causes seeds to remain dormant

    _____

    c. causes cells to grow and causes apical dominance _____

    d. stimulates growth of stems and leaves, and causes enzymes to be made that convert starch into sugar

    _____

    e. promotes the ripening of fruit and the falling of leaves _____

6. Imagine that you are observing the responses of various plants to different stimuli. Identify the kind of plant response that is most clearly illustrated in each of the following observations. (15 points)

    a. A chrysanthemum comes into bloom when the nights become long and the days become short.

    _____

    b. A beetle is caught by a Venus' flytrap. _____

    c. A carrot grows downward into the ground. _____

    d. The tendrils of a sweet pea curl around a trellis. _____

    e. A sunflower turns in the direction of the sun. _____

7. Design an experiment to test the effect of gravity on roots. The experiment should also rule out the possibility of downward growth as a negative response to light. Include a description of materials and equipment. Also describe how you would use a control, and tell what kinds of data you would collect. (16 points)

_____

_____

_____

_____

_____

_____

_____

_____

_____

_____

_____

_____

_____

_____

_____

_____

_____

_____

Unit 5 Test A

Choose the best answer for each question and write its letter in the blank.

_____ 1. Thin strands of cells that resemble plant roots in bryophytes are called
  a. guard cells.   c. rhizoids.
  b. liverworts.   d. capsules.

_____ 2. Which of the following is needed by the alga *Coleochaete* for reproduction?
  a. water   c. eggs that can swim
  b. rich soil   d. pollen

_____ 3. An angiosperm with an embryo containing two cotyledons is called a
  a. monocot.   c. petiole.
  b. tracheid.   d. dicot.

_____ 4. Which of the following food chains involving plants is in the correct order?
  a. human to fruit to insect to bird   c. plant to insect to bird to cat
  b. plant to bird to insect to human   d. none of the above

_____ 5. What is one characteristic that all vascular plants share?
  a. alternation of generations   c. true leaves
  b. reproduction through use of cones   d. seeds

_____ 6. Although bryophytes lack true roots, many have root-like structures called
  a. true leaves.   c. rhizoids.
  b. seeds.   d. flowers.

_____ 7. Cones are specialized reproductive structures that produce seeds
  a. encased in a fruit.   c. with two cotyledons.
  b. without a fruit.   d. with root hairs.

_____ 8. Which of the following plants needs water to reproduce?
  a. tulip   c. conifer
  b. moss   d. ginkgo

_____ 9. Vascular plants fall into one of two basic groups. These two groups are
  a. seedless plants and seed plants.   c. Lycophyta and Pterophyta.
  b. bryophytes and nonvascular plants.   d. mosses and ferns.

_____ 10. Seeds are reproductive structures that contain the plant embryo and
  a. sperm.   c. stored food.
  b. the cuticle.   d. the fruit.

_____ 11. Which of the following functions does the gametophyte of a moss perform for its
  sporophyte?
  a. respiration   c. the diploid phase
  b. encapsulation   d. photosynthesis

_____ 12. What substance does a moss sporophyte lack that keeps it from performing
  photosynthesis?
  a. chlorophyll   c. rhizoids
  b. a foot   d. a stem

_____ 13. Like most other bryophytes, mosses have what characteristic?
  a. a complicated vascular system   c. true leaves
  b. true roots   d. no vascular system

_____ 14. A peat bog is a wet ecosystem formed by large mats of
  a. sphagnum.   c. hornworts.
  b. liverworts.   d. ferns.

_____ **15.** The most prominent phase in the life cycle of a whisk fern is the
  a. gametophyte generation.   **c.** sporophyte generation.
  b. development of fruit.   **d.** growth of the seed.

_____ **16.** The most atypical kind of bryophyte is the
  a. hornwort.   **c.** horsetail.
  b. liverwort.   **d.** fern.

_____ **17.** A capsule is the structure of a moss that forms
  a. diploid spores.   **c.** diploid gametes.
  b. haploid spores.   **d.** new gemmae.

_____ **18.** Mosses alternate between haploid gametophyte and diploid sporophyte phases.
  To what do "haploid" and "diploid" refer?
  a. number of chromosomes   **c.** number of sperm
  b. shape of the leaves   **d.** none of the above

_____ **19.** The sperm-producing organ of a moss is known as a(n)
  a. archegonium.   **c.** antheridium.
  b. rhizome.   **d.** vascular capsule.

_____ **20.** The underside of a fern leaf contains a group of spore-capsules known as the
  a. blade.   **c.** petiole.
  b. gemmae.   **d.** sori.

_____ **21.** The cells of a root's endodermis are coated with a casparian strip. Why is this necessary?
  a. to block water movement between the cells
  b. to keep water out of the vascular cylinder
  c. to absorb excess water
  d. to prevent root absorption

_____ **22.** As water evaporates from the cells of a leaf or stem, replacement water is pulled from the
  a. phloem tissue.   **c.** xylem tissue.
  b. spore cases.   **d.** pistil.

_____ **23.** Which of the following is *not* composed of sclerenchyma cells?
  a. walnut shell   **c.** flax
  b. strings of celery stalk   **d.** linen

_____ **24.** Long, narrow cells of xylem with thin separations between them are known as
  a. vessel elements.   **c.** endodermis.
  b. vascular bundles.   **d.** tracheids.

_____ **25.** The enlarged primary root of a plant is known as the
  a. fibrous root.   **c.** taproot.
  b. stomata.   **d.** palmate.

_____ **26.** Where does the Calvin cycle occur in C_4 plants?
  a. root   **c.** bundle sheath
  b. mesophile   **d.** seed

_____ **27.** Turgor in a plant cell is caused by
  a. osmotic pressure.   **c.** rigid cell walls.
  b. a double nucleus.   **d.** mitochondrial pressure.

_____ **28.** Whereas veins in monocot leaves run parallel, those in dicot leaves
  a. form diamond shapes.   **c.** always overlap.
  b. form a branched network.   **d.** all radiate from a single point.

_____ **29.** Sugars made in photosynthetic cells are pumped into sieve tubes by
  a. transpiration.   **c.** photosynthesis.
  b. respiration.   **d.** active transport.

_____ **30.** Which type of tissue is most impotant in plant growth?
  a. meristematic   **c.** ground
  b. vascular   **d.** xylem

Unit 5 Test A

_____ **31.** Stomata are pores in the epidermis of leaves that allow
    a. carbon dioxide to enter.   **c.** minerals to enter.
    b. light to enter.   **d.** veins to criss-cross.

_____ **32.** In compound leaves, the words *pinnate* and *palmate* refer to the arrangement of
    a. vascular bundles.   **c.** stomata groups.
    b. photosynthetic cells.   **d.** leaflets around the petiole.

_____ **33.** Which of the following draws water upward in a plant?
    a. evaporation of water from leaves   **c.** division of spores
    b. processing of nitrogen   **d.** pigmentation

_____ **34.** Which structure gives rise to the roots of a plant?
    a. epicotyl   **c.** anther
    b. hypocotyl   **d.** pistil

_____ **35.** In a pine tree's life cycle, the gametophyte generation begins with meiosis and ends with
    a. flowering.   **c.** fertilization.
    b. leaf loss.   **d.** tropism.

_____ **36.** What function is served by the sterile parts of flowers?
    a. egg transport   **c.** attraction
    b. germination   **d.** ovulation

_____ **37.** If the anther of a flower were removed, which of the following would no longer be possible?
    a. photosynthesis   **c.** active transport
    b. pollen production   **d.** fertilization by pollen

_____ **38.** Botanists cross-pollinated two kinds of tulips to make a new hybrid. This is an example of
    a. sexual reproduction.   **c.** asexual reproduction.
    b. cloning.   **d.** grafting.

_____ **39.** The style is the structure that connects the stigma to the
    a. anther.   **c.** filament.
    b. sepal.   **d.** ovary.

_____ **40.** How does resin work as an advantage for female gymnosperms in windy weather?
    a. It's sticky enough to trap and hold pollen grains.
    b. It glues the cones together.
    c. It seals out water loss.
    d. It allows light to pass through for photosynthesis.

_____ **41.** Which part of the plant embryo is positioned above the cotyledon?
    a. the monocot   **c.** the epicotyl
    b. the petiole   **d.** the stomata

_____ **42.** Which reproductive method involves fusing the ends of two different plants?
    a. cutting   **c.** tissue culturing
    b. planting   **d.** none of the above

_____ **43.** A plant that lacked phytochrome would probably not be able to
    a. perform photosynthesis.   **c.** respond to changes in the length of day.
    b. produce leaf scars.   **d.** perform active transport.

_____ **44.** The radicle of an embryo will form the
    a. primary root.   **c.** primary shoot.
    b. meristem.   **d.** cambium.

_____ **45.** Bark is composed of cork, cork cambium, and
    a. vascular cambium.   **c.** secondary phloem.
    b. radicles.   **d.** axillary buds.

_____ **46.** Which of the three steps in the primary growth of roots leads to the formation of phloem tissue?
    a. elongation   **c.** differentiation
    b. division   **d.** none of the above

_____ **47.** If a plant lacked the nourishment it needed during secondary growth, which of the following might result?
    a. stems too thin for support   **c.** very short stems
    b. extremely thick stems   **d.** thicker roots

_____ **48.** In pruning a plant, how could you put a stop to apical dominance?
    a. cutting the roots   **c.** cutting the apical meristem
    b. cutting the axillary buds   **d.** grafting the apical meristem

_____ **49.** The Darwins discovered that a plant curves because some its cells are sensitive to light. Which cells were sensitive to light?
    a. those in the curving region   **c.** those in the tip of the meristem
    b. those that grew longer   **d.** those that reacted to auxin

_____ **50.** What is one way to make an apple ripen faster?
    a. spray it with ethylene   **c.** keep it away from other apples
    b. spray it with gibberellin   **d.** spray it with water

Chapter 26 Test A

Choose the best answer for each question and write its letter in the blank.

_____ 1. The body of an animal gets its basic shape and support from
    a. its cell walls.   **c.** its cell cytoskeletons.
    b. its cell membranes.   **d.** its skeletal system.

_____ 2. Organisms that are permanently attached to one spot are called
    a. sessile.   **c.** flagella.
    b. dorsals.   **d.** bilaterals.

_____ 3. The animals described in question 2 also have a free-moving stage in their life cycle.
    a. motile.   **c.** dormant.
    b. vertebrate.   **d.** flexible.

_____ 4. Why are there no animal remains from before 750 million years ago?
    a. There probably were no animals on Earth that long ago.
    b. There were no animals with hard body parts that long ago.
    c. Animal fossils from that period were destroyed by plate tectonics.
    d. none of the above

_____ 5. The body plans of most animals can be compared on the basis of symmetry and
    a. protostome development.   **c.** ganglia clusters.
    b. hermaphroditism.   **d.** segmentation.

_____ 6. When an animal has body parts arranged in pairs on either side of a central axis, the animal is said to have
    a. radial symmetry.   **c.** a ventral bottom.
    b. bilateral symmetry.   **d.** asymmetry.

_____ 7. Which body part or parts would you have to examine to determine the segmentation of a snake?
    a. scales   **c.** skeleton
    b. muscles   **d.** nerves

_____ 8. Although animals with radial symmetry have a dorsal and ventral surface, they never have
    a. an anterior end or posterior end.   **c.** a top or a bottom.
    b. sense organs.   **d.** sessile characteristics.

_____ 9. Which is an advantage of segmentation?
    a. specialization of body parts   **c.** inflexibility
    b. sharper sense organs   **d.** none of the above

_____ 10. When you go to the beach and see a sea star on a rock, which surface is most likely to be visible to you?
    a. the ventral surface   **c.** the dorsal surface
    b. the anterior surface   **d.** the bilateral surface

_____ 11. On which end of your body is your head located?
    a. ventral   **c.** posterior
    b. anterior   **d.** opposing

_____ 12. Which phrase is true of a bilaterally symmetrical animal?
    a. sense organs at anterior end   **c.** sessile characteristics
    b. sense organs at posterior end   **d.** no posterior

_____ 13. The first step of embryo development is a division of the fertilized egg, known as
    a. colomate development.   **c.** cleavage.
    b. the gastrula.   **d.** zygote formation.

_____ 14. The fully lined body cavity formed by the mesoderm of some animals is called the
    a. colomate.   **c.** protostome.
    b. coelom.   **d.** endoskeleton.

_____ **15.** The first several divisions of an embryo do not increase it's overall size. These divisions form a hollow ball of cells called a
    a. pseudocoelom.
    b. coelom.
    c. blastula.
    d. gastrula.

_____ **16.** Which of these animals do *not* have a coelom?
    a. flatworms
    b. annelids
    c. vertebrates
    d. humans

_____ **17.** An animal with a blastopore that develops into a mouth is called a
    a. deuterostome.
    b. pseudocoelom.
    c. gastrula.
    d. protostome.

_____ **18.** A gastrula is a many-celled embryo that is
    a. single-layered and cup-shaped.
    b. two-layered and cup-shaped.
    c. two-layered and perfectly spherical.
    d. single-layered and perfectly spherical.

_____ **19.** The coelom represents an evolutionary improvement in animals because it provides a protective space for
    a. bone tissue.
    b. oxygen.
    c. complex internal organs.
    d. blastula cells.

_____ **20.** Which of the following body parts or traits links echinoderms and chordates?
    a. a blastula
    b. an anus
    c. radial symmetry
    d. a gastrula

_____ **21.** Unlike plants, animals need a support system that is flexible enough to
    a. move.
    b. withstand temperature changes.
    c. absorb blood.
    d. be broken down by enzymes.

_____ **22.** Which of the following animals has a hydrostatic skeleton?
    a. snail
    b. earthworm
    c. human
    d. insect

_____ **23.** A cluster of nerve cell bodies is called a
    a. ganglion.
    b. nerve net.
    c. tract.
    d. nerve framework.

_____ **24.** A hard encasement on the surface of an animal is known as a(n)
    a. endoskeleton.
    b. coelom.
    c. exoskeleton.
    d. protostome.

_____ **25.** In the hydra, food enters an opening to the digestive cavity and leaves by
    a. the anus.
    b. the tentacles.
    c. the same opening.
    d. the bladder.

Chapter 26 Test B

Read each question or statement and respond in the space provided.

1. State six general characteristics of animals. (12 points)

_____

_____

_____

_____

2. Name five phyla of animals and give an example of an animal in each. (10 points)

_____

_____

_____

3. Suppose you are a biotechnologist of the future and you are developing new kinds of animals. For each of the following characteristics and abilities, state whether the animal should have radial symmetry or bilateral symmetry. Explain your answers. (14 points)

a. fast-moving, good sensory system _____

_____

_____

b. sessile, able to defend itself from any approach_____

_____

_____

4. Look at the drawing of the insect shown below. Identify each of the labeled sides and ends as either ventral, dorsal, posterior, or anterior. (8 points)

a. _____   **c.** _____

b. _____   **d.** _____

5. a. Describe the development of the embryo into a blastula and a gastrula. (7 points)

_____

_____

_____

b. What three cell layers typically form during embryo development? What body parts and systems form from each? (7 points)

_____

_____

_____

6. a. How do coelomates differ structurally from animals with no coelom at all and from animals with a pseudocoelom? (5 points)

_____

_____

_____

_____

_____

_____

b. What two major advantages do coelomates have? (5 points)

_____

_____

_____

c. How do protostomes differ from deuterostomes? (5 points)

_____

_____

_____

7. Classify each of the following animals as having either a hydrostatic skeleton, an exoskeleton, or an endoskeleton. Also explain what is meant by each skeletal form. (12 points)

a. crab _____

b. dog_____

c. earthworm _____

_____

8. Contrast the two adaptations in each of the following examples. (15 points)

a. a tube-within-a-tube body plan and a two-way digestive cavity _____

_____

_____

b. a nerve net and a nervous system that includes clustered ganglia _____

_____

_____

c. a hermaphrodite and a nonhermaphrodite reproductive system _____

_____

_____

Chapter 27 Test A

Choose the best answer for each question and write its letter in the blank.

_____ **1.** What characteristic of sponges made the Greeks think they were plants?
   a. asymmetry
   b. porousness
   c. lack of movement
   d. none of the above

_____ **2.** What other characteristic do all sponges share that proves the Greeks were wrong?
   a. movement
   b. heterotrophy
   c. autotrophy
   d. lack of movement

_____ **3.** Sponges cannot withstand water pollution because they
   a. eat large fish.
   b. perform photosynthesis.
   c. swim to great depths.
   d. act as filters.

_____ **4.** Which cells of sponges move about supplying nutrients and removing wastes?
   a. amebocytes
   b. spicules
   c. collar cells
   d. osculi

_____ **5.** An animal that can produce both female and male gametes is known as a(n)
   a. spongin.
   b. gemmule.
   c. hermaphrodite.
   d. spermatozoan.

_____ **6.** A dormant mass of amebocytes surrounded by protective layers of spicules is known as a(n)
   a. gemmule.
   b. osculum.
   c. hermaphrodite.
   d. cnidocyte.

_____ **7.** Whereas sponges cannot hunt prey, cnidarians can. Cnidarians gain this ability through the use of
   a. contractile cells.
   b. sessile cells.
   c. filtering pores.
   d. amebocytes.

_____ **8.** Cnidarians have two basic body plans, a polyp and a
   a. medusa.
   b. larva.
   c. vase shape.
   d. tentacle.

_____ **9.** Which of the following is free-floating or swimming?
   a. a polyp
   b. a sponge
   c. a medusa
   d. none of the above

_____ **10.** How do cnidocytes help a cnidarian to survive?
   a. by storing food
   b. by paralyzing prey
   c. by forming colonies
   d. by providing movement

_____ **11.** A planula can be described as a free-swimming, ciliated
   a. porifera.
   b. turbellaria.
   c. adult medusa.
   d. larva.

_____ **12.** Which of the following characteristics do we share with flatworms?
   a. no ventral side
   b. segmentation
   c. cephalization
   d. no dorsal side

_____ **13.** A certain kind of flatworm has algae living within its cells. How does this help the flatworm survive in environments that lack oxygen?
   a. Algae provides the oxygen through respiration.
   b. Algae helps the worm digest dead organic matter.
   c. Algae provides oxygen through photosynthesis.
   d. none of the above

_____ **14.** What might be the result of a planarian's loss of the ability to secrete slime?
   a. poor digestion
   b. difficulty moving
   c. less sensory awareness
   d. inability to breathe

_____ **15.** The excretory system of planarians is composed primarily of bulblike structures called
  a. flame cells.
  b. pharynxes.
  c. trematoda.
  d. cephalites.

_____ **16.** How are the eggs of blood flukes expelled from the human body?
  a. through the kidneys
  b. through saliva
  c. through the intestines
  d. through the skin

_____ **17.** The word *tapeworm* is a common name for a class of Platyhelminthes known as
  a. Cestoda.
  b. Nematodes.
  c. Scolex.
  d. Roundworms.

_____ **18.** The proglottid of a tapeworm has a complete
  a. female reproductive system.
  b. hermaphroditic reproductive system.
  c. digestive system.
  d. respiratory system.

_____ **19.** It may be dangerous to eat undercooked pork chops because they could contain
  a. hosts.
  b. porifera cysts.
  c. *Trichinella.*
  d. cnidarian cysts.

_____ **20.** One difference between nematodes and flatworms is that in nematodes, wastes leave the body through the
  a. posterior end.
  b. anterior end.
  c. mouth.
  d. same opening that food enters.

_____ **21.** In which of the following ways do rotifers resemble protists?
  a. eyespots
  b. ganglia
  c. microscopic size
  d. pseudocoeloms

_____ **22.** Eggs produced by females in a process called parthenogenesis will result in offspring that are
  a. all male.
  b. all female.
  c. all deformed.
  d. 50% male and 50% female.

_____ **23.** Which of these organisms causes root knot disease?
  a. *Heterodera*
  b. *Bidens pilosa*
  c. *Trichinella*
  d. *Ascaris*

_____ **24.** Species that interact closely adapt to each other in a process known as
  a. regeneration.
  b. leeching.
  c. coevolution.
  d. predatorship.

_____ **25.** Why are blood flukes common in irrigated rice fields?
  a. Both humans and snails are found there.
  b. The flukes feed on rice.
  c. The flukes need to hide under rice plants.
  d. Both ants and oxen are found there.

Chapter 27 Test B

Read each question or statement and respond in the space provided.

1. a. State the general characteristics of the phylum Porifera. (7 points)

_____

b. What is the common name for animals in this phylum? (7 points)

_____

2. If you were to observe sponges carefully, you might see the following structures. State what each is, and give its function. (15 points)

a. osculum

_____

_____

b. amebocytes

_____

_____

c. spongin

_____

_____

d. spicules

_____

_____

e. collar cells

_____

_____

3. a. Describe the characteristics of cnidarians, such as hydras and jellyfish. (8 points)

_____

_____

_____

b. Suppose you placed some tiny prey animals into an aquarium that contained a hydra. Describe the feeding behavior you would observe and the structures that make this behavior possible. (8 points)

_____

_____

_____

_____

_____

4. Describe sexual reproduction in a jellyfish such as *Aurelia*. (15 points)

_____

_____

_____

_____

_____

5. a. In what phylum are flatworms classified? (5 points) _____

    b. Describe the characteristics of planarians, including the ways in which they reproduce. (5 points)

_____

_____

_____

6. a. In what phylum are roundworms classified? (5 points)_____

_____

    b. Describe the characteristics of a roundworm, including the way in which it reproduces. (5 points)

_____

_____

_____

7. a. Describe the life cycle of the parasitic flatworm called the beef tapeworm. (10 points)

_____

_____

_____

_____

_____

_____

_____

    b. What adaptations in parasites such as tapeworms and hookworms were developed through coevolution? How are those adaptations helpful to the parasites? (10 points)

_____

_____

_____

_____

_____

_____

_____

Chapter 28 Test A

Choose the best answer for each question and write its letter in the blank.

_____ 1. Members of the phylum Annelida include earthworms, leeches, and
   a. many segmented marine worms.   **c.** some mollusks.
   b. chitons.   **d.** cephalopods.

_____ 2. Which three characteristics are shared by annelids and mollusks?
   a. blastophores, trochophores, and endoskeletons
   b. blastophores, trochophores, and no true coelom
   c. blastophores, a coelom, and segmentation
   d. none of the above

_____ 3. Which of the following functions is served by a trochophore?
   a. circulation and respiration   **c.** feeding and movement
   b. sight and hearing   **d.** none of the above

_____ 4. Which characteristic do some annelids and mollusks share with members of the phylum Porifera?
   a. segmentation   **c.** an exoskeleton
   b. filter feeding   **d.** complex digestive systems

_____ 5. Earthworms increase the nutrients available to plants by
   a. breaking down large pieces of organic matter.
   b. destroying harmful bacteria.
   c. organizing soil into larger clumps.
   d. leaving parts of their prey to decay in the soil.

_____ 6. The three *classes* of annelids include the Oligochaeta, the Polychaeta, and the
   a. Nephridia.   **c.** Sessile.
   b. Hirudinea.   **d.** Leeches.

_____ 7. Earthworms have four small setae on each segment. How many parapodia do they have on each segment?
   a. two   **c.** four
   b. zero   **d.** eight

_____ 8. An earthworm can shrink to a shorter length by using
   a. turgor pressure.   **c.** contraction of longitudinal muscles.
   b. contraction of circular muscles.   **d.** setae.

_____ 9. Which of the earthworm's digestive organs is used to store undigested food?
   a. gizzard   **c.** intestine
   b. crop   **d.** nephridia

_____ 10. Why would an earthworm die if it's skin lost all of its moisture?
   a. Respiration would be impossible.   **c.** Earthworms need moisture to see.
   b. Digestion would stop at the gizzard.   **d.** none of the above

_____ 11. Earthworms are hermaphrodites that cannot fertilize their own eggs. This means that to mate
   a. a female must find a male.
   b. they must lay eggs to be fertilized by other species.
   c. they must find any other earthworm.
   d. they perform asexual reproduction.

_____ 12. The circulatory system of an earthworm has simple heart-like organs called
   a. aortic arches.   **c.** dorsal blood vessels.
   b. dorsal aortas.   **d.** ventral aortas.

_____ **13.** Fanworms live in tubes that are made of mucus and
  a. seaweed.   **c.** protein.
  b. sand.   **d.** cuticle.

_____ **14.** Which of the following is a free-swimming polychaete?
  a. fanworm   **c.** clam worm
  b. hydra.   **d.** porifera

_____ **15.** To ensure long feeding sessions, leech saliva contains both anticlotting chemicals and
  a. pain-killing chemicals.   **c.** pharynx particles.
  b. reproductive sperm.   **d.** ovules.

_____ **16.** The soft, outer layer of a mollusk's body is called a
  a. visceral mass.   **c.** mantle.
  b. gill.   **d.** coelom.

_____ **17.** The snail, the clam, and the squid all have one large, common feature. This feature is the
  a. eye.   **c.** tentacle.
  b. foot.   **d.** stinging cell.

_____ **18.** Which of the following food-obtaining adaptations makes filter-feeding unnecessary for a squid?
  a. mantle cavity   **c.** beaklike jaws
  b. visceral mass   **d.** foot

_____ **19.** Which excretory organs do annelids and mollusks share?
  a. coronary tract   **c.** nephridia
  b. bladder   **d.** visceral mass

_____ **20.** Squids have a complex brain and a thick bundle of nerves called the
  a. cephalon.   **c.** giant nerve fiber.
  b. nephron.   **d.** complex ganglion.

_____ **21.** Chitons eat algae using a tonguelike organ called a
  a. crop.   **c.** bivalve.
  b. pharynx.   **d.** radula.

_____ **22.** Why can gastropods *not* perform respiration in the same way as earthworms?
  a. Unlike earthworms, gastropods have little exposed body surface area.
  b. Unlike earthworms, gastropods have no lungs.
  c. Unlike worms, gastropods have no mantle.
  d. none of the above

_____ **23.** In bivalves, particles of food are trapped by mucus that coats the
  a. stomach.   **c.** gills.
  b. radula.   **d.** pharynx.

_____ **24.** Cephalopods and humans have similarly structured
  a. eyes.   **c.** feet.
  b. skeletons.   **d.** circulatory systems.

_____ **25.** A cephalopod's tentacles are connected to its
  a. feet.   **c.** shell.
  b. head.   **d.** swim bladder.

Chapter 28 Test B

Read each question or statement and respond in the space provided.

1. What similarities between annelids and mollusks have led scientists to think such animals share a distant ancestor that is not shared by other animals? (16 points)

_____

_____

_____

_____

2. How are annelids and mollusks useful to people? (15 points)

_____

_____

_____

_____

3. Identify each of the labeled structures in the drawing of the earthworm below. Choose from among the following answers: crop, mouth, ventral blood vessel, dorsal blood vessel, intestine, coelom, brain, nerve cord, gizzard, seta, aortic arch. (11 points)

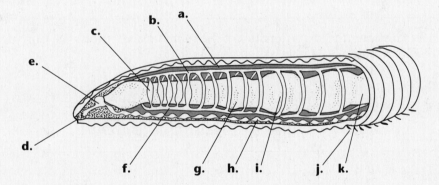

a._____

b. _____

c._____

d. _____

e._____

f. _____

g._____

h. _____

i. _____

j. _____

k. _____

4. a. Suppose you were observing members of the different classes of annelids. How could you tell the difference between polychaetes, leeches, and earthworms? (9 points)

_____

_____

_____

_____

_____

_____

b. What characteristics do annelids in all these classes have in common? (9 points)

_____

_____

_____

_____

5. What characteristics do all mollusks have in common? (16 points)

_____

_____

_____

_____

6. The table below illustrates the characteristics of the four classes of mollusks. Complete the table by filling in the correct information. (24 points)

CLASS	BILATERAL SYMMETRY	BRAIN, GANGLIA, OR NEITHER?	RADULA PRESENT?	USUALLY EXTERNAL SHELL?	CLOSED CIRCULATORY SYSTEM?	SAMPLE ORGANISM
a. Polyplacophora						
b. Gastropoda						
c. Bivalvia						
d. Cephalopoda						

Chapter 29 Test A

Choose the best answer for each question and write its letter in the blank.

_____ 1. An arthropod is a segmented invertebrate with an exoskeleton and
    a. straight appendages.   **c.** jointed appendages.
    b. a closed circulatory system.   **d.** an endothermal system.

_____ 2. Why is molting a risky period in the life of an arthropod?
    a. no protection from its exoskeleton   **c.** opening of circulatory system
    b. poisons excreted by decaying chitin   **d.** none of the above

_____ 3. Which animal has no exoskeleton or jointed appendages?
    a. spider   **c.** centipede
    b. *Peripatus*   **d.** ant

_____ 4. *Peripatus* may represent an evolutionary link between
    a. arthropods and cnidarians.   **c.** arthropods and annelids.
    b. annelids and mollusks.   **d.** annelids and Platyhelminthes.

_____ 5. An arthropod's exoskeleton is composed of protein bound to a tough polysaccharide called
    a. cellulose.   **c.** pheromone.
    b. spiracle.   **d.** chitin.

_____ 6. One difference between centipedes and millipedes is that millipedes do not have
    a. two pairs of legs on each segment.   **c.** segmented bodies.
    b. paired appendages.   **d.** poisonous fangs.

_____ 7. The fused head and chest region to which the legs and other appendages of a crustacean are attached is called the
    a. cephalothorax.   **c.** abdomen.
    b. mandible.   **d.** segmented thorax.

_____ 8. All crustaceans have a pair of jawlike appendages called
    a. the pharynx.   **c.** the swimmerets.
    b. the mandibles.   **d.** the fangs.

_____ 9. Which of these crayfish organs is most like the nephridia of an earthworm?
    a. mandible   **c.** ventral nerve
    b. green gland   **d.** cephalothorax

_____ 10. When are a crayfish's gill bailers likely to be most active?
    a. while walking   **c.** while remaining in one place
    b. while avoiding an enemy   **d.** while on land

_____ 11. Copepods are tiny crustaceans that are a main component in
    a. plankton.   **c.** peat.
    b. algae.   **d.** swimmerets.

_____ 12. Isopods (or wood lice) are crustaceans. Therefore, they are most closely related to what group of organisms?
    a. clams   **c.** beetles
    b. crabs   **d.** annelids

_____ 13. The pedipalps of arachnids are adapted to
    a. bite prey.   **c.** hold and chew food.
    b. filter wastes.   **d.** digest food.

_____ 14. In arachnids, excretory organs that filter wastes from body fluids are known as
    a. Malpighian tubules.   **c.** nephridia.
    b. kidneys.   **d.** spiracles.

_____ **15.** The book lungs of arachnids are similar in structure to
   a. human lungs.   **c.** gills.
   b. pseudocoeloms.   **d.** pedipalps.

_____ **16.** Tarantulas have well-developed eyes, whereas web-weaving spiders have relatively poor eyesight. How can you explain this difference in terms of the feeding habits of each type of spider?
   a. Tarantulas hunt much smaller prey.
   b. Web-weaving spiders do not have to look for prey.
   c. Tarantulas need to migrate.
   d. Web-weaving spiders have sharper mouth parts.

_____ **17.** Horseshoe crabs are classified as
   a. arachnids.   **c.** chelicerates.
   b. crabs.   **d.** cephalons.

_____ **18.** Male moths can locate females at great distances by sensing which female-produced substance?
   a. pheromones   **c.** slime deposits
   b. spiracles   **d.** filaments

_____ **19.** A series of changes during which young insects develop into adults is known as
   a. the nymph stage.   **c.** metamorphosis.
   b. polymorphism.   **d.** ventriculation.

_____ **20.** Once a butterfly larva reaches a certain size, it forms a protective case around itself and enters the
   a. segmented phase.   **c.** fertilization phase.
   b. nymph phase.   **d.** pupal stage.

_____ **21.** Which of these organisms is a member of the order Lepidoptera?
   a. fly   **c.** butterfly
   b. beetle   **d.** cockroach

_____ **22.** How do some praying mantises avoid predators?
   a. by looking like a twig   **c.** by looking like a bee
   b. by looking like a large eye   **d.** by looking like a thorn

_____ **23.** The primary diet of some whales is a crustacean known as
   a. an aphid.   **c.** krill.
   b. a weevil.   **d.** yucca.

_____ **24.** Which of the following two arthropods behave in a way beneficial to plants?
   a. aphids and honeybees   **c.** aphids and cicadas
   b. cicadas and honeybees   **d.** honeybees and yucca moths

_____ **25.** Which of the following fabrics is made from a substance produced by an arthropod?
   a. linen   **c.** muslin
   b. flax   **d.** silk

Chapter 29 Test B

Read each question or statement and respond in the space provided.

1. What characteristics do arthropods have in common? (12 points)

_____

_____

2. Suppose you are a taxonomist who is studying arthropods. You are out in the field and observe arthropods with each of the following characteristics. Classify each as either a crustacean, uniramian, or chelicerate. (10 points)

a. eight legs, no antennae _____

b. many legs, one pair of antennae _____

c. chewing mouthparts, claws, two pairs of antennae _____

d. one pair of antennae, six legs, no claws _____

e. pincerlike mouthparts, no antennae _____

3. Identify the labeled structures in the drawing of the crayfish below. Choose among the following possible answers: green gland, telson, carapace, cephalothorax, anus, digestive gland, walking leg, nerve cord, testis or ovary, brain, stomach, mandible, swimmeret, antenna, abdomen, heart, intestine, jaw foot, eye, mouth. (20 points)

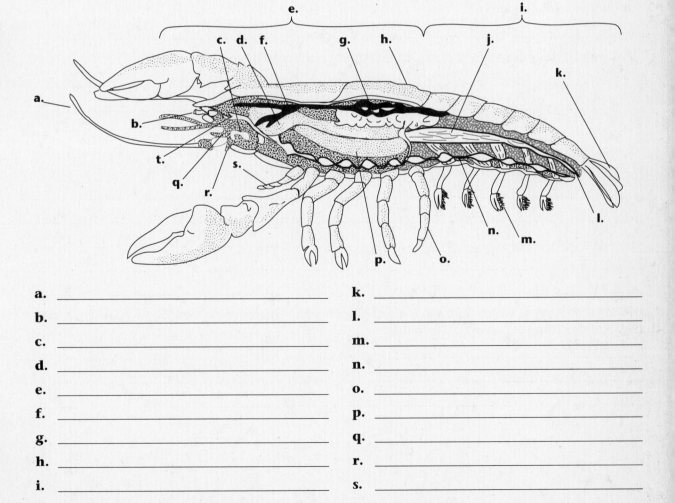

a. _____	**k.** _____
b. _____	**l.** _____
c. _____	**m.** _____
d. _____	**n.** _____
e. _____	**o.** _____
f. _____	**p.** _____
g. _____	**q.** _____
h. _____	**r.** _____
i. _____	**s.** _____
j. _____	**t.** _____

4. State the function of each of the following structures in arachnids. (12 points)

a. pedipalps _____

b. Malpighian tubules _____

c. book lungs _____

d. spinnerets _____

5. State the names of the structures that carry out each of the following functions in insects. (12 points)

a. exchange and movement of gases _____

b. nerve response _____

c. digestion _____

d. excretion _____

6. a. What is meant by metamorphosis in insects? (3 points)

_____

b. Name one kind of insect in which metamorphosis does not occur. (3 points)

_____

c. Name the three stages of incomplete metamorphosis. Name one kind of insect that passes through these stages. (3 points)

_____

d. Name the four stages of complete metamorphosis. Name one kind of insect that passes through these stages. (3 points)

_____

7. Describe three examples of insect camouflage or mimicry. (10 points)

_____

_____

_____

8. Name three orders of insects. Also describe their characteristics and give an example of each. (12 points)

_____

_____

_____

_____

_____

9. List four ways in which arthropods affect people or the environment. Include two positive and two negative effects in your answer. (10 points)

_____

_____

_____

Name _____ Class _____ Date _____

Chapter 30 Test A

Choose the best answer for each question and write its letter in the blank.

_____ 1. Echinoderms have a spiny skin, radial symmetry, an endoskeleton, and
      a. amebocyte cells.   **c.** fully developed arms and legs.
      b. a water vascular system.   **d.** a five-chambered heart.

_____ 2. In the deuterostome embryo of an echinoderm, the blastopore first develops into a(n)
      a. anus.   **c.** tentacle.
      b. mouth.   **d.** larva.

_____ 3. What evidence suggests that chordates and echinoderms are related?
      a. the lack of an anus   **c.** the fact that both are deuterostomes
      b. the fact that both are protostomes   **d.** the fact that both live in water

_____ 4. What trait of the sea urchin and the feather star is often associated with more primitive invertebrates?
      a. bilateral symmetry   **c.** radial symmetry
      b. an anus   **d.** asymmetry

_____ 5. Which of the following phrases does not describe a typical characteristic of an echinoderm?
      a. radial symmetry   **c.** five-part body plan
      b. fast-moving   **d.** sessile

_____ 6. Echinoderms move by a network of fluid-filled tubes known as a the
      a. water vascular system.   **c.** dorsal pouch.
      b. notochord.   **d.** tube pouch.

_____ 7. Tube feet in echinoderms are actually a part of the organism's
      a. ampulla.   **c.** water vascular system.
      b. nerve ring.   **d.** regeneration organ.

_____ 8. What happens in an sea star when muscles in the ampullae contract?
      a. The tube feet shorten.   **c.** The tube feet extend.
      b. Digestion stops.   **d.** The tube feet are dehydrated.

_____ 9. What supports the shape of a sea star's body?
      a. a prickly exoskeleton   **c.** suction cups
      b. hardened calcium plates   **d.** bivalves

_____ 10. What structure surrounding the mouth of a sea star coordinates its movements?
      a. eyespots   **c.** a radial nerve
      b. a nerve net   **d.** a nerve ring

_____ 11. Since sea stars are carnivorous, what organism would they be unlikely to feed on?
      a. a clam   **c.** a coral polyp
      b. a mussel   **d.** none of the above

_____ 12. A sea star feeds on other organisms by
      a. extending its stomach into them.   **c.** filtering them out of water.
      b. pulling them in with cilia.   **d.** paralyzing them with stingers.

_____ 13. Suppose a sea star were isolated from the other members of its species. How could one make it produce offspring?
      a. by cutting off an arm without the central nerve ring
      b. by joining its male and female parts
      c. by cutting off an arm that had a piece of the central nerve ring
      d. by mating it with a larva

_____ **14.** What makes scientists suspect that modern echinoderms evolved from free-swimming, bilaterally symmetrical ancestors?
   a. bilateral symmetry of echinoderm larva
   b. radial symmetry of adult echinoderms
   c. the sessile life style of echinoderms
   d. the hermaphroditism of echinoderms

_____ **15.** A muscular sac that forces water through the vascular system of a sea star is known as a(n)
   a. vasculator.   **c.** gill pouch.
   b. ampulla.   **d.** heart.

_____ **16.** Members of the class Ophiuroidea include the brittle star and the
   a. basket star.   **c.** sea star.
   b. feather star.   **d.** sea urchin.

_____ **17.** What characteristic of basket stars distinguishes them from brittle stars?
   a. long, slender arms and a small central disk
   b. highly branched arms
   c. compact size
   d. ability to move quickly

_____ **18.** What advantage does a brittle star gain from having spines on its arms?
   a. flexibility   **c.** traction
   b. increased respiration   **d.** protection

_____ **19.** One of the few adult echinoderms with bilateral symmetry is the
   a. sea lily.   **c.** sea cucumber.
   b. sand dollar.   **d.** sea urchin.

_____ **20.** The flexible tube located just below the nerve tube in a chordate is called the
   a. gill pouch.   **c.** gill slit.
   b. notochord.   **d.** dorsal tube.

_____ **21.** Which of the following do humans share with other chordates at some point in their development?
   a. tentacles   **c.** tube feet
   b. a tail   **d.** none of the above

_____ **22.** In early chordates, the function of the gill slits was probably
   a. breathing.   **c.** feeding.
   b. excretion.   **d.** reproduction.

_____ **23.** Sea squirts belong to the subphylum
   a. Urochordata.   **c.** Cephalochordata.
   b. Lancelet.   **d.** Tunicate.

_____ **24.** Tunicates are named for their leathery
   a. gill slits.   **c.** outer covering.
   b. notochord.   **d.** dorsal fin.

_____ **25.** Although lancelets can swim, where do they spend most of their time?
   a. on dry rock   **c.** floating on the ocean surface
   b. buried in sand   **d.** on the backs of free-swimming animals

Name _____ Class _____ Date _____

Chapter 30 Test B

Read each question or statement and respond in the space provided.

1. If you examined various echinoderms in their natural environment, what would you notice about each of the following? (21 points)

a. symmetry

_____

b. number of parts in body plan

_____

c. skin

_____

d. system used for motion and respiration

_____

e. embryo type

_____

f. skeleton

_____

g. environment

_____

2. Describe each of the following processes in sea stars. (24 points)

a. feeding and digestion of mollusk prey

_____

_____

_____

_____

_____

_____

b. response

_____

_____

_____

_____

c. asexual and sexual reproduction

_____

_____

_____

_____

3. Compare any two of the following with sea stars: brittle stars, sea lilies, sea urchins, sand dollars, sea cucumbers. (20 points)

_____

_____

_____

_____

_____

4. State the general characteristics of all chordates. (19 points)

_____

_____

_____

_____

5. Suppose you observed chordates with each of the following characteristics. Classify each as either a vertebrate, lancelet, or tunicate. (16 points)

a. The larva shows all the major characteristics of chordates. The adult is sessile and has gill slits but no nerve cord, tail, or backbone.

_____

b. The adult has gills, lives in the ocean, and has a backbone.

_____

c. The adult shows all major chordate characteristics, can swim, filters food from water, and has no backbone.

_____

d. The adult has a leathery outer covering, has gill slits but no notochord, filters food from water, and has no backbone.

_____

Unit 6 Test A

Choose the best answer for each question and write its letter in the blank.

_____ **1.** In some animals, the mesoderm forms a fully-lined body cavity known as the
    a. protostome.
    b. coelom.
    c. deuterostome.
    d. ganglia.

_____ **2.** The major differences between the blastula and the gastrula are that the former is neither two-layered nor
    a. cup-shaped.
    b. embryonic.
    c. multicellular.
    d. hydrostatic.

_____ **3.** Sessile organisms are usually not
    a. very good at feeding.
    b. able to remain in one place.
    c. able to move great distances.
    d. able to reproduce by themselves.

_____ **4.** Animals without a backbone are known as
    a. chordates.
    b. cephalons.
    c. primates.
    d. invertebrates.

_____ **5.** Which is the dorsal surface of a fish?
    a. bottom surface
    b. front end
    c. top surface
    d. rear end

_____ **6.** The coelom is an evolutionary improvement in animals because it prevents an animal's muscles from being restricted by its
    a. internal organs.
    b. nerve endings.
    c. skin.
    d. environment.

_____ **7.** A skeletal system in which muscles are supported by a water-filled cavity is known as a(n)
    a. endoskeleton.
    b. hydrocephalic skeleton.
    c. hydrostatic skeleton.
    d. appendicular skeleton.

_____ **8.** Which is the most fully developed embryo?
    a. newly fertilized egg
    b. gastrula
    c. blastula
    d. spermocyte

_____ **9.** An animal with a blastopore that develops into a mouth is known as a
    a. deuterostome.
    b. aphid.
    c. protostome.
    d. coelomate.

_____ **10.** Bilateral symmetry is the term for body parts arranged
    a. in a radial configuration.
    b. on one side of an axis.
    c. in pairs on either side of a central axis.
    d. around a circle.

_____ **11.** A dormant mass of amebocytes surrounded by protective layers of spicules is called a
    a. gemmule.
    b. medusa.
    c. porifera.
    d. osculum.

_____ **12.** When a female animal undergoes parthenogenesis, which of the following is unnecessary?
    a. eggs
    b. embryo development
    c. males
    d. offspring

_____ **13.** Because a tapeworm contains a proglottid, it can
    a. produce offspring by itself.
    b. survive without many nutrients.
    c. reproduce without fertilized eggs.
    d. live underwater.

_____ **14.** The contractile cells of cnidarians allow them the advantage of
    a. lung respiration.
    b. an endoskeleton.
    c. movement.
    d. a hard outer skeleton.

_____ **15.** Which of the following organisms does algae help survive in anaerobic environments by providing oxygen?
    a. a species of turbellarians
    b. a kind of jellyfish
    c. a species of Trematoda
    d. a sand dollar

_____ **16.** Why is it impossible for a sponge to feed on large pieces of organic matter?
    a. It's not an animal.
    b. It is photosynthetic.
    c. Its teeth are very tiny.
    d. It is a filter feeder with small pores that strain particles from water.

_____ **17.** A muscular tube that can suck in food is called a
    a. pharynx.
    b. snout.
    c. spongin.
    d. phalanx.

_____ **18.** A medusa is one of the two basic body stages of a
    a. porifera.
    b. flatworm.
    c. cnidarian.
    d. planarian.

_____ **19.** In tropical regions of the world, a series disease called schistosomiasis is caused by a
    a. Cestoda.
    b. Platyhelminth.
    c. Cnidarian.
    d. Porifera.

_____ **20.** Like parasitic flatworms, parasitic nematodes usually have
    a. very simple life cycles.
    b. one host.
    c. two or more hosts.
    d. hermaphroditic characteristics.

_____ **21.** In order for air to enter and leave the body, gastropods have a
    a. moist, exposed skin.
    b. a network of pores like those of sponges.
    c. gills or blood vessels in the mantle cavity.
    d. symbiotic relationship with algae.

_____ **22.** A nautilus's shell is divided into chambers, one of which contains the
    a. heart only.
    b. entire living creature.
    c. lungs only.
    d. ganglia only.

_____ **23.** An earthworm's ability to break up and aerate soil comes partly from its
    a. filter feeders.
    b. aortic arches.
    c. visceral mass.
    d. gizzard.

_____ **24.** A typical trochophore is pear-shaped and has tufts of
    a. cilia.
    b. flagella.
    c. capillaries.
    d. ganglia.

_____ **25.** Why do scientists study mollusks to learn about ecology?
    a. Mollusks do not use up any food supply.
    b. Mollusks never overbreed.
    c. Mollusks are filter feeders and can be used to monitor water purity.
    d. none of the above

_____ **26.** All mollusks have a soft, outer layer called a
    a. mantle.
    b. visceral mass.
    c. pharynx.
    d. carapace.

_____ **27.** Chitons eat algae using a tonguelike organ called a
    a. crop.
    b. cephalon.
    c. radula.
    d. fang.

_____ **28.** Pearl formation in oysters begins when a small foreign object lodges between the shell and the
    a. bivalve.
    b. mantle.
    c. gills.
    d. gastropod.

Unit 6 Test A

_____ 29. What happens to the water drawn into the tubule of an earthworm's nephridia?
    a. All of it is excreted.
    b. Some of it is reabsorbed and some is excreted.
    c. All of it is reabsorbed.
    d. It remains in the tubule.

_____ 30. Annelids are classified by the presence and number of bristles on their skin. What are these bristles called?
    a. parapodia   **c.** setae
    b. gemmae   **d.** polyps

_____ 31. Both the antennae and legs of arthropods are classified as
    a. segments.   **c.** mandibles.
    b. part of the cephalothorax.   **d.** appendages.

_____ 32. Which animal would be most likely to have swimmerets?
    a. crustacean   **c.** bumble bee
    b. moth   **d.** earthworm

_____ 33. The long, segmented abdomen of the scorpion ends in
    a. two legs.   **c.** a poisonous stinger.
    b. Malpighian tubules.   **d.** pedipalps.

_____ 34. In the grasshopper, air enters the trachea through openings in the
    a. cuticle.   **c.** coelom.
    b. larvae.   **d.** pupa.

_____ 35. Crustaceans have a long, narrow tail region divided into seven segments. What is it called?
    a. the cephalothorax   **c.** the abdomen
    b. the mandible   **d.** the pedipalp

_____ 36. Crustaceans have three pairs of mouth parts. Two pairs hold the food and one pair
    a. sucks it in.   **c.** crushes it.
    b. secretes an enzyme onto it.   **d.** coats it in mucus.

_____ 37. Insects communicate with each other by secreting pheromones that other insects
    a. smell and taste.   **c.** carry to save in nests.
    b. sense underwater.   **d.** always flee from.

_____ 38. Flies belong to an order of insect that have
    a. two pairs of hard wings.   **c.** two pairs of membranous wings.
    b. one pair of hard wings.   **d.** one pair of membranous wings.

_____ 39. Beetle grubs endanger the health of trees by eating their
    a. fruit.   **c.** bark.
    b. roots.   **d.** leaves.

_____ 40. What are the thin, flexible sound-detecting membranes in grasshoppers called?
    a. sensors   **c.** spiracles
    b. tympanic membranes   **d.** waggles

_____ 41. As adults, tunicates lose their
    a. notochord.   **c.** gill slits.
    b. sessile life style.   **d.** leathery outer covering.

_____ 42. Unlike the ventral, solid nerve cord common in invertebrates, chordates have a(n)
    a. dorsal, hollow nerve tube.   **c.** posterior nerve tube.
    b. uncovered mass of ganglia.   **d.** anterior nerve tube.

_____ **43.** Segmentation in lancelets allows muscle bundles to pull independently against the notochord, resulting in
  a. better digestion.
  b. bivalve circulation.
  c. smooth side-to-side movements.
  d. tentacle flexibility.

_____ **44.** In a deuterostome embryo, the mouth forms from the
  a. blastopore.
  b. protostrome.
  c. gastrula.
  d. epiderm.

_____ **45.** If the water vascular system of an echinoderm stopped working, which of the following activities might be affected?
  a. digestion
  b. respiration only
  c. movement only
  d. both movement and respiration

_____ **46.** A sea star belongs to a class of echinoderms known as
  a. Asteroidea.
  b. Crinoidea.
  c. Ophiuroidea.
  d. Carbonifera.

_____ **47.** Which of the following has nothing to do with a sea cucumber's system of defense?
  a. its digestive system.
  b. poison.
  c. sticky tubules.
  d. mandibles.

_____ **48.** Water is forced through the vascular system of a sea star by the
  a. ampulla.
  b. ventricle.
  c. polyp.
  d. tube foot.

_____ **49.** How does a sea star open the shell of a captured mollusk?
  a. by secreting poison
  b. by attaching tube feet and pulling
  c. by using mandibles to cut the shell tendon
  d. none of the above

_____ **50.** A sea star's nervous system contains a nerve ring, radial nerves, and
  a. receptor cells sensitive to chemicals.
  b. both a and c.
  c. eyespots.
  d. neither a nor c.

Chapter 31 Test A

Choose the best answer for each question and write its letter in the blank.

_____ **1.** Which of the following traits is shared by all vertebrates?
  a. an exoskeleton
  b. ten fingers and ten toes
  c. an endoskeleton
  d. jaws and teeth

_____ **2.** Approximately how many known vertebrate species exist today?
  a. 11,000
  b. 78,000
  c. 43,000
  d. 1,000,000

_____ **3.** What advantages are provided by an endoskeleton?
  a. The skeleton grows in proportion to the body.
  b. The animal can run faster.
  c. The animal can process information faster.
  d. none of the above

_____ **4.** Which of the following is a part of the appendicular skeleton?
  a. pelvis
  b. skull
  c. spine
  d. femur

_____ **5.** The earliest known vertebrate fossils are of a group of animals called
  a. chondrichthyes.
  b. amphibians.
  c. agnatha.
  d. ostracoderms.

_____ **6.** Bones are made hard and rigid by
  a. mineral deposits.
  b. vertebrae.
  c. bone marrow.
  d. cartilage.

_____ **7.** Bony fishes have evolved much more rapidly than cartilaginous fishes. This is the result of their
  a. poisonous secretions.
  b. armored protection.
  c. gargantuan size.
  d. responses to environmental changes.

_____ **8.** Which of the following is classified in class chondrichthyes?
  a. sharks
  b. plankton
  c. salmon
  d. lungfish

_____ **9.** The lateral line system is a special sensory structure possessed by most fish. What is its function?
  a. to detect vibrations and changes in water pressure
  b. to detect electrical signals in the water
  c. to detect body heat
  d. none of the above

_____ **10.** Most sharks must swim constantly in order to avoid
  a. predators.
  b. suffocation.
  c. sleep.
  d. paralysis.

_____ **11.** In sharks and other vertebrates, excretory structures are combined in a pair of organs called
  a. kidneys.
  b. lungs.
  c. glands.
  d. gills.

_____ **12.** The spiral valve of a shark's digestive system helps to
  a. slow the movement of food through the intestine.
  b. crush bones of prey.
  c. remove metabolic wastes from the system.
  d. expel poisons consumed in the diet.

_____ **13.** How does the lateral line system assist the shark during the moment of attacking its prey?
  a. by detecting electrical signals
  b. by detecting blood
  c. by detecting movements
  d. none of the above

_____ **14.** Ray-finned fishes are the only fishes with a swim bladder. What is the function of the swim bladder?
  a. to help swim faster
  b. to digest food quickly
  c. to remain stationary
  d. to conserve water

_____ **15.** Because they are ectothermic, fish body temperature varies with
  a. caloric intake.
  b. electrical currents.
  c. external temperatures.
  d. lateral line movements.

_____ **16.** The only remaining species of lobe-finned fish is the
  a. lungfish.
  b. coelacanth.
  c. Atlantic salmon.
  d. Pacific salmon.

_____ **17.** What hypothesis can be drawn from the skeletal structure of the lobe-finned fish?
  a. Ray-finned fishes evolved from lobe-finned fishes.
  b. Lobe-finned fishes evolved from ray-finned fishes.
  c. Terrestrial vertebrates evolved from lobe-finned fishes.
  d. none of the above

_____ **18.** A layer of mucus covers the scales of ray-finned fishes, which
  a. contains poisonous secretions.
  b. deflects sunlight.
  c. provides insulation.
  d. none of the above

_____ **19.** When the level of oxygen in the water becomes very low, lungfishes
  a. die.
  b. rise to the surface and gulp air.
  c. mate.
  d. migrate.

_____ **20.** Why do scientists consider ray-finned fishes to be the most successful group of fish?
  a. They have adapted to all aquatic environments.
  b. They have developed strong poisonous secretions.
  c. They produce only one offspring at a time.
  d. all of the above

_____ **21.** The pattern of scales on a ray-finned fish, unlike those of the shark, help the fish to
  a. move up and down.
  b. steer and brake.
  c. create less friction.
  d. none of the above

_____ **22.** Most fish produce too many offspring to be supported by their environment. Why does this help ensure survival of the species?
  a. The fish clean up polluted environments.
  b. Only the strongest, best-adapted fish survive.
  c. The increased number of fish raise oxygen levels.
  d. none of the above

_____ **23.** How do fish that migrate long distances, such as salmon, navigate?
  a. by detecting visual cues
  b. by detecting aural cues
  c. by detecting the earth's magnetic field
  d. none of the above

_____ **24.** How does the African lungfish survive when its rivers dry up?
  a. by hiding itself in a cocoon
  b. by migrating to other streams
  c. by crossing land
  d. none of the above

_____ **25.** Why is gene transfer a more economical means than growth hormones for increasing fish growth rates?
  a. The fish can be released into the environment.
  b. The fish are more willing to eat genes.
  c. Growth hormones are too expensive.
  d. none of the above

Chapter 31 Test B

Read each question or statement and respond in the space provided.

1. What are the characteristics of vertebrates? (7 points)

_____

_____

_____

2. Name three vertebrate classes and give an example of an organism in each. (6 points)

_____

_____

_____

3. Briefly describe the evolution of jawless, cartilaginous, and bony fishes. (15 points)

_____

_____

_____

_____

_____

_____

_____

_____

4. Suppose you were observing a number of different kinds of fishes. Use the information below to classify each fish as a member of either class Agnatha, Chondrichthyes, or Osteichthyes. (18 points)

a. cartilaginous skeleton, hinged jaws

_____

b. larval stage that resembles a lancelet, no paired fins

_____

c. paired fins, placoid scales, lateral line system

_____

d. skeleton made of bone, hinged jaws

_____

e. scaleless skin, cartilaginous skeleton, notochord as adult

_____

f. internal fertilization, leathery skin, no means of pumping water over gills

_____

5. Describe the main differences between lobe-finned fishes, lungfishes, and ray-finned fishes. Give an example of each. (14 points)

_____
_____
_____
_____
_____
_____

6. Identify the labeled structures in the drawing of the ray-finned bony fish below. Choose from among the following answers: pelvic fin, gills, stomach, brain, lateral line, swim bladder, heart, anus, dorsal fin, ovary or testis, nerve cord, liver, intestine. (26 points)

a. _____   h. _____
b. _____   i. _____
c. _____   j. _____
d. _____   k. _____
e. _____   l. _____
f. _____   m. _____
g. _____

7. Describe the life cycle of a salmon. (14 points)

_____
_____
_____
_____
_____
_____

Chapter 32 Test A

Choose the best answer for each question and write its letter in the blank.

_____ 1. Amphibians were the first vertebrates to
    a. migrate great distances.
    b. fertilize eggs externally.
    c. live on land.
    d. lay eggs on land

_____ 2. Which phase is true of all amphibians?
    a. start life as aquatic larvae
    b. start life on land
    c. migrate daily between water and land
    d. lay hard-shelled eggs

_____ 3. Fossil evidence suggests that modern amphibians descended from
    a. ray-finned fishes.
    b. terrestrial vertebrates.
    c. lobe-finned fishes.
    d. none of the above

_____ 4. What conditions were most likely responsible for the development of amphibian life forms?
    a. alternating floods and droughts
    b. volcanoes
    c. electrical storms
    d. earthquakes

_____ 5. The development of primarily land-oriented amphibians during the Carboniferous period occurred as a result of what conditions?
    a. fewer competitors for food
    b. fewer predators
    c. abundance of food
    d. all of the above

_____ 6. Which of the following is not an amphibian?
    a. toad
    b. lung fish
    c. salamander
    d. caecilian

_____ 7. What is the function of the bright colorings on certain salamanders?
    a. to attract mates
    b. warn of poisonous secretions
    c. camouflage
    d. they have no function

_____ 8. Amphibians of the order Urodela typically retain their tails
    a. only through adolescence.
    b. for approximately two years.
    c. throughout life.
    d. never have tails.

_____ 9. The first amphibians developed stronger limb bones and muscles than their aquatic predecessors because
    a. air pressure is greater than water pressure.
    b. the effects of gravity are stronger on land than in water.
    c. they had to travel longer distances.
    d. they needed to support the weight of their bodies.

_____ 10. The warts and bumps on a toad's skin are actually
    a. poisonous glands.
    b. parasites.
    c. tumors.
    d. skeletal plates.

_____ 11. During the larval stage of life, through what kind of organ do most amphibians breathe?
    a. lungs
    b. skin
    c. gills
    d. aortic arches

_____ 12. The toxins secreted by poisonous frogs are mostly
    a. alkaloids.
    b. bile.
    c. enzymes.
    d. cytokines.

_____ 13. What is the digestive function of the liver in the frog?
    a. to secrete bile
    b. to secrete poisons
    c. to absorb nutrients
    d. to secrete acid

_____ **14.** Amphibians have adapted to the challenge of distributing oxygen more efficiently to all cells of the body by
   a. developing a double-loop circulatory system.
   b. breathing more quickly.
   c. breathing only out of water.
   d. developing a one-way respiratory system.

_____ **15.** The kidneys of an amphibian maintain
   a. a constant, unchanging water balance.
   b. a water balance that responds to the environment.
   c. the heart rate.
   d. oxygen in the bloodstream.

_____ **16.** The three-chambered heart helps amphibians to
   a. maintain water balance.
   b. regulate body temperature.
   c. increase flow of oxygen-rich blood throughout the body.
   d. eliminate toxins from the bloodstream.

_____ **17.** What is the function of a frog's tympanic membrane?
   a. to receive sound waves   **c.** to protect the eyes
   b. to absorb nutrients   **d.** to catch food

_____ **18.** Many frogs and salamanders return from long distances to breed in the same place each year. How do they navigate?
   a. sensing visual cues   **c.** sensing the earth's magnetic fields
   b. sensing chemical traces   **d.** following each other

_____ **19.** Freshly laid amphibian eggs are covered with a jellylike coating. What is one of the functions of this jelly?
   a. provide nutrients for the embryos   **c.** surround the eggs with protective poisons
   b. provide camouflage for the eggs   **d.** none of the above

_____ **20.** Some species of frogs deposit their young on land. How are the tadpoles transported to water?
   a. in the mother's mouth   **c.** in the father's mouth
   b. in a special pouch   **d.** on the parent's backs

_____ **21.** Metamorphosis in frogs is triggered by
   a. neoteny.   **c.** thyroxine.
   b. electrical signals.   **d.** auxin.

_____ **22.** When reproductive adults retain larval characteristics, the condition is called
   a. cloaca.   **c.** neoteny.
   b. molting.   **d.** larvateny.

_____ **23.** What is the function of the inflatable pouch in a male frog's throat?
   a. to retain oxygen longer   **c.** to amplify mating calls
   b. to frighten predators   **d.** to hold food

_____ **24.** Which digestive organ secretes enzymes into the frog's small intestine to help break down foods?
   a. cloaca   **c.** pancreas
   b. kidney   **d.** spleen

_____ **25.** What membrane protects the frog's eyes in water and keeps them moist in air?
   a. tympanic membrane   **c.** mucous membrane
   b. nictitating membrane   **d.** spleen

Name _____ Class _____ Date _____

Chapter 32 Test B

Read each question or statement and respond in the space provided.

1. State the general characteristics of amphibians. (14 points)

_____

_____

_____

_____

_____

_____

2. Describe the theory of amphibian evolution. (12 points)

_____

_____

_____

_____

_____

3. Compare and contrast members of the orders Urodela, Anura, and Apoda. Also give an example of each. (14 points)

_____

_____

_____

_____

_____

_____

_____

4. Describe respiration in typical amphibians. (12 points)

_____

_____

_____

_____

5. Suppose you are a biologist observing reproduction and metamorphosis in frogs. Write a descriptive, step-by-step report of what you would observe. (14 points)

_____

_____

_____

_____

_____

6. Identify each of the labeled structures in the two drawings of the frog below. The first drawing illustrates the digestive system. The second illustrates the circulatory, reproductive, and excretory systems. Choose among the following possible answers: large intestine, liver, lung, ovary or testis, heart, cloaca, esophagus, anus, atrium, fat body, small intestine, ventricle, pancreas, bladder, stomach, kidney, gall bladder. (34 points)

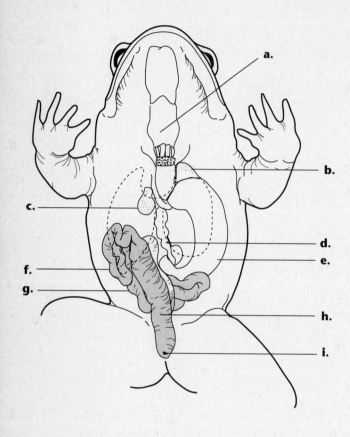

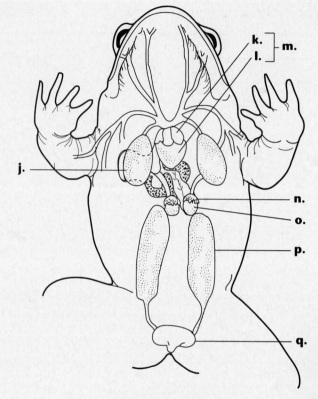

Digestive system

Circulatory, Reproductive and Excretory systems

a. _____

b. _____

c. _____

d. _____

e. _____

f. _____

g. _____

h. _____

i. _____

j. _____

k. _____

l. _____

m. _____

n. _____

o. _____

p. _____

q. _____

Chapter 33 Test A

Choose the best answer for each question and write its letter in the blank.

_____ **1.** During which period did reptiles first appear in the fossil record?
  a. Carboniferous   **c.** Permian
  b. Mesozoic   **d.** Devonian

_____ **2.** Mass extinction occurred among amphibians and reptiles at the end of the Permian period as a result of
  a. shortages of food supplies.   **c.** meteorites.
  b. climate and terrain changes. **d.** none of the above

_____ **3.** The legs of the therapsid were placed more in line with its body, which gave it the advantage of
  a. running faster than most reptiles. **c.** being able to dig for food.
  b. the ability to climb trees.   **d.** none of the above

_____ **4.** How could people help the endangered tuatuara to survive?
  a. cut back factory pollution   **c.** increase Polynesian rat populations
  b. till the soil   **d.** control Polynesian rat populations

_____ **5.** Modern turtles and tortoises are direct descendants of
  a. dinosaurs.   **c.** crocodiles.
  b. stem reptiles.   **d.** geckos.

_____ **6.** If confined to a body of salt water with no access to land, which of the following reptiles would be most likely to survive longest?
  a. freshwater turtle   **c.** tortoise
  b. sea turtle   **d.** crocodile

_____ **7.** The keratin in a reptile's skin helps it to
  a. conserve moisture.   **c.** deflect sunlight.
  b. climb vertical surfaces.   **d.** defend itself.

_____ **8.** Many reptiles periodically shed their skins because
  a. their scales do not grow with their bodies.
  b. the skins become too dry and scaly.
  c. the skins become too moist.
  d. the scales begin to decay.

_____ **9.** Most reptiles have feeding habits best described as
  a. omnivorous.   **c.** carnivorous.
  b. herbivorous.   **d.** none of the above

_____ **10.** An animal whose body temperature is determined by the external environment is a(n)
  a. endotherm.   **c.** hypotherm.
  b. ectotherm.   **d.** hydrotherm.

_____ **11.** A pit viper is able to strike accurately at animals even in darkness by
  a. detecting body heat.   **c.** sensing smells.
  b. detecting electrical signals. **d.** sensing vibrations.

_____ **12.** The venom of the *Bothrops jararaca* affects its victim by
  a. causing paralysis.   **c.** causing coma.
  b. causing blood pressure to drop. **d.** destroying tissues.

_____ **13.** Generally, reptiles that live in colder climates reproduce by
  a. giving birth to live young.   **c.** laying eggs on land.
  b. laying eggs in water.   **d.** asexual reproduction.

_____ **14.** Why do alligators lay eggs under a pile of soil and rotting plant material?
    a. Decomposition keeps the eggs cool.
    b. Decomposition keeps the eggs warm.
    c. Decomposition provides nutrients to the eggs.
    d. The smell of rotting plants drives away predators.

_____ **15.** Why are newly hatched reptiles better equipped to deal with their environments than are newly hatched amphibians?
    a. They have larger, better-provisioned eggs.
    b. They are threatened by fewer predators.
    c. They are given food by their parents.
    d. They are endothermic.

_____ **16.** Studies of dinosaur bones have shown blood circulation patterns to be similar to those of
    a. amphibians.   **c.** birds and mammals.
    b. fish.   **d.** insects.

_____ **17.** The first reptiles that stood upright on two hind legs were the
    a. dinosaurs.   **c.** amphibians.
    b. thecodonts.   **d.** therapsids.

_____ **18.** The largest two-legged dinosaur in the fossil record is called
    a. *Tyrannosaurus rex.*   **c.** *Apatosaurus.*
    b. *Pterodactyl.*   **d.** *Archaeopteryx*

_____ **19.** Scientists infer that snakes evolved from
    a. poisonous frogs.   **c.** burrowing lizards.
    b. turtles.   **d.** ray-finned fish.

_____ **20.** Some scientists hypothesize that the larger body of some dinosaurs was an adaptation for
    a. maintaining body temperature.   **c.** running faster.
    b. intimidating predators.   **d.** having larger offspring.

_____ **21.** Burrowing lizards, like caecilians, lack something that most other reptiles have. What do they lack?
    a. good eyesight   **c.** tails
    b. dry, scaly skin   **d.** legs

_____ **22.** Which of the following is not among the orders of modern reptiles?
    a. Squamata   **c.** Chelonia
    b. Crocodilia   **d.** Therapsid

_____ **23.** The gecko can escape predators by
    a. changing colors to camouflage itself.   **c.** casting off its tail.
    b. burrowing underground.   **d.** injecting them with venom.

_____ **24.** Most reptiles digest their food very slowly because
    a. they have several stomachs.   **c.** they do not eat often.
    b. they do not chew their food.   **d.** they lack digestive enzymes.

_____ **25.** Which reptile would be most likely to survive in a very dry climate?
    a. kingsnake   **c.** freshwater turtle
    b. spiny lizard   **d.** alligator

Chapter 33 Test B

Read each question or statement and respond in the space provided.

1. Describe the evolution of each of the following. (15 points)

   a. stem reptiles

_____

_____

   b. therapsids and thecodonts

_____

_____

   c. dinosaurs

_____

   d. crocodiles

_____

2. Imagine that you are a taxonomist who specializes in reptiles. Would you classify each of the following as a snake, turtle, tortoise, lizard, tuatara, crocodile, or alligator? Also state the order of reptiles to which each belongs: Crocodilia, Squamata, Chelonia, or Rhynchocephalia. (24 points)

   a. four legs, rough skin, parietal eye

_____

   b. legless, blind

_____

   c. four-chambered heart, broad snout

_____

   d. webbed feet, flat shell

_____

   e. legless, good eyesight

_____

   f. terrestrial, domed carapace

_____

   g. pointed snout, narrow jaw, cares for young

_____

   h. four legs, rough skin, no parietal eye

_____

3. Describe the special adaptations that helped the reptiles solve each of the following problems presented by life on land. (25 points)

   a. need to protect against dehydration

_____

_____

_____

b. need for extra support on land

_____

c. need to catch and feed on large or fast-moving terrestrial prey

_____

d. need to maintain warmth under changing conditions

_____

_____

e. need to obtain oxygen and use it efficiently

_____

_____

_____

_____

4. Identify each of the labeled structures or substances in the drawing of the reptile egg below. Choose from among the following possible answers: amnion, shell, yolk, allantois, amniotic fluid, embryo, albumin, chorion. (16 points)

a. _____

b. _____

c. _____

d. _____

e. _____

f. _____

g. _____

h. _____

5. Describe each of the following aspects of reproduction in reptiles. (20 points)

a. fertilization

_____

b. egg-laying and live birth

_____

_____

c. nest building

_____

_____

d. care of eggs and young

_____

_____

_____

Chapter 34 Test A

Choose the best answer for each question and write its letter in the blank.

_____ 1. Which of the following traits is found only in birds?
  a. wings
  b. four chambered heart
  c. feathers
  d. beak

_____ 2. Fossils have been found that show close evolutionary links between
  a. birds and fish.
  b. birds and dinosaurs.
  c. birds and thecodonts.
  d. birds and amphibians.

_____ 3. The earliest known fossil with identifiable feathers is called
  a. *Archaeopteryx.*
  b. *Pterodactyl.*
  c. *Protoavis.*
  d. *Pterosaurus.*

_____ 4. Scientists believe that birds developed the ability to fly in order to
  a. perform mating rituals.
  b. move toward the sun.
  c. escape predators.
  d. capture prey.

_____ 5. Which group of birds displays the greatest range of evolutionary adaptations?
  a. waterfowl
  b. birds of prey
  c. game birds
  d. perching songbirds

_____ 6. The fossil record of birds is fragmented and incomplete because
  a. bird fossils are confusingly similar to those of reptiles.
  b. feathers and fragile bones do not fossilize well.
  c. birds usually die in inaccessible locations.
  d. birds are very rare animals.

_____ 7. The differences between a bird's body and a reptile's body are the result of adaptations for
  a. living out of water.
  b. walking on land.
  c. flight.
  d. none of the above

_____ 8. The function of down feathers is to
  a. provide a smooth flying surface.
  b. streamline the body.
  c. interlock with other feathers.
  d. insulate the body.

_____ 9. How are a bird's bones a good example of its adaptation for flight?
  a. They are made of cartilage.
  b. They are flexible.
  c. They are thin and wide.
  d. They are hollow.

_____ 10. Which of the following substances, if placed on a bird's feathers, might prevent it from flying?
  a. tap water
  b. table salt
  c. petroleum
  d. all of the above

_____ 11. Fused bones in a bird's skeleton eliminate the need for
  a. bone marrow.
  b. ligaments.
  c. blood vessels.
  d. muscles.

_____ 12. Which bird expends the most energy during its flights?
  a. hawk
  b. Andean condor
  c. ruby-throated hummingbird
  d. Californian condor

_____ 13. Birds are called endotherms because they
  a. generate their own body heat.
  b. can survive in warm climates.
  c. are cold blooded.
  d. can survive at high altitudes.

_____ **14.** Birds consume more energy than reptiles. What adaptive feature(s) allow(s) them to meet their energy needs?
  a. claws and beaks
  b. more efficient respiratory, circulatory and digestive systems
  c. feathers
  d. hollow bones

_____ **15.** What striking similarity exists between birds and crocodiles?
  a. hollow bones   **c.** eye structure
  b. endothermy   **d.** four-chambered heart

_____ **16.** The respiratory system of birds is unique in that
  a. airflow is one way.   **c.** they have only one lung.
  b. they breathe carbon dioxide.   **d.** the lungs are very large.

_____ **17.** Birds do not have a
  a. gizzard.   **c.** bladder.
  b. crop.   **d.** villus.

_____ **18.** Before digestion, a bird's food is softened and stored in an esophagal pouch known as the
  a. gizzard.   **c.** crop.
  b. villi.   **d.** bile duct.

_____ **19.** The function of the fingerlike projections called villi in the intestinal walls is to
  a. increase surface area for absorption.   **c.** move stones in the gizzard.
  b. grasp and hold food.   **d.** push food through the intestine quickly..

_____ **20.** Why does a bird often swallow small stones?
  a. to help clean out its intestines
  b. to help break down food in the gizzard
  c. to increase body weight
  d. to force food from the crop

_____ **21.** Because birds are endothermic, their eggs must be
  a. kept cool.   **c.** laid in water.
  b. kept warm.   **d.** laid at high altitudes.

_____ **22.** The concept of imprinting holds that much of a bird's behavior is
  a. instinctive from birth.   **c.** sporadic and impulsive.
  b. learned only as adults.   **d.** learned soon after birth.

_____ **23.** During mating season, most species of birds are
  a. exogamous.   **c.** promiscuous.
  b. polygamous.   **d.** monogamous.

_____ **24.** Many bird behaviors are dependent upon
  a. amount of daylight.   **c.** body size.
  b. tides.   **d.** amount of available food.

_____ **25.** What advantage might be provided by the internal location of reproductive organs in birds?
  a. simplifies mating behavior   **c.** streamlines body for flight
  b. produces more eggs   **d.** saves energy during reproduction

Chapter 34 Test B

Read each question or statement and answer it in the space provided.

1. Describe the evolution of birds. Include an explanation of the significance of *Protoavis* and *Archaeopteryx*. (14 points)

_____

_____

_____

_____

_____

_____

_____

_____

_____

_____

_____

2. List three orders of birds and give an example of each. (12 points)

_____

_____

_____

3. Distinguish between contour feathers and down feathers. Also state the main purpose of each. (12 points)

_____

_____

_____

_____

4. Suppose you were an ornithologist, or expert on birds. You have been asked to give a lecture on how adaptations make flight possible and enable birds to obtain the energy they need for flight. What would you say in your lecture about each of the following structures? (20 points)

    a. skeleton

_____

_____

_____

    b. muscles

_____

_____

_____

c. circulatory system

_____

_____

_____

d. respiratory system

_____

_____

_____

5. Explain the importance of endothermy in birds. (7 points)

_____

_____

_____

_____

_____

6. Describe the role of the digestive system of birds in providing energy efficiently. (8 points)

_____

_____

_____

_____

_____

7. Describe general reproductive structures and processes in birds. (7 points)

_____

_____

_____

_____

8. Describe special behaviors, mating patterns, and biological rhythms associated with reproduction in birds. (8 points)

_____

_____

_____

_____

9. Describe the beak and foot adaptations that help two different types of birds obtain food. (12 points)

_____

_____

_____

_____

_____

Chapter 35 Test A

Choose the best answer for each question and write its letter in the blank.

_____ 1. What do the mammary glands secrete?
    a. hemoglobin   **c.** serotonin
    b. oil   **d.** milk

_____ 2. Which of the following animals is not a mammal?
    a. sperm whale   **c.** kangaroo
    b. gecko   **d.** *Homo sapiens*

_____ 3. Scientists believe that the earliest mammals
    a. lived in harmony with the dinosaurs.
    b. fed upon the dinosaurs.
    c. foraged at night to avoid the dinosaurs.
    d. coevolved with the dinosaurs.

_____ 4. In order to generate and maintain body heat, endothermic animals must consume
    a. less food than ectothermic animals.
    b. more food than ectothermic animals.
    c. angiosperms.
    d. only meat.

_____ 5. How do some scientists suppose that the development of angiosperms contributed to the extinction of dinosaurs?
    a. They were poisonous.
    b. The dinosaurs were unable to eat them.
    c. They deprived the air of oxygen.
    d. They made better food for mammals.

_____ 6. A monotreme is a mammal that has
    a. a pouch to carry its young.
    b. only one opening for intake of both air and food.
    c. only one opening for both reproductive and digestive functions.
    d. only one breast.

_____ 7. Which of the following is a monotreme?
    a. kangaroo   **c.** koala
    b. duck-billed platypus   **d.** skunk

_____ 8. All native Australian mammals are marsupials. Why are there no placental mammals native to Australia?
    a. Austrialia was isolated before placental mammals evolved.
    b. Australia had no Ice Age.
    c. other continents experienced severe drought.
    d. none of the above

_____ 9. Almost ninety-five percent of all mammals are
    a. marsupial.   **c.** placental.
    b. monotreme.   **d.** egg-laying

_____ 10. Which of the following animals is not of the order Carnivora?
    a. lion   **c.** weasel
    b. panda   **d.** pig

_____ 11. Elephants are on the brink of extinction because of
    a. food shortages.   **c.** pollution.
    b. ivory trading.   **d.** disease.

_____ **12.** Most mammals can eat a wide range of foods because they
    a. have various kinds of teeth.   **c.** have several stomachs.
    b. process food quickly.   **d.** do not need a special diet.

_____ **13.** How would a mammal's kidneys adapt to the challenge of maintaining water balance in a very dry environment?
    a. by producing more urine   **c.** by filtering water out of the blood
    b. by producing less urine   **d.** by producing more bile

_____ **14.** Certain artiodactyls possess a second stomach chamber called the
    a. albumin.   **c.** diaphragm.
    b. placenta.   **d.** rumen.

_____ **15.** Scientists believe that the folded shape of the mammalian brain is the result of
    a. disease.   **c.** inbreeding.
    b. malnutrition.   **d.** skull size.

_____ **16.** Bats navigate in the dark by emitting and receiving
    a. electrical impulses.   **c.** magnetic fields.
    b. radio waves.   **d.** sound waves.

_____ **17.** The fact that bats live in dense populations makes them
    a. less vulnerable.   **c.** more vulnerable.
    b. carnivorous.   **d.** none of the above

_____ **18.** The only group of mammals that lays its eggs externally is the
    a. marsupials.   **c.** placentals.
    b. monotremes.   **d.** Carnivora.

_____ **19.** What adaptive advantage do marsupial mothers possess over monotreme mothers?
    a. The eggs are encased in a hard protective shell.
    b. The mother can locomote while the young develop.
    c. The father takes care of the young.
    d. The young can be left to care for themselves.

_____ **20.** The gestation period varies among placental mammals according to
    a. temperature and climate.
    b. body size.
    c. amount of food consumed during pregnancy.
    d. shape of the animal.

_____ **21.** The abdominal muscle that forces air into the lungs is the
    a. rumen.   **c.** quadracep.
    b. placenta.   **d.** diaphragm.

_____ **22.** What organs does a blue whale use in respiration?
    a. skin   **c.** lungs
    b. gills   **d.** none of the above

_____ **23.** In comparison to the newborn marsupial mammal, the newborn placental mammal is
    a. much less developed.   **c.** slightly less developed.
    b. equally developed.   **d.** more developed.

_____ **24.** A mammal that had a damaged or defective cerebellum probably would have difficulty
    a. walking a straight line.   **c.** speaking.
    b. thinking.   **d.** breathing.

_____ **25.** Which of the following is a mammalian adaptation for endothermy?
    a. keen sense of smell   **c.** hair
    b. sharp hearing   **d.** large molar teeth

Chapter 35 Test B

Read each question or statement and respond in the space provided.

1. State the general characteristics of mammals. (12 points)

_____

_____

2. Briefly describe the evolution of mammals. (8 points)

_____

_____

_____

_____

3. Explain how their characteristics helped mammals to become the dominant vertebrates. (7 points)

_____

_____

4. The table below illustrates the characteristics of monotremes, marsupials, and placental mammals. Complete the table by filling in the correct information. (12 points)

GROUP	NOURISHED IN POUCH, NOURISHED BY INTERNAL STRUCTURE, OR HATCHED?	HAVE CLOACA?	COMPLETE BODY-TEMPERATURE CONTROL?	EXAMPLE
a. Monotremes				
b. Marsupials				
c. Placentals				

5. Suppose you go on a field trip and you observe mammals that have the following characteristics. Based on the information, identify each mammal as belonging to one of the following orders: Rodentia, Chiroptera, Lagomorpha, Carnivora, Cetacea, Sirenia, Artiodactyla, Perissodactyla, Insectivora, Proboscidea, Primates. Then give an example of a mammal in that order. (18 points)

a. even number of toes, herbivorous grazer, flat teeth for grinding

_____

b. reproduce entirely in water, no hind limbs, broad flat tail, flipperlike forelimbs, torpedo-shaped body

_____

c. muscular boneless trunk, massive body, thick skin with little hair

_____

d. hands with opposable thumbs, large eyes that face forward

_____

e. able to fly, nocturnal

_____

f. meat-eating, pair of long sharp teeth, clawed toes

_____

g. five clawed toes per limb, herbivorous, pair of very long teeth in each jaw for gnawing

_____

h. odd number of toes, special digestive chamber to break down cellulose

_____

i. long ears, stubby tail, strong hind limbs

_____

6. Contrast the structure, placement, and function of incisors, canines, and molars. (7 points)

_____

_____

_____

_____

7. Explain how the size, shape, and/or type of teeth in three different kinds of mammals relates to function or diet in those mammals. (6 points)

_____

_____

_____

8. Name two ways in which mammals are specially structured to be able to carry out each of the following functions. (18 points)

a. respiration _____

_____

_____

b. circulation _____

_____

_____

c. response _____

_____

_____

_____

9. Explain the advantages of marsupial reproduction over monotreme reproduction. (6 points)

_____

_____

10. Explain the advantages of placental reproduction over marsupial reproduction. (6 points)

_____

_____

_____

Chapter 36 Test A

Choose the best answer for each question and write its letter in the blank.

_____ **1.** Which of the following best applies to all human behaviors?
    a. reflexes   **c.** instincts
    b. learned   **d.** none of the above

_____ **2.** Which of the following best describes innate behavior?
    a. unchangeable   **c.** easily changed
    b. learned   **d.** quickly forgotten

_____ **3.** Something in the environment to which an animal can respond is a
    a. factor.   **c.** stimulus.
    b. behavior.   **d.** reflex.

_____ **4.** Which of the following is not a complex, programmed behavior?
    a. bird building nest   **c.** beaver building dam
    b. wasp building nest   **d.** child building sandcastle

_____ **5.** As animals grow older, learning becomes
    a. more difficult.   **c.** easier.
    b. more innate.   **d.** more instinctive.

_____ **6.** When an animal learns to ignore a given stimulus, it is called
    a. retardation.   **c.** boredom.
    b. habituation.   **d.** imprinting.

_____ **7.** Learning that is acquired during the earliest, critical period of an animal's life is known as
    a. habituation.   **c.** imprinting.
    b. innate.   **d.** none of the above

_____ **8.** A human baby soon learns that it can cause its mother to appear by crying. This is an example of
    a. classical conditioning.   **c.** reasoning.
    b. habituation.   **d.** operant conditioning.

_____ **9.** Chemicals with which animals mark their territories are called
    a. testosterones.   **c.** serotonins.
    b. myoglobins.   **d.** pheromones.

_____ **10.** When a beehive is threatened, its residents will attack in unison. The presence of a threat is communicated among the bees by
    a. warning sounds.   **c.** visual displays.
    b. pheromones.   **d.** buzzing.

_____ **11.** Imagine an experiment in which two groups of birds hatched from the same mother are isolated from each other, and several generations of their offspring are raised in isolation under identical circumstances. The tenth generation of birds from each group is then combined, but the birds in the combined group do not mate. Why might this occur?
    a. The birds' feathers may have changed color.
    b. The birds' species may have changed.
    c. The birds' courtship rituals may have changed.
    d. The birds' reproductive organs may have changed.

_____ **12.** A complex innate behavior is called a
    a. reflex.   **c.** fixed-action pattern.
    b. conditioned response.   **d.** none of the above

_____ **13.** The theory of imprinting was developed by
    a. Konrad Lorenz.   **c.** B.F. Skinner.
    b. Sigmund Freud.   **d.** Ivan Pavlov.

_____ **14.** Pavlov's dogs learned to respond to the sound of a bell. How did they respond?
    a. urinating   **c.** barking
    b. playing dead   **d.** salivating

_____ **15.** Learning that takes place as a result of rewards given to accidental behaviors is known as
    a. imprinting.   **c.** operant conditioning.
    b. classical conditioning.   **d.** habituation.

_____ **16.** When a chimpanzee stacks several boxes on the floor to reach a string of bananas suspended from the ceiling, the behavior is an example of
    a. operant conditioning.   **c.** imprinting.
    b. reasoning.   **d.** communication.

_____ **17.** Which of the following animals has exhibited signs of reasoning in laboratory experiments?
    a. ants   **c.** octopus
    b. cow   **d.** snake

_____ **18.** Jane Goodall was a pioneer in the study of
    a. primate behavior.   **c.** fish behavior.
    b. reptile behavior.   **d.** human behavior.

_____ **19.** A chicken that pecks at other chickens is probably
    a. subordinate.   **c.** retarded.
    b. dominant.   **d.** courting mates.

_____ **20.** When an animal sacrifices its life or the opportunity to mate in order to help another member of its species, this is known as
    a. communication.   **c.** territorial behavior.
    b. imprinting.   **d.** altruism.

_____ **21.** A simple innate, involuntary response by the body to a particular stimulus is a(n)
    a. instinct.   **c.** reflex.
    b. fixed-action pattern.   **d.** imprint.

_____ **22.** The physical state of fear is a complex biological response made up of several
    a. learned behaviors.   **c.** fixed-action patterns.
    b. reflexes.   **d.** none of the above

_____ **23.** The songs of songbirds are
    a. learned.   **c.** innate.
    b. both learned and innate. **d.** operant conditioning.

_____ **24.** The fact that newly hatched goslings identify the first animal they see as their mother is an example of
    a. habituation.   **c.** imprinting.
    b. reasoning.   **d.** operant conditioning.

_____ **25.** The ability to employ reason requires a large
    a. cerebellum.   **c.** brain stem.
    b. cerebrum.   **d.** medulla.

Chapter 36 Test B

Read each question or statement and respond in the space provided.

1. What is meant by *behavior*, in a scientific sense? (6 points)

_____

_____

2. What is the difference beween a stimulus and a response? Give an example that illustrates the difference. (8 points)

_____

_____

_____

3. What is the difference between innate behavior and learned behavior? Give an example of each. (8 points)

_____

_____

4. Suppose you are studying animals and you observe each of the following examples of innate behavior. In each case, tell whether the behavior is a reflex, a fixed-action pattern, or a complex programmed behavior. (16 points)

a. a bird gathers various materials and makes a nest

_____

b. a dog draws back its paw from a hot surface

_____

c. a fish tries to attack any object that is blue and of a certain size

_____

d. a cat salivates when it smells food

_____

5. For each of the following, state which type of learned behavior is being defined. Choose among the possible answers: habituation, imprinting, classical conditioning, operant conditioning, reasoning. Then give an example of each. (10 points)

a. learning in which an animal's reflexes are trained to respond to a new stimulus

_____

_____

b. learning that occurs through insight, or thinking about a solution to a problem

_____

_____

c. learning in which an animal comes to ignore a particular stimulus

_____

_____

d. quick, early learning of a behavior that becomes a permanent response to a particular stimulus

_____

_____

e. learning in which the enviroment rewards behavior that an animal performs accidentally

_____

_____

6. Give an example of each of the following types of animal communication. (16 points)

　a. pheromone release

_____

　b. visual display

_____

_____

　c. courtship ritual

_____

_____

　d. territorial behavior

_____

7. State two advantages of social behavior in animals. (8 points)

_____

_____

8. Explain what is meant by dominance hierarchy and give an example of it.(8 points)

_____

_____

_____

9. Explain what is meant by kin selection and give an example of it. (8 points)

_____

_____

_____

10. Design an experiment whose object is to see whether a monkey can be conditioned to play a three-note tune on a piano. Include a description of any materials you would use and of the procedure you would follow to test your hypothesis. (12 points)

_____

_____

_____

_____

_____

_____

_____

_____

_____

_____

Unit 7 Test A

Choose the best answer for each question and write its letter in the blank.

_____ 1. Mouse A has a damaged cerebellum. Mouse B has a damaged brain stem. Which mouse would have more difficulty maintaining its balance?
  a. mouse A   c. Both would have equal difficulty.
  b. mouse B   d. Neither mouse would have difficulty.

_____ 2. Which two animals are most closely related?
  a. humans and birds   c. birds and reptiles
  b. birds and fish   d. humans and fish

_____ 3. Which two animals are most closely related?
  a. pigs and camels   c. pigs and humans
  b. humans and camels   d. pigs and hedgehogs

_____ 4. The need to molt is eliminated by what adaptation?
  a. scales   c. endoskeleton
  b. exoskeleton   d. amniote eggs

_____ 5. What advantage is provided by the fact that the backbone is comprised of numerous small vertebrae, rather than one large bone?
  a. flight   c. flexibility
  b. speed   d. none of the above

_____ 6. Which of the following fishes belongs to the group Agnatha?
  a. lamprey   c. shark
  b. tuna   d. skate

_____ 7. The inflatable pouch that helps ray-finned fishes to move up and down and to remain stationary in the water is the
  a. kidney.   c. air sac.
  b. swim bladder.   d. dorsal fin.

_____ 8. How does a shark detect motion in the water?
  a. eyesight   c. lateral line system
  b. nictitating membrane   d. tympanic membrane

_____ 9. Terrestrial vertebrates probably evolved from
  a. lobe-finned fishes.   c. ray-finned fishes.
  b. agnathans.   d. chondrichthyes.

_____ 10. Which of the following animals is poisonous?
  a. king snake   c. gecko
  b. lungfish   d. beaded lizard

_____ 11. Sound waves are received by the
  a. mucous membrane.   c. nictitating membrane.
  b. tympanic membrane.   d. nasal membrane

_____ 12. Which amphibian lays its eggs on land and carries them to water on its back?
  a. poison-arrow frog   c. horny toad
  b. spadefoot toad   d. leopard frog

_____ 13. What disadvantage would be encountered by a male frog whose throat pouch became damaged and did not heal?
  a. could not carry its young   c. could not attract mates
  b. could not swallow food   d. could not catch insects

_____ 14. The first identifiable reptile to appear in the fossil record is the
  a. *Apatosaurus*.   c. *Protoavis*.
  b. cotylosaur.   d. caecilian.

_____ **15.** Suppose a pit viper were enclosed in a dark room with the following four animals. Which of the animals would be least likely to be struck by the viper?
    a. rabbit
    b. cat
    c. toad
    d. mouse

_____ **16.** Scientists believe that larger bodies are an adaptation for reducing
    a. parasite-to-body ratio.
    b. heat loss.
    c. energy needs.
    d. water needs.

_____ **17.** Which animal does not typically chew its food well?
    a. human
    b. pig
    c. cow
    d. lizard

_____ **18.** The ancestor of modern birds was the
    a. *Archaeopteryx.*
    b. *Pterosaur.*
    c. *Pterodactyl.*
    d. none of the above

_____ **19.** When birds come into contact with an oil spill, why does the oil often prevent them from flying?
    a. It weighs them down.
    b. It disrupts the smooth consistency of their feathers.
    c. It confuses them.
    d. It destroys feathers.

_____ **20.** What adaptation for endothermy do birds possess?
    a. four-chamber heart
    b. hair
    c. varied teeth
    d. scaly skin

_____ **21.** Which of the following mammals is not of the order Rodentia?
    a. beaver
    b. porcupine
    c. chipmunk
    d. hare

_____ **22.** There are approximately how many known species of bats?
    a. 73
    b. 3,000
    c. 925
    d. 10,000

_____ **23.** Which two animals are most closely related?
    a. caecilian and snake
    b. toad and snake
    c. caecilian and toad
    d. snake and eel

_____ **24.** What can humans do to prevent the extinction of elephants?
    a. feed elephants
    b. control ivory trade
    c. control tigers
    d. reduce the number of giraffes

_____ **25.** Legends of mermaids probably originated from sightings of what aquatic mammal?
    a. manatee
    b. porpoise
    c. dolphin
    d. ungulate

_____ **26.** Which animal has the longest gestation period?
    a. human
    b. horse
    c. rat
    d. blue whale

_____ **27.** Which group of mammals give birth to the most developed young?
    a. marsupials
    b. monotremes
    c. placentals
    d. none of the above

_____ **28.** When Konrad Lorenz's geese mistook Lorenz for their mother, the behavior was evidence of
    a. classical conditioning.
    b. fixed-action patterns.
    c. operative conditioning.
    d. imprinting.

_____ **29.** Pavlov's dogs were taught to salivate when they heard the sound of a bell. This is an example of
    a. classical conditioning.
    b. reflex.
    c. operative conditioning.
    d. imprinting.

Unit 7 Test A

_____ **30.** Which of these animals is least likely to be caught by the tail?
    a. mouse   **c.** spiny lizard
    b. gecko   **d.** chipmunk

_____ **31.** Hares, rabbits and pikas are examples of
    a. lagomorphs.   **c.** carnivores.
    b. rodents.   **d.** ungulates.

_____ **32.** The panda bear is unique to its order because it
    a. lives in arctic weather.   **c.** does not eat meat.
    b. has an odd number of claws.   **d.** sometimes eats meat.

_____ **33.** Where are most marsupials found today?
    a. North America   **c.** Asia
    b. Australia   **d.** Antarctica

_____ **34.** Which of the following is not a mammal?
    a. dolphin   **c.** rhinoceros
    b. whale   **d.** caecilian

_____ **35.** Frogs and toads are members of the order
    a. Anura.   **c.** Urodela.
    b. Apoda.   **d.** Tuatuara.

_____ **36.** Salamanders walk with a side-to-side gait because their legs
    a. are too short.   **c.** are in line with the body.
    b. extend outward from the body.   **d.** swing under the body.

_____ **37.** Before they can diffuse into or out of animals, oxygen and carbon dioxide must first dissolve in
    a. blood.   **c.** water.
    b. acid.   **d.** none of the above

_____ **38.** Lungs are internal air sacs lined with membranes that must remain
    a. moist.   **c.** dry.
    b. acidic.   **d.** none of the above

_____ **39.** The function of the frog's pancreas is to
    a. secrete bile.   **c.** secrete enzymes.
    b. filter out toxins.   **d.** balance water.

_____ **40.** On what do most amphibians feed?
    a. plant roots   **c.** angiosperms
    b. insects   **d.** conifers

_____ **41.** Which two animals are most closely related?
    a. porpoise and lungfish   **c.** porpoise and whale
    b. whale and manatee   **d.** porpoise and manatee

_____ **42.** A defining feature of the order Primates is
    a. ten fingers and ten toes.   **c.** hands with opposable thumbs.
    b. body hair.   **d.** bipedalism.

_____ **43.** The ability to extract nutrition from normally undigestible plant fibers is an adaptation possessed by
    a. lagomorphs.   **c.** rodents.
    b. primates.   **d.** ungulates.

_____ **44.** Drugs obtained from poisonous frogs can be used to
    a. increase intelligence.   **c.** purify the blood.
    b. lower blood pressure.   **d.** cure cancer.

_____ **45.** The diaphragm aids in the processes of
   a. circulation.   **c.** respiration.
   b. digestion.   **d.** excretion.

_____ **46.** Humans differ from most mammals in having a poor sense of
   a. smell.   **c.** vision.
   b. touch.   **d.** taste.

_____ **47.** The ability of cats to land on their feet when they fall is a
   a. learned behavior.   **c.** stimulus.
   b. complex programmed behavior.   **d.** reflex.

_____ **48.** Bats are useful to humans because they
   a. frighten away birds.   **c.** eat insects.
   b. breathe carbon dioxide.   **d.** clean up caves.

_____ **49.** The theory of operant conditioning was developed by
   a. B.F. Skinner.   **c.** Ivan Pavlov.
   b. Konrad Lorenz.   **d.** Jane Goodall.

_____ **50.** When a cat rubs its jawline along a person's leg, it is a display of
   a. affection.   **c.** territorial behavior.
   b. hunger.   **d.** courtship behavior.

Chapter 37 Test A

_____ **173**

Choose the best answer for each question and write its letter in the blank.

_____ 1. The front of the body is known as the
    a. ventral side.   **c.** dorsal side.
    b. lateral.   **d.** caudal end.

_____ 2. The thoracic cavity is separated from the abdominal cavity by a thin sheet of muscle called the
    a. cranium.   **c.** diaphragm.
    b. epithelium.   **d.** cardiac muscle.

_____ 3. Which of the following is *not* part of the integumentary system?
    a. skin   **c.** hair
    b. nails   **d.** triceps

_____ 4. The function of the endocrine glands is to secrete
    a. pheromones.   **c.** bile.
    b. hormones.   **d.** enzymes.

_____ 5. Which of the following is an example of connective tissue?
    a. cartilage   **c.** epithelium
    b. mucous glands   **d.** biceps

_____ 6. A group of cells that are specialized for contraction make up the
    a. epithelial tissue.   **c.** muscle tissue.
    b. nervous tissue.   **d.** connective tissue.

_____ 7. What is the main function of nervous tissue?
    a. cause contractions   **c.** secrete hormones
    b. secrete pheromones   **d.** transfer information

_____ 8. About how many bones make up the human skeleton?
    a. 948   **c.** 96
    b. 796   **d.** 206

_____ 9. Which of the following is *not* among the functions of the bones?
    a. transfer information   **c.** anchor muscles
    b. make blood cells   **d.** store minerals

_____ 10. The outer surfaces of bones are covered by a membrane called the
    a. humerus.   **c.** bone marrow.
    b. periosteum.   **d.** cartilage.

_____ 11. Yellow bone marrow is made up primarily of
    a. fat cells.   **c.** cartilage.
    b. connective tissue.   **d.** blood cells.

_____ 12. The Haversian canals are spaces in bones through which
    a. nerves pass.   **c.** hormones are secreted.
    b. tendons pass.   **d.** ligaments pass.

_____ 13. The skeletal system of the developing fetus is made mostly of
    a. ligaments.   **c.** tendons.
    b. bone marrow.   **d.** cartilage.

_____ 14. Which of the following joints is typical of a ball and socket joint?
    a. elbow   **c.** base of thumb
    b. shoulder   **d.** head and neck

_____ 15. Which of these organs is made up of cells that *do not* undergo cytokinesis after mitosis?
    a. the biceps   **c.** the stomach
    b. the skin   **d.** none of the above

    Chapter 37: Skeletal, Muscular, Integumentary Sys.   **173**

_____ **16.** Where is cardiac muscle located in the human body?
   a. throughout the body.
   b. only in the heart.
   c. only in the heart and lungs.
   d. only in the lungs.

_____ **17.** How do skeletal muscles function?
   a. by contracting
   b. by pushing
   c. by expanding
   d. none of the above

_____ **18.** The action of skeletal muscles is directly triggered by
   a. hormones.
   b. endocrines.
   c. nerve impulses.
   d. none of the above

_____ **19.** Which of these body parts is made of striated tissue?
   a. skin
   b. the hamstrings
   c. the intestines
   d. the lungs

_____ **20.** The blood vessels in the skin release excess body heat by
   a. dilating.
   b. bursting.
   c. contracting.
   d. none of the above

_____ **21.** The top layer of the epidermis is made of
   a. healthy, living cells.
   b. melanin.
   c. tough, dead cells.
   d. collagen.

_____ **22.** Which is a function of sweat?
   a. increase melanin count
   b. regulate body temperature
   c. increase keratin
   d. excrete cholesterol

_____ **23.** Hair and nails are made of substances similar to those in the
   a. nervous tissue.
   b. connective tissue.
   c. dermis.
   d. epidermis.

_____ **24.** Why do scientists expect cases of skin cancer to increase in coming years?
   a. polluted water supplies
   b. malnutrition
   c. depleted ozone layer
   d. none of the above

_____ **25.** The muscles of the digestive system consist of
   a. smooth muscle.
   b. cardiac muscle.
   c. skeletal muscle.
   d. connective tissue.

Chapter 37 Test B

Read each question or statement and respond in the space provided.

1. State the term used to describe each of the following parts of the human body. (12 points)

   a. front side of the body _____

   b. back side of the body _____

   c. cavity inside the head _____

   d. cavity that contains the lungs and heart _____

   e. cavity that contains the digestive and urinary system _____

   f. structure that divides the ventral cavities _____

2. Name two structures in each of the following organ systems. (14 points)

   a. integumentary system _____

   b. skeletal system _____

   c. nervous system _____

   d. circulatory system _____

   e. respiratory system _____

   f. excretory system _____

   g. digestive system _____

3. Suppose you are a biologist studying functions of human tissues. Identify each of the following types of tissues as either connective, muscle, epithelial, or nervous tissue. (12 points)

   a. tissue that contracts and moves limbs _____

   b. tissue that covers the body and that lines organs _____

   c. tissue that supports and protects the inner organs _____

   d. tissue that produces responses to stimuli _____

   e. tissue that makes up the stomach _____

   f. tissue that makes up blood _____

4. List four of the general functions of bones. (8 points)

_____

_____

_____

5. Identify each of the following. Choose among the possible answers: periosteum, red marrow, yellow marrow, osteoblast, Haversian canal, cartilage, joint, ligament, tendon. (18 points)

   a. tissue that joins one bone to another _____

   b. tough, flexible tissue that is often later replaced by bone _____

   c. space through which nerves and blood vessels pass in bones _____

   d. connective tissue that joins a bone and a muscle _____

   e. material in bones that produces blood cells _____

   f. membrane that covers the outside of bones _____

6. a. Contrast the structure and function of the three types of muscles. (6 points)

_____

_____

_____

_____

b. How do muscles move body parts? How are they able to work together to do so? (6 points)

_____

_____

_____

_____

c. What does the sliding filament theory explain? (6 points)

_____

_____

_____

_____

7. Identify each of the labeled structures in the drawing of a section of skin below. Choose among the following answers: dermis, sweat gland, pore, hair follicle, sebaceous gland, epidermis, fat layer, blood vessel, nerve ending. (18 points)

a. _____	**f.** _____
b. _____	**g.** _____
c. _____	**h.** _____
d. _____	**i.** _____
e. _____	

Chapter 38 Test A

Choose the best answer for each question and write its letter in the blank.

_____ 1. Which of the following is *not* an essential nutrient?
    a. carbohydrates   **c.** fats
    b. minerals   **d.** hormones

_____ 2. The food pyramid suggests that a person should eat
    a. more meat than breads.
    b. more breads than meats.
    c. more dairy products than vegetables.
    d. more dairy products than breads.

_____ 3. The cells of the body obtain most of their energy from
    a. carbohydrates.   **c.** fats.
    b. minerals.   **d.** vitamins.

_____ 4. Which of the following is *not* a carbohydrate?
    a. cellulose   **c.** starch
    b. sugar   **d.** amino acid

_____ 5. Which of the following provides the body with energy over an extended period of time?
    a. single sugars   **c.** starches
    b. cellulose   **d.** minerals

_____ 6. Which of the following aids in digestion and elimination?
    a. sugars   **c.** cellulose
    b. fats   **d.** starches

_____ 7. Most of the lipids that your body needs come from
    a. starches.   **c.** cellulose.
    b. fats.   **d.** proteins.

_____ 8. A chain of carbon and hydrogen atoms with a weak acid group attached to one end is a(n)
    a. fatty acid.   **c.** polysaccharide.
    b. hydrochloric acid.   **d.** disaccharide.

_____ 9. Heart disease and some cancers have been linked to dietary excesses of
    a. starch.   **c.** cellulose.
    b. fats.   **d.** glycogens.

_____ 10. Proteins are made of smaller units called
    a. lipids.   **c.** amino acids.
    b. glycogens.   **d.** villi.

_____ 11. When the body is starved, it grows thin because it
    a. releases gas through the skin.
    b. draws nutrients from its own tissues.
    c. loses water.
    d. none of the above

_____ 12. Scurvy occurs as a result of what deficiency?
    a. vitamin C   **c.** vitamin A
    b. protein   **d.** riboflavin

_____ 13. Inorganic substances that perform vital functions in the body are
    a. lipids.   **c.** minerals.
    b. vitamins.   **d.** proteins.

_____ 14. The sum of all the chemical processes that occur within an organism is known as the
    a. epiglottis.   **c.** peristalsis.
    b. villi.   **d.** metabolism.

_____ **15.** A calorie is the amount of energy needed to
    a. raise the temperature of the body by 1 degree Celsius.
    b. raise the temperature of 1 gram of water by 1 degree C.
    c. raise the temperature of 1 gram of fat by 1 degree C.
    d. none of the above

_____ **16.** The number of kilocalories an animal must use in a set amount of time just to maintain life is the
    a. kilocalorie factor.   **c.** basal metabolism rate.
    b. anabolic rate.   **d.** lipid consumption rate.

_____ **17.** People who mistakenly believe they are overweight and refuse to eat may be
    a. bulimic.   **c.** peristaltic.
    b. anorexic.   **d.** hormonal.

_____ **18.** The passage that carries food between the pharynx and the stomach is the
    a. chyme.   **c.** bolus.
    b. epiglottis.   **d.** esophagus.

_____ **19.** The stomach breaks down food into a soft, partially digested mixture called
    a. bolus.   **c.** chyme.
    b. villi.   **d.** none of the above

_____ **20.** The digestive enzyme pepsin works best in what kind of environment?
    a. watery   **c.** fatty
    b. balanced   **d.** acidic

_____ **21.** Water is extracted from food in the body primarily by the
    a. colon.   **c.** gallbladder.
    b. pancreas.   **d.** bladder.

_____ **22.** Three jars of fat used for cooking labeled A, B, and C are at room temperature. The fat in Jar A is liquid, the fat in Jar B is semi-solid, and the fat in Jar C is solid. Which of the three jars contains the most unsaturated fat?
    a. Jar A
    b. Jar B
    c. Jar C
    d. The jars have equal amounts of unsaturated fat.

_____ **23.** Which jar contains a fat with the lowest ratio of hydrogen atoms to carbon-carbon bonds in its molecules?
    a. Jar A, a liquid at room temperature
    b. Jar B, a semi-solid at room temperature
    c. Jar C, a solid at room temperature
    d. None of the fats has carbon-carbon bonds in its molecules.

_____ **24.** Compounds made from carbon, hydrogen, and oxygen in a 1:2:1 ratio are
    a. polyunsaturates.   **c.** fatty acids.
    b. carbohydrates.   **d.** hydrogenates.

_____ **25.** Which of the following is *not* a function of the liver?
    a. converts glucose to glycogen   **c.** removes ammonia
    b. stores iron   **d.** peristalis

Name _____ Class _____ Date _____

Chapter 38 Test B

Read each question or statement and respond in the space provided.

1. The table below is designed to illustrate the five kinds of nutrients. Complete the table by filling in the missing information. (10 points)

NUTRIENT	FUNCTIONS IN BODY	MAIN SITE(S) OF DIGESTION
a. carbohydrates		
b. fats		
c. proteins		
d. vitamins		
e. minerals		

2. Compare and contrast each of the following substances. (15 points)

  a. sugars, starches, and cellulose _____

  _____

  _____

  _____

  _____

  b. saturated, monounsaturated, and polyunsaturated fats _____

  _____

  _____

  _____

  c. essential amino acids, nonessential amino acids, and proteins _____

  _____

  _____

  _____

3. Suppose you are a nutritionist. You analyzed a patient's diet and found that he eats too much fat and does not take in enough water-soluble vitamins. What specific changes in diet would you recommend? What foods would you suggest the person eat more of? Less of? (16 points)

_____

_____

_____

4. a. What is a calorie? A kilocalorie? A Calorie? (5 points) _____

_____

b. How many kilocalories are there per gram of carbohydrates? Of fats? Of proteins? (5 points)

_____

c. What is meant by *basal metabolims rate* (BMR)? What is the approximate BMR for adult males?

For adult females? (5 points) _____

_____

5. Identify each of the labeled structures in the drawing of the human digestive system below. Choose from among the following possible answers: esophagus, rectum, pancreas, large intestine, pharynx, anus, epiglottis, small intestine, mouth, liver, stomach, salivary gland, gallbladder. (26 points)

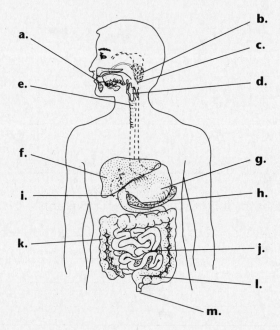

a. _____   **h.** _____

b. _____   **i.** _____

c. _____   **j.** _____

d. _____   **k.** _____

e. _____   **l.** _____

f. _____   **m.** _____

g. _____

6. a. State three functions of the liver. (6 points) _____

_____

_____

b. State the main function of the gallbladder. (6 points) _____

_____

c. State the main function of the pancreas. (6 points) _____

_____

_____

Chapter 39 Test A

Choose the best answer for each question and write its letter in the blank.

_____ **1.** What is the loose-fitting sac that surrounds the heart?
    a. cardiac   **c.** pericardium
    b. atrium   **d.** ventricle

_____ **2.** Oxygen-poor blood is received on the right side of the heart and
    a. pumped into the lungs.   **c.** converted into bone marrow.
    b. distributed throughout the body.   **d.** none of the above

_____ **3.** Blood coming into the heart is pumped through
    a. the septum into the ventricles.   **c.** the septum into the atria.
    b. the ventricles into the atria.   **d.** the atria into the ventricles.

_____ **4.** What prevents blood from moving through the heart in the wrong direction?
    a. blood pressure   **c.** speed
    b. valves   **d.** villi

_____ **5.** The sound of a heartbeat is caused by
    a. dilation of cardiac muscle.   **c.** contraction of smooth muscle.
    b. closing valves.   **d.** echoes in the chest cavity.

_____ **6.** What mass of tissue electrically controls the heart rate?
    a. sinoatrial node   **c.** atrioventricular node
    b. sinoventricular node   **d.** sinotricular node

_____ **7.** The thick, yellowish liquid in which blood cells are suspended is (are)
    a. hemoglobin.   **c.** plasma.
    b. iron.   **d.** T-cells.

_____ **8.** What causes the red color of blood?
    a. white blood cells   **c.** plasma
    b. platelets   **d.** iron

_____ **9.** What is the condition in which the blood does not transport enough oxygen to the cells of the body?
    a. atherosclerosis   **c.** anemia
    b. hypertension   **d.** antibody

_____ **10.** White blood cells are essential for the function of which system?
    a. immune system   **c.** digestive system
    b. respiratory system   **d.** excretory system

_____ **11.** Blood will *not* clot at a wound if the blood lacks
    a. plasma.   **c.** cholesterol.
    b. lymph.   **d.** platelets.

_____ **12.** Which of the following does *not* facilitate the flow of blood?
    a. platelets   **c.** veins
    b. capillaries   **d.** arteries

_____ **13.** Artery walls are protected from blood pressure by
    a. ligaments.   **c.** connective tissue.
    b. smooth muscle.   **d.** cardiac muscle.

_____ **14.** During pollen season, a woman went to her doctor to complain of sneezing, a runny nose, and watery eyes. Which of the following blood cells is likely to have contributed to her symptoms?
    a. monocytes   **c.** basophils
    b. platelets   **d.** neutrophils

                         Chapter 39: Circulatory System   **181**

_____ **15.** Which pathway carries blood through the lungs for oxygenation?
     a. pulmonary circuit   **c.** systemic circuit
     b. lymphatic system   **d.** spleen

_____ **16.** Plasma is drawn from the intercellular regions and reprocessed by the
     a. circulatory system.   **c.** pulmonary circuit.
     b. lymphatic system.   **d.** excretory system.

_____ **17.** Where do the veins carry blood?
     a. to the capillaries   **c.** to the arteries
     b. from the heart   **d.** to the heart

_____ **18.** Atherosclerosis is a condition in which the arteries have
     a. become narrowed.   **c.** become dilated.
     b. ruptured.   **d.** become tangled.

_____ **19.** When the pressure of blood pumping through the veins is constantly too high, the condition is known as
     a. arteriosclerosis.   **c.** hypertension.
     b. atherosclerosis.   **d.** anemia.

_____ **20.** James does not exercise, and he eats mostly dairy products. John exercises five times a day. He eats mostly breads and vegetables. Who is more likely to develop atherosclerosis?
     a. James
     b. John
     c. James and John are equally likely to develop atherosclerosis.
     d. Neither James nor John is likely to develop atherosclerosis.

_____ **21.** Who is more likely to develop hypertension?
     a. a person with low blood pressure
     b. a person whose parents have high blood pressure
     c. a person whose parents have low blood pressure
     d. none of these people

_____ **22.** In which of these vessels would the blood contain the most oxygen?
     a. veins of the systemic circuit
     b. capillaries of the systemic circuit
     c. arteries of the systemic circuit
     d. arteries of the pulmonary circuit

_____ **23.** Particles such as old red blood cells, bacteria, and platelets are removed from the blood by the
     a. spleen.   **c.** lymph.
     b. lymph vessels.   **d.** atrium.

_____ **24.** The measure of the force of blood in the arteries when the ventricles contract is called the
     a. diastolic pressure.   **c.** systolic pressure.
     b. blood pressure.   **d.** pulmonary pressure.

_____ **25.** The large vessels that carry blood away from the heart are the
     a. veins.   **c.** capillaries.
     b. arteries.   **d.** lymph vessels.

Chapter 39 Test B

Read each question or statement and respond in the space provided.

1. a. State the main functions of the circulatory system. (5 points)

_____

_____

_____

_____

b. Name the three major parts of the circulatory system. (5 points)

_____

_____

c. State the difference between the pulmonary circuit and the systemic circuit. (5 points)

_____

_____

_____

2. a. Describe the main parts of the heart. (6 points)

_____

_____

_____

b. Describe how the two sides of the heart differ in terms of the kind of blood they receive and pump. (6 points)

_____

_____

_____

_____

3. a. Explain the difference between diastole and systole. (6 points)

_____

_____

_____

b. How is heart contraction rate controlled? (6 points)

_____

_____

_____

_____

_____

4. Suppose you were making a study of blood cell functions. You might observe cytoplasmic structures that have each of the following characteristics. Identify each structure as one of the following: erythrocyte, phagocyte, lymphocyte, platelet. (15 points)

a. Cell engulfs bacteria.

_____

b. Cell has no nucleus.

_____

c. Piece of cytoplasm clumps with similar structures at a wound location.

_____

d. Cell produces antibodies.

_____

e. Cell contains hemoglobin and carries oxygen.

_____

5. Compare arteries, veins, and capillaries. In your answer, discuss the types of tissue in them, function, and type of blood generally carried. (15 points)

_____

_____

_____

_____

_____

_____

_____

6. Describe the structure, operation, and function of the lymphatic system. (15 points)

_____

_____

_____

_____

_____

_____

_____

7. Suppose you were a physician and you diagnosed patients as having the following cardiovascular diseases. In each case, explain what the disease is and the main problems it can cause. (16 points)

a. atherosclerosis

_____

_____

_____

_____

_____

b. hypertension

_____

_____

_____

_____

_____

Chapter 40 Test A

Choose the best answer for each question and write its letter in the blank.

_____ 1. The cells of the human body constantly produce which waste product?
   a. carbon monoxide   c. carbon dioxide
   b. hydrogen peroxide   d. hydrogenated oil

_____ 2. The process by which the body derives energy from the oxidation of glucose is known as
   a. internal respiration.   c. glucose conversion.
   b. external respiration.   d. cellular respiration.

_____ 3. What stuctures trap foreign particles and bacteria in the nose and trachea?
   a. cilia   c. bronchioles
   b. villi   d. the epiglottis

_____ 4. Talking when you have food in your mouth can cause choking and even death in some cases. Why is this so?
   a. Talking inteferes with the digestive process.
   b. Talking enlarges the larynx.
   c. Talking seals off the larynx and prevents food from entering.
   d. Talking requires air, which opens the epiglottis.

_____ 5. What prevents the trachea from collapsing?
   a. circular bones   c. rings of cartilage
   b. bronchi   d. alveoli

_____ 6. What causes vocal cords to make sounds?
   a. rushes of air   c. electrical impulses
   b. muscle contractions   d. none of the above

_____ 7. The bronchioles open onto bunches of air sacs called
   a. tubelets.   c. nodes.
   b. alveoli.   d. diaphragms.

_____ 8. Air is forced into the lungs by the contraction of the
   a. diaphragm.   c. bronchioles.
   b. alveoli.   d. heart.

_____ 9. What is the name of the condition in which the alveoli lose elasticity and become damaged?
   a. tuberculosis   c. emphysema
   b. pneumonia   d. hemophilia

_____ 10. Someone whose blood could *not* carry enough oxygen to the cells of the body might have a deficiency of
   a. estrogen.   c. carbon dioxide.
   b. hemoglobin.   d. lactose.

_____ 11. A toxic gas that strongly binds to hemoglobin and deprives the body of oxygen is
   a. hydrogen peroxide.   c. carbon dioxide.
   b. carbon monoxide.   d. sodium bicarbonate.

_____ 12. The brain's breathing center usually regulates breath rate according to what factor?
   a. pH level in the blood   c. pH level in the cells
   b. oxygen level in the blood d. oxygen level in the cells

_____ 13. Why might aerobic exercise and endurance training benefit a weightlifter who wanted to build and maintain strong arms?
   a. increase flow of white blood cells to skeletal muscles
   b. increase flow of oxygen-rich blood to skeletal muscles
   c. increase flow of white blood cells to smooth muscles
   d. increase flow of oxygen-rich blood to smooth muscles

_____ **14.** The main organs that excrete nitrogen waste is (are) the
     a. lymph nodes.   **c.** sweat glands.
     b. liver.   **d.** kidneys.

_____ **15.** What are the parts of kidneys that remove wastes from the blood and from urine?
     a. vitrioles   **c.** nephrons
     b. alveoli   **d.** tubules

_____ **16.** The urinary bladder is made of
     a. smooth muscle.   **c.** cardiac muscle.
     b. skeletal muscle.   **d.** connective tissue.

_____ **17.** Which of the following is *not* a diuretic?
     a. caffeine   **c.** alcohol
     b. sarsaparilla   **d.** tobacco

_____ **18.** Which of the following is *not* contained in tobacco?
     a. caffeine   **c.** nicotine
     b. cyanide   **d.** carbon monoxide

_____ **19.** The driving force behind gas exchange in the body is
     a. fusion.   **c.** diffusion.
     b. air pressure.   **d.** blood pressure.

_____ **20.** Many animals contain an oxygen-carrying substance called
     a. hemoglobin.   **c.** filtrate.
     b. chyme.   **d.** lymph.

_____ **21.** What percentage of the total amount of fluid that passes through the kidneys each day ends up as urine?
     a. 10%   **c.** all of it
     b. about 30%   **d.** less than 2%

_____ **22.** The brain regulates the rate of filtration in the kidneys by sending
     a. electrical signals.   **c.** hormonal signals.
     b. red blood cells.   **d.** white blood cells.

_____ **23.** Which of the following is *not* part of a nephron?
     a. lymph   **c.** glomerulus
     b. renal tubule   **d.** Bowman's capsule

_____ **24.** Where are the vocal cords located in the body?
     a. larynx   **c.** pharynx
     b. trachea   **d.** bronchi

_____ **25.** A substance that prevents reabsorption of water in the kidneys is a
     a. carcinogen.   **c.** toxin.
     b. diuretic.   **d.** nephron.

Chapter 40 Test B

Read each question or statement and respond in the space provided.

1. For each of the following, state where the respiration occurs and what happens in the process. (18 points)

a. cellular respiration _____

_____

b. internal respiration _____

_____

c. external respiration _____

_____

2. Identify each of the labeled structures in the drawing of the respiratory system below. Choose from the following possible answers: trachea, bronchiole, larynx, bronchus, alveolus, epiglottis, lung, nostril, diaphragm, vocal cord. (20 points)

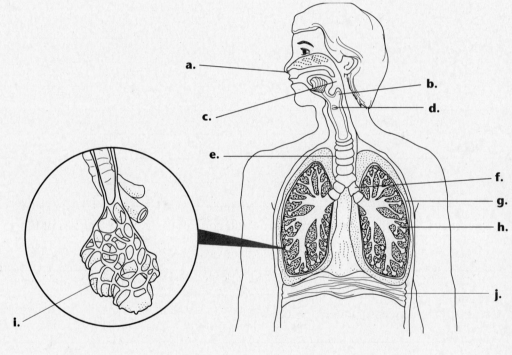

a. _____	**f.** _____
b. _____	**g.** _____
c. _____	**h.** _____
d. _____	**i.** _____
e. _____	**j.** _____

3. Explain the mechanisms involved in inhalation and exhalation. (18 points)

_____

_____

_____

_____

4. Explain how gas exchange occurs between capillaries and alveoli, and between capillaries and body tissues. (20 points)

_____

_____

_____

_____

_____

_____

_____

_____

5. a. State the main purpose of the excretory system. (6 points)

_____

_____

b. Describe the main parts of the kidneys and their functions. (6 points)

_____

_____

_____

_____

_____

_____

_____

c. By what three processes do the kidneys form urine and control the volume and pH of blood? (6 points)

_____

_____

d. What is the role of the urinary bladder? (6 points)

_____

_____

_____

_____

_____

Chapter 41 Test A

Choose the best answer for each question and write its letter in the blank.

_____ **1.** The brain and spinal cord are the
    a. peripheral nervous system.   **c.** central nervous system.
    b. endocrine system.   **d.** lymphatic system.

_____ **2.** What is the basic functional unit of the nervous system?
    a. reflex   **c.** reflex arc
    b. neuron   **d.** neutron

_____ **3.** Which of the following is true?
    a. Dendrites carry information toward the cell body.
    b. Axons carry information toward the cell body.
    c. Dendrites carry information away from the cell body.
    d. none of the above

_____ **4.** Neurons carry information through the body in the form of
    a. nerve impulses.   **c.** dendrites.
    b. axons.   **d.** protons.

_____ **5.** The axons and dendrites of neurons are collectively called
    a. sensory receptors.   **c.** myelin sheaths.
    b. glial cells.   **d.** nerve fibers.

_____ **6.** Which neurons conduct information toward the central nervous system?
    a. sensory neurons   **c.** motor neurons
    b. interneurons   **d.** none of the above

_____ **7.** Which of the following has a similar function to the plastic coating around electrical wiring in your home?
    a. sensory neurons   **c.** Schwann cells
    b. Broca's neurons   **d.** dendrites

_____ **8.** Glial cells are also called
    a. interneurons.   **c.** neuroglia.
    b. dendrites.   **d.** axons.

_____ **9.** Neurons with myelin sheaths conduct nerve impulses
    a. faster than neurons without myelin sheaths.
    b. slower than neurons without myelin sheaths.
    c. at the same speed as neurons without myelin sheaths.
    d. in greater numbers than neurons without myelin sheaths.

_____ **10.** The most numerous glial cells in the central nervous system are
    a. sensory receptors.   **c.** Schwann cells.
    b. astrocytes.   **d.** sensory neurons.

_____ **11.** What is a wave of chemical and electrical change that is conducted along the membrane of a neuron?
    a. electrocardiogram   **c.** cytogram
    b. nerve impulse   **d.** motor neuron

_____ **12.** The reversal and restoration of electrical charges across the cell membrane of a neuron is called the
    a. resting potential.   **c.** action potential.
    b. reflex arc.   **d.** synapse.

_____ **13.** What are the spaces between adjacent neurons and between neurons and effectors?
    a. reflex arcs   **c.** sinuses
    b. synapses   **d.** resting potentials

_____ **14.** What is the function of neurotransmitters?
  a. hurl neurons through synapses to create nerve impulses
  b. chemically link neurons across the synapses to conduct impulses
  c. receive and transmit ultrasound waves across synapses
  d. none of the above

_____ **15.** A pathway of neurons that carries the nerve impulses for an automatic response is a(n)
  a. reflex arc.   **c.** synapse.
  b. neurotransmitter.   **d.** action potential.

_____ **16.** Some color-blind people cannot distinguish between red and green. What structure in their eyes is not functioning properly?
  a. the cornea   **c.** the rods
  b. the retina   **d.** the cones

_____ **17.** What is the stucture that links the endocrine and nervous systems?
  a. brain stem   **c.** cerebrum
  b. thalamus   **d.** hypothalamus

_____ **18.** An infection in which of the following structures might cause dizziness?
  a. eardrum   **c.** oval window
  b. semicircular canals   **d.** outer ear

_____ **19.** Which of the following is *not* among the functions of the cerebrum?
  a. coordinate speech
  b. coordinate memory
  c. coordinate balance and equilibrium
  d. control voluntary muscle movements

_____ **20.** For a neuron to return to its resting potential, it must
  a. lose negative charge.   **c.** lose positive charge.
  b. gain negative charge.   **d.** gain more sodium ions.

_____ **21.** Someone who has suffered an injury to Broca's area often cannot
  a. walk.   **c.** remember recent events.
  b. speak.   **d.** understand speech.

_____ **22.** The activities of smooth muscles, organs, and glands are controlled by what part of the peripheral nervous system?
  a. autonomic nervous system   **c.** somatic nervous system
  b. smooth nervous system   **d.** none of the above

_____ **23.** The responses of the body to stressful situations are regulated by the
  a. somatic nervous system.   **c.** sympathetic nervous system.
  b. parasympathetic nervous system.   **d.** none of the above

_____ **24.** What is the organ of the inner ear that contains mechanoreceptors for hearing?
  a. cochlea   **c.** eardrum
  b. retina   **d.** auditory canal

_____ **25.** Why can brain surgery be performed on fully conscious patients without causing pain?
  a. The brain secretes anaesthetic chemicals.
  b. The brain has no pain receptors.
  c. The entire brain is easily anaesthetized with a single injection.
  d. none of the above

Name _____ Class _____ Date _____

Chapter 41 Test B

Read each question or statement and respond in the space provided.

1. a. State the four main functions of the nervous system. (8 points)

_____

_____

_____

_____

_____

b. Name the two main parts of the nervous system. Also state the main purpose of each. (8 points)

_____

_____

_____

_____

_____

2. a. What is a neuron? (6 points)

_____

b. What are the two types of fiberlike structures in neurons? What is the function of each? (6 points)

_____

_____

c. What are the three types of neurons? What is the main function of each? (6 points)

_____

_____

_____

_____

_____

d. What are glial cells? Name two types of glial cells. (6 points)

_____

_____

_____

3. a. Suppose you could directly observe the process in which a nerve impulse is received by a neuron and transmitted along the cell fiber. Describe this four-step process. (8 points)

_____

_____

_____

_____

_____

_____

_____

b. Describe the process in which an impulse passes from one neuron to another. (8 points)

_____

_____

_____

_____

_____

4. Identify each of the labeled structures in the drawing of the central nervous system below. Choose among the following possible answers: brain stem, cerebrum, spinal cord, pons, thalamus, cerebellum, meninges, hypothalamus, medulla oblongata. (18 points)

a. _____

b. _____

c. _____

d. _____

e. _____

f. _____

g. _____

h. _____

i. _____

5. Discuss the theory of the neural basis of each of the following. (14 points)

a. memory _____

_____

_____

_____

_____

b. speech and understanding of language _____

_____

_____

_____

_____

6. a. Compare and contrast the somatic nervous system and the autonomic nervous system. (6 points)

_____

_____

_____

b. Compare and contrast the sympathetic and parasympathetic nervous systems. (6 points)

_____

_____

_____

Chapter 42 Test A

Choose the best answer for each question and write its letter in the blank.

_____ 1. What are ductless glands that release hormones directly into the blood called?
   a. salivary glands   **c.** pituitary glands
   b. endocrine glands   **d.** pineal glands

_____ 2. What gland is part of both the endocrine system and the digestive system?
   a. pituitary gland   **c.** pancreas
   b. testis   **d.** thymus

_____ 3. When epinephrine is secreted by the adrenal gland, its molecules bind to receptors on the membranes of cells. Judging from this, epinephrine must be a(n)
   a. protein hormone.   **c.** insulin hormone.
   b. steroid hormone.   **d.** thyroid hormone.

_____ 4. Testosterone can alter the genetic activity of some body cells. Judging from this, it must be a(n)
   a. protein hormone.   **c.** insulin hormone.
   b. steroid hormone.   **d.** thyroid hormone.

_____ 5. Someone who has suffered damage to the pancreas might
   a. have trouble walking a straight line.
   b. be unable to remember a recent event.
   c. have periods of very low energy.
   d. have trouble making a fist.

_____ 6. What is the regulation of the rate of a bodily process by the last step in the process?
   a. feedback control   **c.** luteinizing
   b. stop gap regulation   **d.** none of the above

_____ 7. What hormone stimulates cells to take up sugar from the blood?
   a. glucagon   **c.** adrenalin
   b. insulin   **d.** luteinizing hormone

_____ 8. What are male organs that produce sperm?
   a. ovaries   **c.** testes
   b. oocytes   **d.** pineal glands

_____ 9. The primary male sex hormone is called
   a. estrogen.   **c.** oxytocin.
   b. testosterone.   **d.** glycogen.

_____ 10. A single drop of semen can contain approximately
   a. 10,000 sperm.   **c.** 200 sperm.
   b. 1000 sperm.   **d.** 5 million sperm.

_____ 11. Sperm are powered by what substance?
   a. air   **c.** blood
   b. urine   **d.** none of the above

_____ 12. What female organ releases eggs and produces estrogen and progesterone?
   a. ovum   **c.** uterus
   b. womb   **d.** ovary

_____ 13. The process by which cells in the male and female reproductive organs make sperm and eggs is known as
   a. ovulation.   **c.** ejaculation.
   b. meiosis.   **d.** intercourse.

_____ **14.** What is the cycle that prepares the lining of the uterus to receive a fertilized egg or discharge an unfertilized egg?
   a. menstrual cycle   **c.** ovarian cycle
   b. luteal phase   **d.** follicle phase

_____ **15.** Fertilization and pregnancy can occur if intercourse happens within
   a. three days of ovulation.   **c.** ten days of ovulation.
   b. fifteen days of ovulation.   **d.** twenty-five days of ovulation.

_____ **16.** The fusion of egg and sperm nuclei is called
   a. cleavage.   **c.** implantation.
   b. fertilization.   **d.** ejaculation.

_____ **17.** What cell is formed as a result of fertilization?
   a. blastocyst   **c.** morula
   b. placenta   **d.** zygote

_____ **18.** When the embryo attaches to the walls of the uterus, the process is
   a. cleavage.   **c.** implantation.
   b. fertilization.   **d.** blastocysty.

_____ **19.** Some health problems can be caused by damage to an embryo in its early stages of development. For example, malfunctioning kidneys can be caused by damage to an embryo's
   a. mesoderm tissue.   **c.** ectoderm tissue.
   b. endoderm tissue.   **d.** phyloderm tissue.

_____ **20.** From the ninth week after fertilization until birth, the developing human is called a(n)
   a. embryo.   **c.** fetus.
   b. organelle.   **d.** zygote.

_____ **21.** After implantation, the blastocyst forms several sections known as
   a. morulas.   **c.** zygotes.
   b. placentas.   **d.** germ layers.

_____ **22.** A surge of what hormone triggers labor?
   a. oxytocin   **c.** testosterone
   b. myoglobin   **d.** estrogen

_____ **23.** What strand of tissue connects mother and fetus?
   a. organelle   **c.** umbilical cord
   b. ligament   **d.** tendon

_____ **24.** During which phase of the menstrual cycle is there a surge in estrogen levels and a sharp increase in amount of LH?
   a. days 1–4   **c.** days 12–14
   b. days 6–10   **d.** days 24–28

_____ **25.** What happens to the follicle during days 12–14 of the menstrual cycle?
   a. It releases an egg.   **c.** It is ejected.
   b. It begins to develop.   **d.** none of the above

Chapter 42 Test B

Read each question or statement and respond in the space provided.

1. a. What is the main function of the endocrine system? (5 points)

_____

b. How do endocrine glands differ from exocrine glands? Give two examples of each. (5 points)

_____

_____

_____

c. Name a hormone produced by each of the endocrine glands you named. State the functions of the hormones. (5 points)

_____

_____

_____

d. How do protein hormones and steroid hormones differ? (5 points) _____

_____

_____

_____

2. a. Explain the role of the hypothalamus and the pituitary in controlling endocrine glands. (8 points)

_____

_____

_____

b. Explain how blood sugar is controlled through feedback. (8 points)

_____

_____

_____

_____

_____

3. Identify the main structures in the male reproductive system. Describe the function of each. (13 points)

_____

_____

_____

_____

_____

4. Identify each of the labeled structures in the drawing of the female reproductive system below. Choose from among the following possible answers: uterus, ovary, follicle, cervix, Fallopian tube, oocyte, vagina, ovum. (16 points)

a._____

b. _____

c._____

d. _____

e._____

f. _____

g._____

h. _____

5. Describe what occurs at each of the following phases of the female reproductive cycle. (15 points)

a. menstrual-flow phase _____

_____

b. follicle phase _____

_____

c. luteal phase _____

_____

_____

_____

6. Briefly describe each of the following stages of the reproductive process. (20 points)

a. fertilization _____

_____

_____

_____

b. cleavage and implantation _____

_____

_____

_____

c. fetal development _____

_____

_____

_____

d. birth _____

_____

_____

Chapter 43 Test A

Choose the best answer for each question and write its letter in the blank.

_____ **1.** Which of the following is *not* caused by a pathogen?
    a. influenza   **c.** botulism
    b. snake bite   **d.** common cold

_____ **2.** The idea that microbes cause disease was first stated by
    a. Louis Pasteur.   **c.** Sigmund Freud.
    b. Marie Curie.   **d.** Joseph Lister.

_____ **3.** Any object or organism that transmits a disease is called a
    a. pathogen.   **c.** pathogenic factor.
    b. contagion.   **d.** vector.

_____ **4.** Syphilis and gonorrhea are examples of
    a. pathogenic fungi.   **c.** sexually transmitted diseases.
    b. flatworms.   **d.** tape worms.

_____ **5.** What kind of food poisoning causes damage to the nervous system?
    a. botulism   **c.** salmonellosis
    b. syphilis   **d.** strep throat

_____ **6.** Bubonic plague, malaria, and Lyme disease are most often transmitted through what vector?
    a. air currents   **c.** insects
    b. birds   **d.** polluted water

_____ **7.** Which of the following diseases is most often transmitted through infected domestic animals?
    a. Bubonic plague   **c.** emphysema
    b. rabies   **d.** botulism

_____ **8.** Bacteria that settle on the skin, in the nose, or in the eye are often killed by
    a. viruses.   **c.** retroactive viruses.
    b. enzymes.   **d.** fungi.

_____ **9.** When tissues are injured or infected, the cells release a hormone called
    a. histamine.   **c.** estrogen.
    b. testosterone.   **d.** oxytocin.

_____ **10.** Against which of the following pathogens would interferon possibly be effective?
    a. malaria   **c.** syphilis
    b. influenza   **d.** botulism

_____ **11.** Natural killer cells attack
    a. fungal spores.   **c.** antibodies.
    b. virus-infected cells.   **d.** toxic substances.

_____ **12.** The specific defenses of the body are collectively known as the
    a. immune response.   **c.** lymphocytes.
    b. antigens.   **d.** immunization.

_____ **13.** A substance that a macrophage identifies as foreign is called a(n)
    a. antibody.   **c.** vaccine.
    b. bacterium.   **d.** antigen.

_____ **14.** A disease-fighting protein produced in response to a specific pathogen is a(n)
    a. humoral immunity.   **c.** antigen.
    b. antibody.   **d.** lymphocyte.

_____ **15.** The special defense cells used in cell-mediated immunity are called
    a. T-cells.   **c.** lymphocytes.
    b. host cells.   **d.** antibodies.

_____ **16.** Suppose a person with an excessively high and active number of suppressor T-cells in the blood were exposed to the influenza virus. What effect could this have on cell-mediated immunity?
    a. suppression of the virus leading to immunity
    b. suppression of the killer T-cells possibly leading to illness
    c. production of interferon by the suppressors
    d. none of the above

_____ **17.** The body's resistance to previously encountered pathogens is called
    a. acquired immunity.   **c.** acquired immune deficiency.
    b. cell-mediated immunity.   **d.** humoral immunity.

_____ **18.** The response of the immune system to a normally harmless substance is called a(n)
    a. specific immune response.   **c.** cell-mediated response.
    b. allergy.   **d.** autoimmune disease.

_____ **19.** An autoimmune disease is one in which
    a. the body cannot produce antibodies.
    b. the body cannot produce antigens.
    c. the body mistakes its own cells for pathogens.
    d. the body mistakes its own cells for antibodies.

_____ **20.** HIV disease attacks the immune system by
    a. killing suppressor T-cells but not T4 cells.
    b. killing T4 cells but not suppressor T-cells.
    c. causing cancer.
    d. causing T-cells to attack the central nervous system.

_____ **21.** Which of the following is not a vector for HIV?
    a. unprotected sexual contact   **c.** sharing needles
    b. toilet seats   **d.** exchanging body fluids

_____ **22.** Which of the following is an opportunistic infection common to people with AIDS?
    a. Kaposi's sarcoma   **c.** Lyme disease
    b. schistosomiasis   **d.** trichinosis

_____ **23.** AIDS can be described as
    a. a specific disease.   **c.** a fungal infection.
    b. a condition caused by a virus.   **d.** an autoimmune disorder.

_____ **24.** Which of the following is *not* a common cause of allergies?
    a. foods   **c.** mold spores
    b. protozoans   **d.** pollen

_____ **25.** The fastest growing epidemic in the world is now
    a. schistosomiasis.   **c.** Lyme disease.
    b. multiple sclerosis.   **d.** HIV infection.

Chapter 43 Test B

Read each question or statement and respond in the space provided.

1. a. What is an infectious disease? (6 points)

_____

_____

b. What is a pathogen? (6 points) _____

_____

c. Name two infectious diseases and the kind of pathogen that is associated with each. (6 points)

_____

_____

2. Imagine that you are a medical research scientist. You suspect that a mysterious cattle disease known as X fever is caused by a certain kind of bacterium carried in the blood. Describe how you would use Koch's postulates to find out if you are correct. (16 points)

_____

_____

_____

_____

_____

_____

_____

_____

_____

3. State the four ways in which infectious diseases are generally spread. Give an example of a disease that is typically spread in each of these ways. (14 points)

_____

_____

_____

_____

4. a. What is meant by a nonspecific defense? (16 points)

_____

_____

b. What is meant by a specific defense? (6 points) _____

_____

c. What is the difference between humoral immunity and cell-mediated immunity? Name one agent of each in the body. (6 points)

_____

_____

_____

_____

5. Suppose you are observing patients who have been able to fight off infections in each of the following ways. In each case, state whether the defense is nonspecific, involves humoral immunity, or involves cell-mediated immunity. (14 points)

   a. Natural killer cells attack body cells that have been infected by a virus.

   _____

   b. A macrophage carries some foreign antigen from viruses to T cells, which then attack the viruses.

   _____

   c. In response to the entry of protozoans into the lungs, pyrogens are released by macrophages, and a fever results.

   _____

   d. Tears wash from the eye a bit of bacteria-infested soil.

   _____

   e. A macrophage carries foreign antigens from bacteria to B lymphocytes, which then produce substances that attack the bacteria.

   _____

   f. Interferon is produced in response to a viral infection.

   _____

   g. Bacteria enter through a cut in the skin, but the area becomes inflamed and phagocytes and macrophages attack the bacteria.

   _____

6. Describe what takes place in the following immune-system disorders. (20 points)

   a. an allergy to pollen

   _____

   _____

   _____

   _____

   _____

   b. HIV infection

   _____

   _____

   _____

   _____

   _____

   _____

   _____

   _____

   _____

Chapter 44 Test A

Choose the best answer for each question and write its letter in the blank.

_____ 1. A nonfood chemical substance that is taken into the body and changes the way the body functions is a(n)
   a. placebo.   **c.** drug.
   b. antigen.   **d.** antibody.

_____ 2. Which of the following is *not* a drug?
   a. tobacco   **c.** alcohol
   b. caffeine   **d.** vitamin C

_____ 3. When a woman who took heroin was suddenly deprived of the drug, she suffered severe muscle spasms. This proves that heroin
   a. causes dependency but not addiction.
   b. is addictive.
   c. is a toxin that causes muscles spasms.
   d. none of the above

_____ 4. Psychoactive drugs affect
   a. transmission of nerve impulses in the brain.
   b. production of hormones in the brain.
   c. regulation of temperature and water in the brain.
   d. transmission of nerve impulses in the spinal cord.

_____ 5. Drugs that increase the activity of the central nervous system are classified as
   a. hallucinogens.   **c.** steroids.
   b. stimulants.   **d.** narcotics.

_____ 6. What kinds of drugs decrease the activity of the central nervous system?
   a. hallucinogens   **c.** depressants
   b. narcotics   **d.** amphetamines

_____ 7. What are drugs that affect the sensory perceptions of the central nervous system?
   a. hallucinogens   **c.** amphetamines
   b. narcotics   **d.** barbituates

_____ 8. Some people have managed to quit smoking with the use of drug patches. Since the patches prevented the withdrawal normally associated with stopping smoking, the patches must contain
   a. carbon monoxide.   **c.** tar.
   b. nicotine.   **d.** cirrhosis.

_____ 9. Cocaine is classified as a(n)
   a. opiate.   **c.** barbiturate.
   b. narcotic.   **d.** stimulant.

_____ 10. What are the risks in smoking?
   a. emphysema   **c.** heart disease
   b. lung cancer   **d.** all of these

_____ 11. The most addictive group of drugs are the
   a. hallucinogens.   **c.** barbiturates.
   b. narcotics.   **d.** steroids.

_____ 12. The most commonly used illegal substance in the U.S. is
   a. marijuana.   **c.** crack.
   b. cocaine.   **d.** heroin.

_____ 13. Bodybuilders sometimes use what illegal drugs to help build muscle?
   a. barbituates   **c.** narcotics
   b. steroids   **d.** peptides

_____ **14.** What do alcoholic beverages contain?
    a. ethanol
    b. methanol
    c. isopropyl alcohol
    d. mixtures of all three kinds

_____ **15.** Alcohol is a
    a. barbituate.
    b. peptide.
    c. stimulant.
    d. depressant.

_____ **16.** Women absorb a higher percentage of alcohol into their blood than do men, which causes women to
    a. get 'drunk' faster than men.
    b. convert more alcohol to glucose.
    c. remain sober longer than men.
    d. none of the above

_____ **17.** Women absorb a higher percentage of alcohol into their blood because
    a. they have fewer alcohol-digesting enzymes than men.
    b. their livers cannot filter out as much alcohol as men's livers.
    c. their urinary processes do not function as quickly.
    d. their digestive processes take place more quickly.

_____ **18.** The most people die from problems related to which of these drugs?
    a. alcohol.
    b. caffeine.
    c. tobacco.
    d. cocaine.

_____ **19.** Something that causes cancer cells to grow is called a
    a. nicotine.
    b. monoxide.
    c. carcinogen.
    d. delirium tremens.

_____ **20.** Which of the following causes lung cancer?
    a. nicotine
    b. carbon monoxide
    c. tar
    d. caffeine

_____ **21.** The number one cause of death among smokers is
    a. lung cancer.
    b. heart disease.
    c. emphysema.
    d. throat cancer.

_____ **22.** Carbon monoxide in cigarettes deprives the body of oxygen by
    a. binding to hemoglobin in the blood.
    b. slowing down the breathing rate.
    c. damaging the kidneys.
    d. suppressing oxygen uptake hormones.

_____ **23.** Loud sounds harm the ears by
    a. rupturing the eardrum.
    b. breaking the bones in the inner ear.
    c. damaging the hair cells in the inner ear.
    d. none of the above

_____ **24.** Which of the following is a stimulant?
    a. cigarettes
    b. marijuana
    c. coffee
    d. beer

_____ **25.** People who drink a lot of alcohol frequently develop a disease called
    a. emphysema.
    b. cirrhosis.
    c. carcinoma.
    d. hemophilia.

Chapter 44 Test B

Read each question or statement and respond in the space provided.

1. **a.** What is a drug? (9 points)

_____

_____

b. Compare drug misuse and drug abuse. (9 points)

_____

_____

_____

_____

2. **a.** Explain what is meant by drug dependency. (6 points)

_____

_____

_____

b. What is meant by drug addiction? (6 points)

_____

_____

_____

c. What is meant by drug withdrawal? (6 points)

_____

_____

_____

3. Suppose you want to classify drugs on the basis of their effects on the body. For each of the effects described below, classify the drug causing the effect as either a stimulant, barbiturate, tranquilizer, hallucinogen, narcotic, or steroid. (18 points)

a. slightly reduces activity of central nervous system, relieves stress, can lead to psychological and physical dependency

_____

b. binds to endorphin receptors in the brain, reduces pain, produces euphoria

_____

c. builds muscle mass, disrupts body functions, causes liver disease

_____

d. increases heart rate, transmission of nerve impulses, and blood pressure, causes sleeplessness, heart attacks, strokes

_____

e. greatly slows down activity of central nervous system, produces sleep, can cause coma or death

_____

f. affects sensory perceptions by central nervous system

_____

Chapter 44: Substance Abuse **203**

4. a. Describe the effects of alcohol on the body. (11 points)

_____

_____

_____

_____

b. Explain what is meant by alcoholism. How can this condition generally be recognized? (11 points)

_____

_____

_____

_____

_____

5. a. Descibe three dangerous substances in tobacco smoke. (8 points)

_____

_____

_____

_____

b. What are the effects of tobacco on the respiratory system? (8 points)

_____

_____

_____

_____

c. What are the effects of tobacco on the circulatory system? (8 points)

_____

_____

_____

_____

Unit 8 Test A

Choose the best answer for each question and write its letter in the blank.

_____ 1. Which of the following is an example of skeletal muscle?
a. colon
b. heart
c. stomach
d. biceps

_____ 2. Someone who eats great quantities of food and then vomits suffers from
a. anorexia nervosa.
b. emphysema.
c. bulimia.
d. colonitis.

_____ 3. What is the function of the nocireceptors?
a. receive painful stimuli
b. filter bright light before it damages the cornea
c. receive motor instructions from the central nervous system
d. none of the above

_____ 4. Blood is circulated to the lungs through the
a. cardiac circuit.
b. peripheral circuit.
c. pulmonary circuit.
d. oxidation circuit.

_____ 5. The vocal cords are located in what part of the body?
a. pharynx
b. larynx
c. trachea
d. alveoli

_____ 6. What carries vibrations through the inner ear?
a. bones
b. ligaments
c. tendons
d. connective tissues

_____ 7. Heavy coffee drinkers are likely to urinate more frequently than the average person because caffeine
a. breaks down water in the blood.
b. inhibits uptake of water in the kidneys.
c. inhibits uptake of glucose in the blood.
d. breaks down glucose in the kidneys.

_____ 8. What is another term for afterbirth?
a. zygote
b. water
c. placenta
d. blastocyst

_____ 9. Which system releases and regulates most hormones?
a. endocrine
b. circulatory
c. respiratory
d. reproductive

_____ 10. The blood vessels in the skin conserve heat in cold situations by
a. dilating.
b. bursting.
c. contracting.
d. retreating further beneath the skin.

_____ 11. What is the name for the group of symptoms experienced by someone who suddenly stops taking a drug to which they are addicted?
a. inflammatory response
b. emphysema
c. pathogenia
d. withdrawal

_____ 12. Cirrhosis is an alcohol-related disease that affects the
a. kidneys.
b. heart.
c. liver.
d. brain.

_____ 13. When natural killer cells mistake the body's own cells for pathogens, the condition that results is a(n)
a. allergy.
b. vector.
c. acquired immune deficiency syndrome.
d. autoimmune disorder.

_____ **14.** The ovum is fertilized by the
   a. sperm.
   b. blastocyst.
   c. zygote.
   d. ovaries.

_____ **15.** Insects are a vector for which of the following diseases?
   a. AIDS
   b. bulimia
   c. emphysema
   d. Lyme disease

_____ **16.** Barbiturates are
   a. depressants.
   b. hallucinogens.
   c. stimulants.
   d. opiates.

_____ **17.** Multiple sclerosis is a(n)
   a. contagious disease.
   b. acquired immune disorder.
   c. fungal infection.
   d. autoimmune disorder.

_____ **18.** Which of the following is the correct order of terms for describing the developing child during the various phases of the gestation period?
   a. zygote, fetus, blastocyst
   b. blastocyst, fetus, zygote
   c. zygote, blastocyst, fetus
   d. blastocyst, zygote, fetus

_____ **19.** Peyote, a drug used in some Native American religious ceremonies, is classified as a
   a. carcinogen.
   b. hallucinogen.
   c. narcotic.
   d. barbiturate.

_____ **20.** Smokers tire more easily than nonsmokers because in smokers their
   a. cells are deprived of oxygen.
   b. adrenal glands produce less adrenalin.
   c. glucose level of the blood is lower.
   d. lymphatic system becomes clogged.

_____ **21.** The tube that leads from the throat into the bronchi is the
   a. bronchiole.
   b. atria.
   c. pharynx.
   d. trachea.

_____ **22.** The function of platelets is to
   a. form blood clots.
   b. manufacture T-cells.
   c. combat specific infections.
   d. secrete antibacterial enzymes.

_____ **23.** The addictive agent in coffee, tea, and some soft drinks is
   a. heroin.
   b. nicotine.
   c. caffeine.
   d. tar.

_____ **24.** Olympic athletes are now screened for the use of what controlled substance?
   a. heroin
   b. caffeine
   c. steroids
   d. nicotine

_____ **25.** The function of T4 cells is to
   a. speed up action of killer T-cells.
   b. inhibit action of killer T-cells.
   c. stimulate production of antibacterial enzymes.
   d. consume macrophages.

_____ **26.** The virus that directly attacks T4 cells is
   a. HIV.
   b. polio.
   c. influenza.
   d. *Pneumocystis carinni.*

_____ **27.** Which of the following causes the greatest number of deaths each year?
   a. injecting heroin
   b. drinking
   c. smoking crack
   d. smoking cigarettes

Unit 8 Test A

_____ 28. Loud rock concerts can affect hearing capacity by
   a. making the eardrum rigid.
   b. shrinking the semicircular canals.
   c. damaging hair cells in the inner ear.
   d. enlarging the outer ear.

_____ 29. What is the function of a macrophage?
   a. produce antibodies   **c.** monitor blood sugar
   b. consume pathogens   **d.** manufacture antigens

_____ 30. When you drink beer, you are consuming a drug that is a
   a. barbiturate.   **c.** depressant.
   b. stimulant.   **d.** narcotic.

_____ 31. The chemical that triggers an inflammatory immune response is
   a. histamine.   **c.** endocrine.
   b. amphetamine.   **d.** endorphin.

_____ 32. Heroin and other opiates function by binding in the brain with
   a. histamine receptors.   **c.** endorphin receptors.
   b. nocireceptors.   **d.** special opiate receptors.

_____ 33. The two lower sections of the heart are known as the
   a. ventricles.   **c.** atria.
   b. cardia.   **d.** septum.

_____ 34. Which causes the fewest deaths each year?
   a. cigarette-related illnesses   **c.** barbiturate-related illnesses
   b. alcohol-related illnesses   **d.** marijuana-related illnesses

_____ 35. Amphetamines are classified as
   a. barbiturates.   **c.** stimulants.
   b. hallucinogens.   **d.** narcotics.

_____ 36. The fluid-filled cavity common to almost all animals is called the
   a. sternum.   **c.** coelum.
   b. thoracic cavity.   **d.** abdominal cavity.

_____ 37. Eating which of the following foods would be linked to a greater chance of heart disease?
   a. animal fat   **c.** candy
   b. artificially flavored food   **d.** starchy food

_____ 38. The tiny blood vessels through which plasma leaks into the intercellular spaces are the
   a. arteries.   **c.** veins.
   b. capillaries.   **d.** nodes.

_____ 39. Approximately how many times does the heart beat per day?
   a. 100,000   **c.** 5,000
   b. 10,000   **d.** 1,000,000

_____ 40. Which of the following is true?
   a. The left lung is larger than the right lung.
   b. The left lung is smaller than the right lung.
   c. The lungs are equal in size.
   d. none of the above

_____ 41. An organ that helps control the amounts of water, salts, minerals, and vitamins in the blood is the
   a. gall bladder.   **c.** kidney.
   b. pancreas.   **d.** liver.

_____ **42.** The central nervous system consists of the
    a. brain and endocrine system.
    b. brain and spinal cord.
    c. spinal cord and endocrine system.
    d. endocrine system and peripheral nervous system.

_____ **43.** The pituitary gland is connected to and regulated by the
    a. brain stem.   **c.** cerebrum.
    b. hypothalamus.   **d.** thalamus.

_____ **44.** What part of the brain contols emotions?
    a. thalamus.   **c.** cerebellum.
    b. hypothalamus.   **d.** brain stem.

_____ **45.** The average human gestation period is approximately
    a. eleven months.   **c.** ten months.
    b. seven months.   **d.** nine months.

_____ **46.** What is the benefit of having the testes located in the scrotum, away from the body?
    a. for protection   **c.** to provide momentum for spermatozoa
    b. to keep them cool   **d.** none of the above

_____ **47.** Which of the following diseases is transmitted primarily by insects?
    a. malaria   **c.** bulimia
    b. strep throat   **d.** gonorrhea

_____ **48.** Which of the following is not a pathogen?
    a. *Streptococcus pyogenes*   **c.** *Vibrio cholerae*
    b. *Spermatozoan*   **d.** *Trichinella spiralis*

_____ **49.** How are contagious diseases often spread?
    a. direct contact   **c.** food and water
    b. animal bites   **d.** all of the above

_____ **50.** Based on what you know about the spread of HIV, which of the following behaviors would seem to be a vector for transmitting the virus?
    a. hugging   **c.** holding hands
    b. sharing soap   **d.** none of the above

Chapter 45 Test A

Choose the best answer for each question and write its letter in the blank.

_____ **1.** What is the study of organisms and their interactions with the environment?
    a. biology   **c.** ecology
    b. environmentalism   **d.** ethology

_____ **2.** The region of the earth that supports all living things is the
    a. life zone.   **c.** biotic factor.
    b. biosphere.   **d.** biozone.

_____ **3.** The role an organism plays in its ecosystem is its
    a. niche.   **c.** abiotic factor.
    b. biotic factor.   **d.** ethos.

_____ **4.** The typical weather pattern of an area over time is called a
    a. temperature.   **c.** climate.
    b. latitude.   **d.** ecosystem.

_____ **5.** Why don't trees grow on the tops of high mountains?
    a. Soil is too rich.   **c.** Not enough sunlight reaches area.
    b. Temperatures are too cold.   **d.** none of the above.

_____ **6.** Development of topsoil takes approximately
    a. one year.   **c.** twenty years.
    b. one hundred years.   **d.** two thousand years.

_____ **7.** Which of the following organisms does not require sunlight to live?
    a. chemosynthetic bacteria   **c.** algae
    b. trees   **d.** none of the above

_____ **8.** Research has shown that chemical fertilizers and pesticides
    a. benefit soil renewal.
    b. inhibit soil renewal.
    c. increase nutritional value of crops.
    d. increase air quality near farms.

_____ **9.** Which of the following is an abiotic factor?
    a. rainfall   **c.** trees
    b. compost   **d.** crops

_____ **10.** The lichens that grow on rocks and form soil eventually disappear because
    a. the rocks do not provide enough nutrients.
    b. the wind carries them away.
    c. rainfall washes them away.
    d. grass overshadows and crowds them out.

_____ **11.** Which of the following represents the typical order of plant life that occurs in a primary succession?
    a. shrubs, pines, grass, deciduous trees
    b. deciduous trees, pines, shrubs, grass
    c. grass, shrubs, pines, deciduous trees
    d. pines, grass, deciduous trees, shrubs

_____ **12.** Succession that occurs in an area where an existing community has been partially destroyed is called
    a. primary succession.   **c.** climax succession.
    b. secondary succession.   **d.** pioneer succession.

_____ **13.** What kind of human population pattern might be called a human climax community?
    a. fluctuating   **c.** rapidly growing
    b. unchanging   **d.** rapidly decreasing

_____ 14. Imagine two recently formed islands, A and B. The islands are of equal size and climate, but A is 30 miles from the mainland, while B is 400 miles from the mainland. Which of the two islands probably will be first to develop a climax community?
  a. Island A
  b. Island B
  c. The islands will develop climax communities simultaneously.
  d. Neither island will ever develop a climax community.

_____ 15. Which of the two islands in question 14 probably will develop a more unique ecosystem?
  a. Island A
  b. Island B
  c. The islands will develop identical ecosystems.
  d. The islands will maintain ecosystems identical to the mainland.

_____ 16. A major ecosystem with its own temperature ranges, rainfall amounts, and types of organisms is called a
  a. biosphere.   c. biome.
  b. bioregion.   d. biozone.

_____ 17. An organism that cannot make its own food is called a
  a. heterotroph.   c. heterophage.
  b. heterosexual.   d. heterogene.

_____ 18. Just below the ocean's photic zone lies the
  a. photosynthetic zone.   c. aphotic zone.
  b. neritic zone.   d. benthic zone.

_____ 19. The environment on the ocean floor is called the
  a. photic zone.   c. continental shelf.
  b. benthic zone.   d. estuary.

_____ 20. Although they are only ten percent of the marine biome, which of the following areas are important because they contain almost ninety percent of marine life?
  a. estuaries   c. continental shelves
  b. intertidal zones   d. oceanic zones

_____ 21. Freshwater ecosystems such as lakes and ponds can be made uninhabitable for animal life by
  a. dumping detergents in them.   c. too many ultraviolet rays.
  b. farming fish in them.   d. growing crops too close to them.

_____ 22. Which of the following is *not* classified as a wetland?
  a. bogs   c. swamps
  b. marshes   d. beaches

_____ 23. Which of the following is *not* classified as a land biome?
  a. swamps   c. rain forest
  b. taiga   d. chaparral

_____ 24. Which of the following is a threat to wetlands in some countries?
  a. alligator overpopulation   c. ozone depletion
  b. housing developments   d. wildfires

_____ 25. Travelers in outer space experience alarming body changes due to the lack of what?
  a. water   c. gravity
  b. oxygen   d. food

Chapter 45 Test B

Read each question or statement and respond in the space provided.

1. Suppose that an ecosystem in a certain area includes the following: grasses, trees, soil, rocks, grass-eating mice, air, water, and mouse-eating owls that nest in trees. (18 points)

a. Which of these factors are biotic? Which are abiotic? _____

_____

b. Describe the niche of the mice, of the owls, and of the trees.

_____

_____

_____

_____

_____

_____

2. a. What is climate? (6 points)

_____

b. What are the two main factors that determine climate in a region? (6 points)

_____

c. Name three factors that determine the typical temperature in a region. Describe the effect of each of these factors. (6 points)

_____

_____

_____

_____

3. In a certain area, there are only rocks at first. Lichens appear, then grasses, then tall weeds, after which there is no large-scale change for a long period. A fire occurs, killing off the weeds. Small shrubs then appear, then pines, then oaks, and finally beeches, after which there is no large-scale change. Discuss the process of succession in the area. Include the concepts of primary succession, pioneer community, secondary succession, and climax community. Also, explain how one stage leads to another. (18 points)

_____

_____

_____

_____

_____

_____

_____

_____

_____

_____

_____

4. Suppose you are an ecologist classifying certain areas of Earth in terms of biomes. You travel to these areas and observe the following conditions and organisms. In which biome would you classify each area? Choose from among the following possible answers: tropical rain forest, desert, chaparral, grasslands, temperate forest, taiga, tundra. (18 points)

a. frequent rain, cold winters; deciduous trees, wolves, deer, and birds present

_____

b. rainy winters, summer drought; scrub oak, manzanita, mice, deer, and reptiles present

_____

c. soil permanently frozen except for a thin layer during the short, cool summer; lichens, moss, reindeer, and musk oxen present

_____

d. rain falls almost every day; very tall trees, dense canopy, monkeys and flying squirrels present

_____

e. long cold winters, short summers; conifers, moose, elk, and lynxes present

_____

f. long dry periods, occasional fires; no large trees; wildflowers, burrowing mammals, and grazing animals present

_____

5. Identify each of the marine zones described below. In each case, choose the best answer from among the following possibilities: photic zone, aphotic zone, intertidal zone, neritic zone, oceanic zone, benthic zone. (12 points)

a. alternately covered and exposed by water_____

b. ocean floor, contains organisms such as crabs and sea stars_____

c. light penetrates, and photosynthesis is possible _____

d. deep, large zone, phytoplankton scarce, relatively few organisms _____

e. light does not penetrate, bioluminescent organisms present_____

f. lies just above the continental shelf _____

6. Describe the characteristics of each of the following aquatic areas. Then give examples of three organisms that live there in large numbers. (16 points)

a. estuary _____

_____

_____

b. wetland_____

_____

_____

c. moving-water biome_____

_____

_____

d. standing-water biome_____

_____

_____

Chapter 46 Test A

Choose the best answer for each question and write its letter in the blank.

_____ 1. What is the term for each step in the transfer of energy and matter within a biological community?
    a. biological transfer.   **c.** biotransfer.
    b. trophic level.   **d.** consumptive transfer.

_____ 2. What is the source of almost all the energy in most ecosystems?
    a. rock   **c.** radiation from the sun
    b. water   **d.** carbon

_____ 3. Organisms that break down and feed on organic matter are
    a. decomposers.   **c.** synthesizers.
    b. omnivores.   **d.** producers.

_____ 4. Carnivores are animals that eat only
    a. plants.   **c.** other animals.
    b. inorganic materials.   **d.** decomposers.

_____ 5. All the interconnected food chains in an ecosystem make up a
    a. biomass.   **c.** food pyramid.
    b. biosphere.   **d.** food web.

_____ 6. A schematic that shows the relationships between producers and consumers at different trophic levels in an ecosystem is called a(n)
    a. biogram.   **c.** ecological sphere.
    b. ecological pyramid.   **d.** biopyramid.

_____ 7. The amount of organic matter at each trophic level is called the
    a. organic mass.   **c.** biomass.
    b. energy pyramid.   **d.** trophic mass.

_____ 8. If all the recyclable household garbage and yard rubbish currently being dumped in landfills were recycled and put to other uses, by what percentage could the need for landfills be reduced?
    a. 10 percent   **c.** 70 percent
    b. 30 percent   **d.** 40 percent

_____ 9. Which of the following can be recycled?
    a. metal cans   **c.** newspapers
    b. glass   **d.** all of the above

_____ 10. The repeated movement of water between Earth's surface and the atmosphere is called the
    a. water cycle.   **c.** climate.
    b. biocycle.   **d.** water vapor.

_____ 11. Photosynthesis and cellular respiration are part of which cycle(s)?
    a. water cycle   **c.** carbon and oxygen cycles
    b. nitrogen cycle   **d.** ethanol cycle

_____ 12. What energy-rich compounds are formed from organic matter by geological processes?
    a. carbon dioxides   **c.** fossil fuels
    b. fossils   **d.** petrified wood

_____ 13. What is the process by which nitrogen gas in the air is converted to usable nitrogen compounds?
    a. nitrogen fixation   **c.** nitrification
    b. ammonification   **d.** denitrification

_____ 14. The nitrogen cycle is carried out primarily by
    a. humans.   **c.** bacteria.
    b. termites.   **d.** the water cycle.

_____ **15.** What is the source of the ammonia in an animal's urine?
    a. nitrogen compounds   **c.** glucose
    b. fats   **d.** hydrogen

_____ **16.** A cheap and renewable resource that could be used in place of gasoline is
    a. natural gas.   **c.** coal.
    b. ethanol.   **d.** petroleum.

_____ **17.** An organism that produces its own food supply from inorganic compounds is called a(n)
    a. autotroph.   **c.** consumer.
    b. heterotroph.   **d.** scavenger.

_____ **18.** An organism that feeds only on plants is a
    a. carnivore.   **c.** photosynthetic.
    b. herbivore.   **d.** parasympathetic.

_____ **19.** The organisms at the bottom of an ecological pyramid are
    a. consumers.   **c.** producers.
    b. decomposers.   **d.** heteromorphs.

_____ **20.** What gas is produced during photosynthesis?
    a. carbon dioxide   **c.** hydrogen
    b. nitrogen   **d.** oxygen

_____ **21.** Which of the following has a direct role in the nitrogen cycle?
    a. bacteria   **c.** legumes
    b. decomposers   **d.** all of the above

_____ **22.** What animals eat both producers and consumers?
    a. omnivores   **c.** scavengers
    b. herbivores   **d.** carnivores

_____ **23.** The 10-percent law states that only 10 percent of
    a. a species can be hunted during a given season.
    b. the total stored energy is passed on at each trophic level.
    c. the nitrogen in the atmosphere enters the nitrogen cycle.
    d. the oxygen an animal breathes is absorbed into the blood.

_____ **24.** The Environmental Protection Agency predicts that four-fifths of the landfills in the U.S. will be closed by the year
    a. 1995.   **c.** 2010.
    b. 2250.   **d.** 2000.

_____ **25.** What kinds of organisms are at the base of a food chain?
    a. producers   **c.** consumers
    b. carnivores   **d.** herbivores

Chapter 46 Test B

Read each question or statement and respond in the space provided.

1. a. What is the difference between an ecosystem and a community? (5 points)

_____

_____

_____

b. What is meant by a trophic level? (5 points) _____

_____

c. Name the three main trophic levels, and describe what is meant by each. (5 points)

_____

_____

_____

_____

_____

_____

2. Suppose you observe the following interactions among organisms A, B, C, and D. Organism A feeds on B. B makes food through photosynthesis. Organism C feeds on D, and D feeds on A. Identify A, B, C, and D as either a producer, primary consumer, secondary consumer, or tertiary consumer. Also give an example of an organism that plays each role. (12 points)

_____

_____

_____

3. A certain ecosystem contains the following organisms:

grass   owls that eat mice and toads

snakes that eat mice   eagles that eat rabbits, snakes, and owls

toads that eat beetles   cougars that eat deer

rabbits, mice, beetles, and deer that eat grass   foxes that eat rabbits and mice

The drawing below shows all these organisms. Create a food web by drawing arrows to show the flow of energy from one organism to another. (16 points)

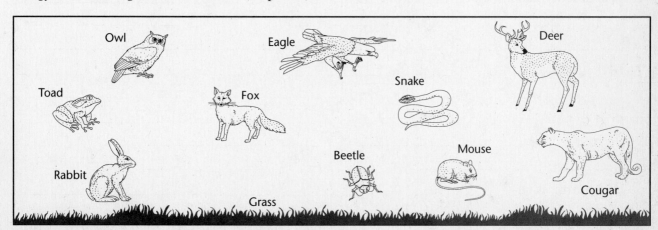

Name _____ Class _____ Date _____

4. a. What is meant by the term biomass? (5 points) _____
_____

b. What is an ecological pyramid? (5 points) _____
_____

c. At higher and higher trophic levels, what happens to the energy available? What happens to the amount of biomass? What happens to the numbers of organisms? (5 points)
_____
_____

5. a. What is the water cycle? (4 points) _____
_____

b. Describe the abiotic and biotic processes involved in the water cycle. (10 points)
_____
_____
_____
_____
_____
_____

6. Explain the role of photosynthesis and respiration in the carbon and oxygen cycles. (8 points)
_____
_____
_____
_____
_____

7. Explain how fossil fuels were made. (4 points)_____
_____
_____
_____
_____

8. Briefly describe what occurs in each of the following processes in the nitrogen cycle. Also state which kind of organism carries out each process. (16 points)

a. nitrogen fixation _____
_____
_____

b. nitrification _____
_____

c. ammonification _____
_____
_____

d. denitrification_____
_____

Chapter 47 Test A

Choose the best answer for each question and write its letter in the blank.

_____
1. Which of the following is a limiting factor on the human population?
  a. cancer   **c.** famine
  b. drought   **d.** all of the above

_____
2. Which of the following human activities does not threaten any population in the biosphere?
  a. toxic dumping   **c.** building dams
  b. deforestation   **d.** respiration

_____
3. The building of the Aswan High Dam in Egypt indirectly caused
  a. a flood of the Nile River Valley.
  b. a rise in cases of heart disease.
  c. a rise in cases of bladder cancer.
  d. hydroelectric failure in Syria and Cambodia.

_____
4. The population of beavers in a certain forest increased by 7 percent over a period of one generation. This is an example of
  a. exponential growth.   **c.** territorial multiplication.
  b. multiplicity.   **d.** emigration.

_____
5. "Change in number of individuals" divided by "time period" is a formula for
  a. emigration.   **c.** immigration.
  b. growth rate.   **d.** exponential growth.

_____
6. The number of organisms that can be supported by the environmental resources in a given ecosystem is called what?
  a. exponent   **c.** ceiling
  b. carrying capacity   **d.** biomass

_____
7. Which of the following is a density-independent limiting factor on population growth?
  a. drought   **c.** competition
  b. predation   **d.** parasitism

_____
8. The number of predators in a population grows in proportion to the population. This is an example of
  a. density-independent limiting factors.
  b. density-dependent limiting factors.
  c. parasitism.
  d. the S-shaped curve.

_____
9. An organism that feeds on the tissues or body fluids of another living organism is called a
  a. herbivore.   **c.** producer.
  b. parasite.   **d.** host.

_____
10. Parasitism is an example of which of the following?
  a. density-dependent limiting factors
  b. density-independent limiting factors
  c. boom-and-bust factors
  d. predation

_____
11. How fast is the human population currently growing?
  a. slowly
  b. exponentially
  c. The population is remaining stable
  d. The population is decreasing

_____
12. Which of the following is a limiting factor for the northern spotted owl?
  a. logging   **c.** hydroelectric dams
  b. cigarette smoke   **d.** none of the above

         Chapter 47: Population Biology   **217**

_____ **13.** Which of the following is now recognized as a major limiting factor for the human population of Cairo, Egypt?
    a. blood flukes   **c.** car accidents
    b. brain cancer   **d.** cigarette smoke

_____ **14.** Which of the following factors might contribute to an exponential growth rate in a given population?
    a. lower death rates   **c.** higher birth rates
    b. less competition   **d.** all of the above

_____ **15.** Darwin observed that populations tend to remain at a stable size because they reach their ecosystem's
    a. carrying capacity.   **c.** population curve.
    b. S-shaped curve.   **d.** boom-and-bust curve.

_____ **16.** What kind of population curve would you expect the population of a growing nation to exhibit?
    a. S-shaped curve   **c.** tailhook curve
    b. boom-and-bust curve   **d.** none of the above

_____ **17.** Which of the following is a parasite?
    a. cat   **c.** flea
    b. baby   **d.** fly

_____ **18.** Which of the following would make it most difficult for a population of beavers to survive the winter?
    a. snow in January   **c.** freezing rain in December
    b. forest fire in October   **d.** none of the above

_____ **19.** During the 200-year period of the Industrial Revolution, the human population
    a. declined.   **c.** doubled.
    b. tripled.   **d.** quadrupled.

_____ **20.** The process of waste-water filtration was developed by
    a. Thomas Malthus.   **c.** Sigmund Freud.
    b. Ellen Richards.   **d.** B.F. Skinner.

_____ **21.** Two hundred years ago, the infant mortality rate was higher, and women often died in childbirth. Yet the population continued to grow. Why?
    a. good health care   **c.** more available resources
    b. high birth rate   **d.** none of the above

_____ **22.** Which of the following is a density-dependent limiting factor?
    a. earthquake   **c.** human interference
    b. blood flukes   **d.** immigration

_____ **23.** When organisms move into a given area from another area, it is known as
    a. immigration.   **c.** emigration.
    b. carrying capacity.   **d.** parasitism.

_____ **24.** When organisms leave their normal ecosystem, it is known as
    a. abandonment.   **c.** emigration.
    b. immigration.   **d.** carrying capacity.

_____ **25.** The primary interaction between organisms for resources in a given area is
    a. competition.   **c.** parasitism.
    b. boom-and-bust.   **d.** carrying capacity.

Chapter 47 Test B

Read each question or statement and respond in the space provided.

1. **a.** What is a population? (8 points) _____
   _____

   b. Explain what is meant by a limiting factor. (8 points) _____
   _____

   c. Name four limiting factors. (8 points) _____
   _____

2. Look at the four growth curves—(1), (2), (3), and (4)—shown below. (15 points)

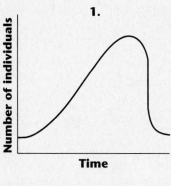

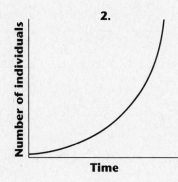

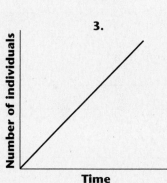

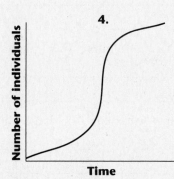

   a. Which curve illustrates the kind of growth that would occur under ideal conditions with unlimited resources? What is such growth called?
   _____
   _____

   b. Which curve illustrates growth that is eventually limited to a number that can be supported by environmental resources? What is that number called?
   _____
   _____

   c. Which curve represents a cycle of nearly unlimited growth and sudden collapse? What is such a curve made up of such cycles called?
   _____
   _____

3. Suppose you were observing the size of a population of deer in an area. You discovered that in a 3-year period the population underwent the following changes: 40 deer were born, 18 deer died, 20 deer migrated into the herd, and 6 deer migrated out of it. Calculate the growth rate, per year, of the population. Do not ignore the changes brought about by immigration and emigration. Show your work. (17 points)

_____

_____

_____

_____

_____

4. Identify each of the following limiting factors as either density-dependent or density-independent, and explain why. (20 points)

   a. The population of lions decreases as the population of zebra prey decreases.

_____

_____

   b. A hurricane destroys a large number of palm trees of a given kind.

_____

_____

   c. The population of host fish decreases as that of parasitic roundworms increases.

_____

_____

   d. Competition for food limits the population of squirrels in a forest.

_____

_____

   e. Normal winter weather kills off a large number of bees.

_____

_____

5. Briefly describe the history of human population change. Compare growth before and after food-storage practices and agriculture developed, and also since the Industrial Revolution. (24 points)

_____

_____

_____

_____

_____

_____

_____

_____

_____

_____

_____

Chapter 48 Test A

Choose the best answer for each question and write its letter in the blank.

_____ 1. What does the Gaia hypothesis state?
  a. The earth functions like a living organism.
  b. The earth is approximately 10,000 years old.
  c. The solar system is collapsing on itself.
  d. The universe is infinite.

_____ 2. Maintaining the resources needed for survival while ensuring that they are still available in the future is a practice called
  a. human adaptation.   **c.** sustainable development.
  b. greenhouse effect.   **d.** biological magnification.

_____ 3. Which of the following factors contributed to the rapid growth of the human population in the last three hundred years?
  a. germ theory of disease   **c.** improved health care
  b. sanitary conditions   **d.** all of the above

_____ 4. Which of the following is an indicator of an ecosystem under strain?
  a. malnutrition   **c.** low death rates
  b. high birth rates   **d.** less competition

_____ 5. Most of the ecological problems now being faced by the earth have been caused by
  a. volcanic eruptions.
  b. earthquakes and hurricanes.
  c. human activities and overpopulation.
  d. biological diversity.

_____ 6. The buildup of pollutants in organisms at higher trophic levels in a food chain is known as
  a. pollutant buildup.   **c.** biological magnification.
  b. extinction.   **d.** toxic disruption.

_____ 7. Because the gases that make up the air can be reused by organisms, scientists classify air as a(n)
  a. renewable resource.   **c.** recycled agent.
  b. pollutant.   **d.** ozone.

_____ 8. Cars harm the environment because they emit
  a. helium.   **c.** carbon monoxide.
  b. petrolatum.   **d.** nitrogen.

_____ 9. An increase in the earth's temperature from the rapid buildup of carbon dioxide and other gases in the atmosphere is called
  a. the greenhouse effect.   **c.** global warming.
  b. ozone depletion.   **d.** particulate dispersal.

_____ 10. The sulfur dioxide in smog can bind with hydrogen to cause
  a. ozone depletion.   **c.** global warming.
  b. acid rain.   **d.** chlorofluorocarbons.

_____ 11. Exposure to the sun's ultraviolet rays can lead to which of the following?
  a. burns   **c.** skin cancer
  b. eye disorders **d.** all of the above

_____ 12. A lot of pollutants enter the atmosphere naturally, through
  a. chlorofluorocarbons.   **c.** volcanic eruptions.
  b. photosynthesis.   **d.** streams and rivers.

_____ 13. Which of the following is not a source of water pollution?
  a. ozone   **c.** chlorinated hydrocarbons
  b. mercury   **d.** sewage

_____ **14.** The wearing away of land and topsoil by water and wind is known as
   a. deforestation.
   b. land management.
   c. erosion.
   d. overgrazing.

_____ **15.** When erosion and other factors cause soil to lose its ability to hold water and other nutrients and to support plant life, it is called
   a. desertification.
   b. landfilling.
   c. deforestation.
   d. waste management.

_____ **16.** The greatest threat today to biological diversity in the rain forest regions is
   a. erosion.
   b. methane poisoning.
   c. desertification.
   d. deforestation.

_____ **17.** How might deforestation contribute to global warming?
   a. decreasing the amount of oxygen consumed by photosynthesis
   b. increasing the amount of oxygen consumed by photosynthesis
   c. decreasing the amount of carbon dioxide consumed by photosynthesis
   d. increasing the amount of carbon dioxide consumed by photosynthesis

_____ **18.** What is the combined production of heat and power?
   a. cogeneration
   b. nuclear fission
   c. a renewable resource
   d. energy displacement

_____ **19.** Perhaps the most economical and efficient means of generating electricity today is (are)
   a. coal-fire power plants.
   b. nuclear fission.
   c. cogeneration plants.
   d. hydroelectric dams.

_____ **20.** Nuclear power plants present a problem because
   a. accidents can harm the environment.
   b. disposal of wastes is extremely difficult.
   c. the plants produce thermal pollution.
   d. all of the above

_____ **21.** Why do hydroelectric dams cause a problem?
   a. They release chlorofluorocarbons into the water.
   b. They don't generate very much electricity.
   c. They flood lands and threaten indigenous species.
   d. They produce bulky waste products.

_____ **22.** Which of the following sources of energy does not produce any pollutants or threaten any organisms in the ecosystem?
   a. nuclear fission
   b. solar power
   c. hydroelectric dams
   d. coal-fire plants

_____ **23.** Individuals within a population of organisms are often protected by
   a. biological diversity.
   b. parasites.
   c. genetic similarity.
   d. pathogens.

_____ **24.** Which of the following ecological threats is magnified by overpopulation?
   a. malnutrition
   b. erosion
   c. disease
   d. all of the above

_____ **25.** Why is the cheetah near extinction?
   a. parasites
   b. hunting
   c. little genetic diversity
   d. factory pollution

Chapter 48 Test B

Read each question or statement and respond in the space provided.

1. a. What is meant by sustainable development? (7 points)

_____

_____

b. Describe three ways in which overpopulation can be defined. (7 points)

_____

_____

_____

_____

2. a. Explain what is meant by biological magnification. (7 points)

_____

_____

b. Illustrate this concept, using DDT as an example. (7 points)

_____

_____

_____

_____

_____

_____

3. Suppose you are visiting a power plant. You observe the following things occurring: a smokestack releasing sulfur dioxide and carbon dioxide gases, and a drain releasing large quantities of hot water into a river. Describe the problems to which such practices might contribute. (15 points)

_____

_____

_____

_____

_____

4. a. Describe the importance of land as a resource. (6 points)

_____

_____

_____

_____

_____

_____

b. Describe three harmful forms of changes in land or forest that are often caused by human activities. Also state the human activities involved in each case. (6 points)

_____

_____

_____

_____

5. Discuss the environmental significance of each of the following. (15 points)

   a. volcanic eruptions _____

_____

_____

   b. human production and use of nonbiodegradable substances _____

_____

_____

   c. release of chlorofluorocarbons into the atmosphere _____

_____

_____

6. a. Describe problems associated with the use of fossil fuels. (5 points)

_____

_____

   b. Describe possible problems associated with the use of nuclear energy. (5 points) _____

_____

_____

_____

   c. Discuss the possible use of less harmful energy sources. (5 points) _____

_____

_____

_____

_____

7. What problems are created by each of the following human activities? (15 points)

   a. destruction of habitats of unknown species _____

_____

_____

   b. creation of single-species communities, such as tree plantations _____

_____

_____

   c. continuation of increase in human population _____

_____

_____

Unit 9 Test A

Choose the best answer for each question and write its letter in the blank.

_____ **1.** Imagine a wetland where the temperatures are usually cool, where the soil is mostly peat, and where great numbers of insects thrive. This would most likely be a
    a. bog.   **c.** swamp.
    b. marsh.   **d.** estuary.

_____ **2.** Although the burning of ethanol instead of gasoline also produces carbon dioxide, ethanol helps solve this problem by the fact that
    a. it produces bacteria that consume carbon dioxide.
    b. the plants from which it is harvested consume some of the carbon dioxide.
    c. the carbon dioxide it produces is more easily broken down.
    d. all of the above

_____ **3.** Which of the following is a population whose growth rate is subject to density-independent limiting factors?
    a. humans   **c.** northern spotted owls
    b. toads   **d.** all of the above

_____ **4.** Migrating salmon must pass through what kind of area on their way to their breeding grounds?
    a. estuaries   **c.** coral reefs
    b. benthic zones   **d.** aphotic zones

_____ **5.** Pollution threatens life in the biosphere by
    a. diminishing biodiversity.   **c.** poisoning food chains.
    b. creating environmental crises.   **d.** all of the above

_____ **6.** Earth's atmosphere is divided into many layers. Which layer is nearest to the surface of the planet?
    a. troposphere   **c.** stratosphere
    b. biosphere   **d.** none of the above

_____ **7.** Rays, skates, and octopi live primarily in the
    a. benthic zone.   **c.** photic zone.
    b. neritic zone.   **d.** aphotic zone.

_____ **8.** As part of the nitrogen cycle, animal urine contains
    a. ethanol.   **c.** methanol.
    b. methane.   **d.** ammonia.

_____ **9.** Bacteria play a role in which of the following cycles?
    a. nitrogen cycle   **c.** carbon and oxygen cycles
    b. digestive cycles   **d.** all of the above

_____ **10.** The clearing of large amounts of trees in small amounts of time is known as
    a. desertification.   **c.** deforestation.
    b. erosion.   **d.** emigration.

_____ **11.** Which of the following is highest on the ecological pyramid?
    a. humans   **c.** foxes
    b. bacteria   **d.** vegetables

_____ **12.** Human garbage production causes problems with
    a. pollution.   **c.** landfill capacity.
    b. dwindling resources.   **d.** all of the above

_____ **13.** Loss of muscle tone, nausea, bone degeneration, and changes in the immune system are all problems experienced by
 a. workers in nuclear power plants.
 b. travelers to outer space.
 c. deep-sea divers.
 d. people near the Aswan High Dam in Egypt.

_____ **14.** The regions where fresh water and salt water meet are known as
 a. wetlands.   **c.** estuaries.
 b. benthic zones.   **d.** aphotic zones.

_____ **15.** Which of the following are considered biomes?
 a. deserts   **c.** prairies
 b. wetlands   **d.** all of the above

_____ **16.** The pioneer community to settle on exposed rocks is usually
 a. grass.   **c.** reptiles.
 b. lichens.   **d.** deciduous trees.

_____ **17.** Farm A uses crop rotation, growing both peas and wheat. Farm B grows only wheat every year. Which of the two farms would probably have better topsoil as a result?
 a. Farm A
 b. Farm B
 c. The farms would both have quality topsoil.
 d. The farms would both have very poor topsoil.

_____ **18.** Which of the following organisms would occupy the most complex niche in a given ecosystem?
 a. plants   **c.** humans
 b. foxes   **d.** rabbits

_____ **19.** Which of the following seems like a trophic level where exchange of energy might take place?
 a. plants and rocks   **c.** rabbits and plants
 b. foxes and plants   **d.** rocks and foxes

_____ **20.** Which of the following organisms are *not* subject to parasites?
 a. humans   **c.** cats
 b. bacteria   **d.** trees

_____ **21.** Which of the following represents a biotic factor?
 a. earthquakes   **c.** thunderstorms
 b. compost heaps   **d.** mountains

_____ **22.** Under ideal conditions, populations
 a. grow at slow rates.   **c.** remain stable.
 b. grow at exponential rates.   **d.** decline slowly exponentially.

_____ **23.** When the number of births is equal to the number of deaths, this results in
 a. biomass.   **c.** a density-independent limiting factor.
 b. immigration.   **d.** an S-shaped curve.

_____ **24.** Which of the following areas is more likely to develop a topsoil where plants can grow?
 a. desert   **c.** polar region
 b. mountaintop   **d.** chaparral

_____ **25.** What chemical is used in wastewater filtration?
 a. nitrogen   **c.** chlorine
 b. sulfur dioxide   **d.** chlorofluorocarbon

_____ **26.** The Gaia hypothesis was developed by
 a. Charles Darwin.   **c.** Ellen Richards.
 b. Harlan Ellison.   **d.** James Lovelock.

Unit 9 Test A

_____ 27. Which of the following gases occurs in smog?
  a. carbon dioxide
  b. sulfur dioxide
  c. carbon monoxide
  d. all of the above

_____ 28. The main factor in global warming is
  a. water pollution.
  b. waste management.
  c. air pollution.
  d. land use.

_____ 29. One of the possible effects of smog is
  a. acid rain.
  b. building decay.
  c. global warming.
  d. all of the above

_____ 30. The major threat to the ozone layer is
  a. mercury contamination.
  b. water pollution.
  c. chlorofluorocarbons.
  d. gaia.

_____ 31. Ozone depletion may result in
  a. carbon dioxide buildup.
  b. global warming.
  c. depleted oxygen level in the biosphere.
  d. excessive ultraviolet light from the sun.

_____ 32. The protection, management, and renewal of resources is known as
  a. land use.
  b. conservation.
  c. waste management.
  d. ecology.

_____ 33. Energy from the sun is captured primarily by
  a. autotrophs.
  b. heterotrophs.
  c. omnivores.
  d. decomposers.

_____ 34. Thomas Malthus was the first to state the theory that
  a. humans evolved from primates.
  b. the human population tends to outgrow its resources.
  c. factory pollution would cause global warming.
  d. chlorofluorocarbons would result in ozone depletion.

_____ 35. An increase in the earth's carrying capacity for humans was brought about by
  a. increased natural vegetation growth.
  b. agricultural improvements during the Industrial Revolution.
  c. depletion of the ozone layer.
  d. drop in average yearly rainfall.

_____ 36. The temperature of an ecosystem is largely determined by
  a. biological diversity.
  b. soil and minerals.
  c. latitude and altitude.
  d. chemosynthetic processes.

_____ 37. Ecologists refer to the loss of available energy up the ecological pyramid as
  a. the 10 percent law.
  b. the Gaia hypothesis.
  c. biomass reduction.
  d. Skinner's law.

_____ 38. In general, population growth rates of a given organism tend to stabilize because
  a. the organisms reach the carrying capacity of their ecosystem.
  b. large numbers of organisms are killed by poisonous animals.
  c. pollution kills off surplus members of the population.
  d. none of the above

_____ 39. The buildup of DDT in fish and then in eagles who ate the fish is an example of
  a. biological diversity.
  b. species adaptation.
  c. biological magnification.
  d. conservation.

_____ **40.** Suppose a population of woodpeckers are almost entirely eliminated by a forest fire, and a new population of tree frogs moves in to take over their territory. This is an example of
    a. biological diversity.
    b. primary succession.
    c. biological magnification.
    d. secondary succession.

_____ **41.** Which of the following proposals for dealing with the garbage crisis seems to fit the definition of *sustainable development?*
    a. deep-sea dumping
    b. garbage burning
    c. outer-space dumping
    d. recycling

_____ **42.** Which of the following organisms is an autotroph?
    a. rabbit
    b. plant
    c. human
    d. digestive bacteria

_____ **43.** Solid pollutants light enough to remain in the air are known as
    a. particulates.
    b. minute solids.
    c. greenhouse factors.
    d. chlorofluorocarbons.

_____ **44.** Which of the following organisms produces its food from inorganic compounds?
    a. chemosynthetic bacteria
    b. northern spotted owl
    c. vulture
    d. human

_____ **45.** Which of the following contributes most effectively to soil renewal?
    a. red algae
    b. landfills
    c. crop rotation
    d. chemical fertilizers

_____ **46.** The presence of lichens on rocks helps to
    a. reduce ozone depletion.
    b. reduce predator populations.
    c. make soil.
    d. make carbon dioxide.

_____ **47.** In a bog, there are more plants than insects, more insects than frogs, and more frogs than alligators. This is an example of
    a. biological diversity.
    b. the ecological pyramid.
    c. the food pyramid.
    d. biomass.

_____ **48.** Rain, snow, sleet, and vapor are elements of
    a. the water cycle.
    b. the carbon and oxygen cycles.
    c. the nitrogen cycle.
    d. the photosynthetic cycle.

_____ **49.** Which of the following is required by plant life?
    a. carbon monoxide
    b. sulfur dioxide
    c. nitrates
    d. chlorofluorocarbons

_____ **50.** The deforestation of the tropical rain forests contributes to
    a. global warming.
    b. biological vulnerability.
    c. carbon dioxide buildup.
    d. all of the above

Name _____ Class _____ Date _____

Final Exam

Choose the best answer for each question and write its letter in the blank.

_____ 1. A group of organisms so similar to one another that they can interbreed is called a
    a. community.
    b. genus.
    c. biome.
    d. species

_____ 2. Several different types of tissues that function together for a specific purpose make up a(n)
    a. organ.
    b. cell.
    c. organ system.
    d. ecosystem.

_____ 3. A possible explanation for an event or set of observations is called a(n)
    a. experiment.
    b. conclusion.
    c. prediction.
    d. hypothesis.

_____ 4. Which of the following separation techniques is being carried out when a mixture of sugar and starch molecules are passed through a gel that has small pores in it?
    a. fractionation
    b. chromatography
    c. electrophoresis
    d. centrifuging

_____ 5. Sodium sulfate (Na_2SO_4) is an example of a(n)
    a. compound
    b. mixture.
    c. element.
    d. isotope.

_____ 6. A chemical reaction in which heat is released is
    a. exothermic.
    b. endothermic.
    c. ionic.
    d. organic.

_____ 7. Each molecule of a certain compound contains 5 carbon atoms, 10 hydrogen atoms, and 5 oxygen atoms. The compound is therefore likely to be a
    a. lipid
    b. carbohydrate.
    c. protein.
    d. nucleic acid.

_____ 8. All proteins are polymers of
    a. amino acids.
    b. fatty acids.
    c. glucose.
    d. DNA.

_____ 9. Cells that contain a nucleus are called
    a. organelles.
    b. prokaryotes.
    c. eukaryotes.
    d. ribosomes.

_____ 10. The membrane of a kind of cell encloses a droplet of a nutrient-rich liquid and carries it into the cell. Of which type of transport is this an example?
    a. active transport
    b. bulk transport
    c. facilitated diffusion
    d. osmosis

_____ 11. The process by which food molecules are broken down to release energy for work is
    a. photosynthesis.
    b. passive transport.
    c. exocytosis.
    d. cellular respiration.

_____ 12. Which of the following is involved in photosynthesis?
    a. Krebs cycle
    b. citric acid cycle
    c. Calvin cycle
    d. lysogenic cycle

_____ 13. At which phase of mitotic cell division are centromeres pulled toward the ends of the cell and sister chromatids separated?
    a. telophase
    b. anaphase
    c. prophase
    d. metaphase

_____ 14. Which of the following occurs in sexual reproduction?
    a. meiosis
    b. mitosis
    c. fragmentation
    d. budding

_____ **15.** The founder of modern genetics was
    a. Koch.   **c.** Pasteur.
    b. Mendel.   **d.** Spallanzani.

_____ **16.** What are the genotypes of F_1 offspring of parents with the genotypes AABB and aabb?
    a. AABB, AaBb, and aabb   **c.** AaBb only
    b. AAbb and aaBB   **d.** AABB only

_____ **17.** The genes for the trait of red plumage color in a kind of bird is found only on the X chromosome. Such a trait is
    a. sex-limited.   **c.** sex-linked.
    b. sex-influenced.   **d.** autosomal.

_____ **18.** What type of mutation occurs when a piece of a chromosome attaches to a chromosome in a different pair?
    a. translocation   **c.** inversion
    b. duplication   **d.** deletion

_____ **19.** Which of the following bases is in DNA but not in RNA?
    a. guanine   **c.** adenine
    b. cytosine   **d.** thymine

_____ **20.** In an RNA molecule, the base sequence CCU translates to the amino acid proline. Such a sequence is an example of a(n)
    a. regulator.   **c.** codon.
    b. operon.   **d.** promoter.

_____ **21.** Small circular pieces of DNA within bacteria are called
    a. vectors.   **c.** mitochondria.
    b. ribosomes.   **d.** plasmids.

_____ **22.** The crossing of distantly related organisms is called
    a. induced polyploidy.   **c.** genetic engineering.
    b. inbreeding.   **d.** outbreeding.

_____ **23.** A human disorder caused by trisomy is
    a. sickle-cell disease.   **c.** cri-du-chat syndrome.
    b. Down syndrome.   **d.** Turner syndrome.

_____ **24.** Which of the following is a sex-linked disorder?
    a. hemophilia   **c.** cystic fibrosis
    b. Huntington's disease   **d.** Klinefelter syndrome

_____ **25.** Which of the following relates to the principle that life comes only from life?
    a. spontaneous generation   **c.** biogenesis
    b. Margulis' hypothesis   **d.** Oparin's hypothesis

_____ **26.** The era in which the dinosaurs lived was the
    a. Cenozoic era.   **c.** Paleozoic era.
    b. Mesozoic era.   **d.** Precambrian era.

_____ **27.** The foreleg of a mammal and the wing of a bird are similar because they were inherited from a common ancestor. These two characteristics are therefore
    a. homologous.   **c.** vestigial.
    b. analogous.   **d.** biogenetic.

_____ **28** Which of the following scientists proposed that acquired characteristics are inherited?
    a. Darwin   **c.** Mendel
    b. Wallace   **d.** Lamarck

_____ **29.** Which of the following is a condition for genetic equilibrium, according to the Hardy-Weinberg principle?
    a. Mating must not be random.   **c.** Only significant mutations occur.
    b. There must be no migration.   **d.** Natural selection must operate.

_____ **30.** Baboons belong to a group of animals called
   a. Old World monkeys.   **c.** apes.
   b. New World monkeys.   **d.** prosimians.

_____ **31.** To which of the following are modern-day *Homo sapiens* most closely related?
   a. *Australopithecus afarensis*   **c.** Neanderthals
   b. *Homo erectus*   **d.** *Homo habilis*

_____ **32.** The taxon that occurs between *class* and *family* is
   a. phylum.   **c.** genus.
   b. species.   **d.** order.

_____ **33.** A certain organism is found to have cells that do not contain a nuclear membrane. In which kingdom should the organism be classified?
   a. Fungi   **c.** Protista
   b. Plantae   **d.** Monera

_____ **34.** The core of all viruses is made of
   a. DNA only.   **c.** either DNA or RNA.
   b. RNA only.   **d.** neither DNA nor RNA.

_____ **35.** Which of the following is the process in which viral replication rapidly kills a host bacterial cell?
   a. lysogenic cycle.   **c.** Krebs cycle.
   b. lytic cycle.   **d.** Calvin cycle.

_____ **36.** Which of the following characteristics would you expect a cyanobacterium to have?
   a. appears pink after Gram staining   **c.** produces methane
   b. appears purple after Gram staining   **d.** uses inorganic compounds as an energy source

_____ **37.** Suppose you are looking through a microscope and observe bacteria that are spherical. You should classify the bacteria as
   a. bacilli.   **c.** cocci.
   b. spirilla.   **d.** archaebacteria.

_____ **38.** What sort of movement would you expect to observe in a sarcodinian?
   a. extension of cytoplasm   **c.** movement by means of flagella
   b. movement by means of cilia   **d.** no independent movement

_____ **39.** Giant kelps are included in the group of protists known as
   a. green algae.   **c.** red algae.
   b. diatoms.   **d.** brown algae.

_____ **40.** Which of the following characteristics would you expect to observe in fungi?
   a. ability to make their own food   **c.** cell walls made of chitin
   b. lack of mitochondria   **d.** production of seeds

_____ **41.** In fungi, the rootlike parts of hyphae that act as anchors to a source of nutrients are called
   a. stolons.   **c.** asci.
   b. basidia.   **d.** rhizoids.

_____ **42.** Bryophytes are kinds of plants that are
   a. nonvascular and lack true leaves and roots.
   b. nonvascular and have true leaves and roots.
   c. vascular and lack true leaves and roots.
   d. vascular and have true leaves and roots.

_____ **43.** Multicellular organisms that are sexually reproducing, autotrophic, and that consist of specialized cells belong to the phylum
   a. Protista.   **c.** Monera.
   b. Fungi.   **d.** Plantae.

_____ **44.** The egg-producing organ in mosses is called the
   a. ovary.   **c.** archegonium.
   b. antheridium.   **d.** gemma.

_____ **45.** Ferns are kinds of plants that are
   a. vascular and bear seeds.
   b. seedless and vascular.
   c. nonvascular and bear seeds.
   d. seedless and nonvascular.

_____ **46.** What sorts of materials would you expect xylem in a plant to carry?
   a. water and dissolved minerals
   b. starches
   c. sugars
   d. sap

_____ **47.** Pores in the epidermis of leaves are called
   a. nodes.
   b. internodes.
   c. stomata.
   d. bundle sheaths.

_____ **48.** Flowering plants are
   a. gymnosperms.
   b. bryophytes.
   c. epicotyls.
   d. angiosperms.

_____ **49.** What structure produces pollen?
   a. style
   b. stigma
   c. anther
   d. sepal

_____ **50.** A meristem that causes plants to grow thicker is
   a. an apical meristem.
   b. cambium.
   c. an axillary meristem.
   d. a radicle.

_____ **51.** Auxins and gibberellins are kinds of
   a. plant hormones.
   b. angiosperms.
   c. meristems.
   d. cytokinins.

_____ **52.** Organisms that are heterotrophic, multicellular, and eukaryotic, and that lack cell walls belong to the kingdom
   a. Monera.
   b. Fungi.
   c. Protista.
   d. Animalia.

_____ **53.** The front part of an organism that has bilateral symmetry is said to be
   a. anterior.
   b. posterior.
   c. dorsal.
   d. ventral.

_____ **54.** If you observed an animal that lacked body symmetry and that had no specialized tissues or organ systems, you should classify the animal as a
   a. hydra.
   b. sponge.
   c. flatworm.
   d. roundworm.

_____ **55.** Worms that are cylindrical, unsegmented, and that have a complete one-way digestive system are classified as
   a. annelids.
   b. nematodes.
   c. planarians.
   d. rotifers.

_____ **56.** What is the term for the bristles of annelids?
   a. parapodia
   b. setae
   c. cilia
   d. nephridia

_____ **57.** Clams, mussels, and oysters are kinds of
   a. gastropods.
   b. chitons.
   c. cephalopods.
   d. bivalves.

_____ **58.** Jointed appendages and an exoskeleton are general characteristics of
   a. mollusks.
   b. echinoderms.
   c. arthropods.
   d. chordates.

_____ **59.** Book lungs are present in
   a. insects.
   b. arachnids.
   c. crustaceans.
   d. echinoderms.

_____ **60.** In which of the following is movement carried out by a water vascular system?
   a. fishes
   b. mollusks
   c. echinoderms
   d. annelids

Name _____ Class _____ Date _____

_____ **61.** The phylum that includes fishes, birds, and mammals is
    a. Echinodermata.   **c.** Platyhelminthes.
    b. Vertebrata.   **d.** Chordata.

_____ **62.** An example of a jawless fish, or agnathan, is a
    a. shark.   **c.** lamprey.
    b. trout.   **d.** ray.

_____ **63.** Which characteristic sets sharks apart from fishes such as salmon and tuna?
    a. Sharks are warmblooded.
    b. Sharks lack true fins.
    c. Sharks have a skeleton made of cartilage.
    d. Sharks are not vertebrates.

_____ **64.** Which of the following is *not* an amphibian?
    a. toad   **c.** caecilian
    b. tuatara   **d.** salamander

_____ **65.** The muscular cavity through which solid wastes pass in amphibians is the
    a. cloaca.   **c.** Malpighian tubule.
    b. rectum.   **d.** bladder.

_____ **66.** The thecodonts were the ancestors of
    a. mammals.   **c.** dinosaurs.
    b. fishes.   **d.** amphibians.

_____ **67.** The only reptiles that have a four-chambered heart are
    a. turtles.   **c.** crocodilians.
    b. lizards.   **d.** snakes.

_____ **68.** Which of the following are characteristic of birds?
    a. four-chambered heart, warmblooded
    b. four-chambered heart, coldblooded
    c. three-chambered heart, warmblooded
    d. three-chambered heart, coldblooded

_____ **69.** In birds, the crop is an organ of
    a. circulation.   **c.** respiration.
    b. digestion.   **d.** excretion.

_____ **70.** Which of the following characteristics is unique to mammals?
    a. hair   **c.** internal skeleton
    b. endothermy   **d.** backbone

_____ **71.** Mammals whose young complete their development in their mother's pouch are called
    a. marsupials.   **c.** monotremes.
    b. placental mammals.   **d.** therapsids.

_____ **72.** A simple, innate, involuntary response by a part of the body to a particular stimulus is called a
    a. fixed-action pattern.   **c.** tropism.
    b. reflex.   **d.** nastic movement.

_____ **73.** What sort of learned behavior takes place when a worm that is repeatedly touched no longer moves away in response to the stimulus?
    a. operant conditioning   **c.** classical conditioning
    b. imprinting   **d.** habituation

_____ **74.** Tissue that covers the body and its organs is
    a. connective tissue.   **c.** epithelial tissue.
    b. parenchyma.   **d.** muscle tissue.

_____ **75.** Which of the following are striated?
    a. voluntary muscles   **c.** involuntary muscles
    b. cardiac muscles   **d.** smooth muscles

_____ **76.** The passageway between the pharynx and the stomach is called the
    a. small intestine.   **c.** trachea.
    b. epiglottis.   **d.** esophagus.

_____ **77.** Carbohydrates and fats are digested in the
    a. stomach.   **c.** large intestine.
    b. small intestine.   **d.** pancreas.

_____ **78.** The upper chambers of the heart are called
    a. ventricles.   **c.** atria.
    b. nodes.   **d.** arterioles.

_____ **79.** What is the complex protein to which oxygen and carbon dioxide bind in blood?
    a. hemoglobin   **c.** abscisic acid
    b. chlorophyll   **d.** RNA

_____ **80.** The two tubes into which the trachea divide are called
    a. larynxes.   **c.** alveoli.
    b. bronchioles.   **d.** bronchi.

_____ **81.** The urine-forming functional units of the kidneys are the
    a. capillaries.   **c.** ureters.
    b. nephrons.   **d.** urethras.

_____ **82.** How would you classify a nerve cell that carries a sensation of heat from the surface of the body to the brain?
    a. motor neuron   **c.** interneuron
    b. glial cell   **d.** sensory neuron

_____ **83.** Which of the following controls the functions of the body associated with rest and digestion?
    a. somatic nervous system   **c.** sympathetic nervous system
    b. parasympathetic nervous system   **d.** skeletal nervous system

_____ **84.** Which of the following is part of the brain stem?
    a. cerebellum   **c.** medulla oblongata
    b. spinal cord   **d.** cerebrum

_____ **85.** Which of the following is *not* an example of an endocrine gland?
    a. pituitary   **c.** testis
    b. salivary gland   **d.** adrenal gland

_____ **86.** A hormone that stimulates cells to take up sugar from blood is
    a. insulin.   **c.** estrogen.
    b. glucagon.   **d.** testosterone.

_____ **87.** During which phase of the female reproductive cycle are large amounts of progesterone and estrogen released as the egg moves through the Fallopian tube to the uterus?
    a. luteal phase   **c.** menstrual-flow phase
    b. follicle phase   **d.** ovulation phase

_____ **88.** Koch's postulates relate to
    a. measuring metabolism.   **c.** identifying causes of infection.
    b. explaining respiration.   **d.** recognizing evolutionary change.

_____ **89.** Which of the following is an example of a specific defense against pathogens?
    a. fever   **c.** inflammatory response
    b. interferon release   **d.** production of antibodies

_____ **90.** HIV is the cause of
    a. botulism.   **c.** syphilis.
    b. malaria.   **d.** AIDS.

_____ **91.** A certain drug tends to produce sleep and slows down the activity of the central nervous system. The drug is an example of a
    a. stimulant.   **c.** depressant.
    b. hallucinogen.   **d.** steroid.

_____ **92.** Cirrhosis often results from excessive and long-term use of
    a. alcohol.   **c.** heroin.
    b. marijuana.   **d.** tobacco.

_____ **93.** Biotic and abiotic factors in an area make up a(n)
    a. niche.   **c.** population.
    b. community.   **d.** ecosystem.

_____ **94.** Which of the following contains only one kind of organism?
    a. community   **c.** biome
    b. population   **d.** ecosystem

_____ **95.** The zone of marine biomes that is located just above the continental shelf is called the
    a. benthic zone.   **c.** aphotic zone.
    b. intertidal zone.   **d.** neritic zone.

_____ **96.** The number of organisms that can be supported by environmental resources in an ecosystem is called the
    a. growth rate.   **c.** carrying capacity.
    b. limiting factor.   **d.** sustainable limit.

_____ **97.** Which of the following limiting factors is density-independent?
    a. competition   **c.** parasitism
    b. predation   **d.** natural disasters

_____ **98.** The buildup of pollutants in organisms at higher trophic levels in a food chain is called
    a. exponential growth.   **c.** biodegradation.
    b. biological magnification.   **d.** greenhouse effect.

_____ **99.** Which of the following is a renewable resource?
    a. coal   **c.** solar energy
    b. oil   **d.** natural gas

_____ **100.** Global warming is most directly tied to the buildup of which gas in the atmosphere?
    a. oxygen   **c.** carbon monoxide
    b. nitrogen   **d.** carbon dioxide

Answer Key

Chapter 1

TEST A

1. b	10. b	19. c
2. c	11. b	20. a
3. c	12. c	21. a
4. c	13. a	22. b
5. a	14. b	23. c
6. a	15. c	24. a
7. c	16. a	25. a
8. d	17. a	
9. c	18. b	

TEST B

1. Zebras feed on grass, lions feed on zebras, vultures feed on dead animals, grass provides oxygen for all the animals, all the animals produce wastes that enrich soil and are used by grasses.

2. Extinction of some species leads to extinction of others that depend on them. Some species are very valuable, serving as important sources of food, etc. Human activities are now causing very large numbers of extinctions. The problem can be lessened by limiting destruction of habitats, reducing pollution, and preventing the hunting of endangered species.

3. Answers will vary, but students should point out that living things provide food, clothing, shelter, and fuel, promote a healthy environment, produce medicines, etc. Knowledge of biology is needed for the proper uses of nature, and for the development of useful related technologies.

4. Like all organisms, a horse is made up of cells. It is highly organized in terms of its internal structures. It responds to its environment. It uses energy that it gets from eating grain for growth and maintenance. It reproduces. It grows and develops. It adapts to its environment.

5. a. Organ; a leaf is a set of tissues that function together.

b. Population; the crows are of the same species and live together in a certain location.

c. Molecular; proteins are molecules made up of atoms.

d. Cellular; a blood cell is the smallest unit of life.

e. Community; the organisms are different populations living in the same place.

f. Tissue; a muscle is a group of cells that performs a function.

g. Ecosystem; they are the community and the nonliving factors of the environment.

h. Organ system; they are organs that function together as the digestive system.

6. a. Genetics
b. Taxonomy
c. Ethology
d. Cytology
e. Botany
f. Physiology
g. Immunology
h. Ecology
i. Molecular biology
j. Zoology
k. Microbiology
l. Anatomy

Chapter 2

TEST A

1. b	10. c	19. a
2. a	11. a	20. a
3. d	12. b	21. c
4. a	13. a	22. a
5. b	14. c	23. b
6. c	15. b	24. b
7. a	16. a	25. a
8. b	17. a	
9. d	18. b	

TEST B

1. a. Science is an ongoing, everchanging process that involves a way of studying and thinking about the natural world.

b. There is always uncertainty in science. Explanations are proposed, tested, and accepted tentatively until new and better ones come along.

c. Hypotheses are possible explanations whose validity can be tested experimentally. If a hypothesis is not borne out in experiments, it is rejected.

d. Successful science generally involves collaboration, communication, and the influence of different points of view.

e. Scientific discoveries, activities, and applications have enormous impact, both good and bad, on everyone. Science must be considered in terms of ethics, values, and consequences in which everyone has a stake.

2. a. This is a hypothesis because it is a possible explanation of observations.

b. This is a prediction because it is an "if . . . then" statement that describes what one thinks will occur in future.

c. This is an observation because it simply states something detected by the senses.

d. This describes an experiment because it discusses an actual activity that can be used to test a hypothesis.

3. a. It is not a good idea scientifically because it would not make clear what was producing the observed effect. It is not a good idea in terms of raising plants because one or both factors might be harmful and could damage all the plants rather than simply one or two of them.

b. In one experiment, keep light, water, and all other factors except food the same. Add food to one (variable), but not to the other (control). In the second experiment, keep food, water, and all other factors except light the same. Give extra light to one (variable), but not to the other (control).

c. Without controls, one cannot isolate factors and determine which one is really causing an effect.

4. Light microscopes cannot resolve objects at this magnification, so the details would be very blurry. She should use an electron microscope, which has a much higher resolving power.

5. Field studies allow scientists to observe animal behaviors that are not possible in a laboratory, such as interactions with the natural environment. Laboratory studies permit better control of experimental conditions and allow for better repeatability and the use of specialized equipment.

6. Electrophoresis would permit separation by differences in the speed and direction of molecules of different shape, mass, and induced charge that are loaded into a gel through which a current is passed. Centrifuging would permit separation by density difference during spinning. Chromatography would permit separation by deposition at different points on paper, solvent layers, or bead columns.

Chapter 3

TEST A

1. a	**10.** c	**19.** b
2. c	**11.** b	**20.** c
3. b	**12.** a	**21.** a
4. c	**13.** d	**22.** b
5. a	**14.** a	**23.** d
6. b	**15.** b	**24.** a
7. d	**16.** b	**25.** a
8. a	**17.** a	
9. b	**18.** c	

TEST B

1. Mass (amount of matter) and volume (amount of space) tell you it is matter. Various physical properties (e.g., density, texture, hardness, brittleness, transparency, physical state) and chemical properties tell you it is glass.

2. a. This is a mixture because it is a combination of different substances not chemically bonded.

b. This is an element because it contains only one kind of atom.

c. This is a compound because it contains more than one kind of atom chemically combined in a definite proportion.

3. a. There are 3 protons.

b. There are 3 electrons.

c. There are 4 neutrons.

d. The total negative charge is -3.

e. The total positive charge is $+3$.

f. The net charge is 0.

g. The atomic number is 3.

h. The atomic mass number is 7.

4. a. They are the atomic numbers, or numbers of protons.

b. Elements with the symbols Ne and Ar have similar properties because they are in the same group.

c. Three.

d. Eight.

e. Group 18.

f. It is the average atomic mass, or average of the masses of the isotopes.

5. a. The bonding is ionic. An electron is transferred from the K to the Br, forming K^+ and Br^- and the two ions attract each other.

b. The bonding is covalent. Each H shares two electrons with S.

6. a. KOH is a base because it produces hydroxide ions. HBr is an acid because it produces hydrogen ions. The pH of the KOH solution is greater than 7 because the solution is basic. The pH of the HBr solution is less than 7 because the solution is acidic.

b. $HBr + KOH \rightarrow KBr + H_2O$ + energy. Exothermic.

Chapter 4

TEST A

1. b	**10.** a	**19.** b
2. d	**11.** a	**20.** b
3. a	**12.** b	**21.** d
4. b	**13.** c	**22.** a
5. a	**14.** a	**23.** b
6. c	**15.** a	**24.** a
7. a	**16.** c	**25.** a
8. b	**17.** a	
9. b	**18.** a	

TEST B

1. a. Organic compounds always contain carbon. Inorganic compounds, with few exceptions, do not contain carbon.

b. organic; inorganic; inorganic; organic

2. a. polymer; monomers; water

b. protein; peptide bond

3. a. glucose; monosaccharide; energy source

b. cellulose; polysaccharide; support

c. starch; polysaccharide; energy storage

4. a. wax; waterproofing

b. fat; energy storage, insulation

c. steroid; control of body functions

d. phospholipids; control of movement of material in and out of cell

e. fat; energy storage

f. steroid; component of cell membranes

5. a. Lipid; this is a compound of glycerol and three fatty acids, and therefore a fat.

b. Carbohydrate; this is a sugar and contains C, H, and O in a 1:2:1 ratio.

c. Nucleic acid; this is a polymer that contains phosphates, sugars, and nitrogen bases.

d. Protein; this is a polymer made up of amino acids.

Chapter 5

TEST A

1. b	10. b	19. a
2. d	11. a	20. b
3. a	12. c	21. c
4. b	13. b	22. b
5. a	14. a	23. a
6. c	15. b	24. a
7. a	16. a	25. b
8. c	17. c	
9. a	18. b	

TEST B

1. a. Cells come only from preexisting cells.

b. Plants come only from plants, animals come only from animals.

c. Cells are the basic units of all life; all organisms are made up of cells.

2. a. acts as control center of the cell, contains hereditary material

b. makes ribosomes which build proteins

c. serves as material in which many biological reactions occur, suspends organelles

d. separates cell contents from surroundings, controls what enters and leaves the cell

3. a. rough endoplasmic reticulum

b. lysosome

c. cytosol

d. smooth endoplasmic reticulum

e. nucleolus

f. nucleus

g. mitochondrion

h. Golgi apparatus

i. ribosome

j. cell membrane

4. a. animal cell

b. prokaryotic cell

c. animal cell

d. plant cell

e. prokaryotic cell

5. Hypertonic: cells will shrink; water will diffuse out of them because osmotic diffusion involves movement down a concentration gradient (from high to low water concentration). Hypotonic: cells will swell and perhaps burst; water will diffuse into them because of osmosis down a concentration gradient. Isotonic: cells will neither shrink nor swell, because there is no water concentration gradient.

6. a. pinocytosis

b. active transport

c. facilitated diffusion

d. osmosis

e. exocytosis

f. phagocytosis

Chapter 6

TEST A

1. c	10. a	19. d
2. a	11. d	20. c
3. a	12. c	21. a
4. a	13. a	22. c
5. d	14. b	23. a
6. a	15. c	24. b
7. a	16. a	25. d
8. c	17. b	
9. b	18. c	

TEST B

1. bush: autotroph, from sunlight, carbon dioxide, and water; caterpillar: heterotroph, from consuming leaves; bird: heterotroph, from consuming caterpillar

2. Adenosine triphosphate; energy released from the breakdown of food and needed for life processes is stored in ATP.

3. a. oxidation: loss of electrons; reduction: gain of electrons;

b. Reduced: Cl_2; atoms are gaining electrons and are becoming negatively charged. Oxidized: H_2 atoms are losing electrons and are becoming positively charged.

4. a. It is the process in which they convert sunlight to usable forms of energy.

b. Carbohydrates (such as glucose) and oxygen are formed from CO_2 and water.

c. Chloroplast: chlorophyll-containing organelle, on the inner membrane of which photosynthesis takes place; Thylakoid: disk-shaped structure that contains photosynthetic pigments and on whose membrane light-dependent reactions occur; Stroma: gel-like matrix that surrounds thylakoids and in which carbon-fixing reactions occur; Grana: stack of thylakoids; Photosystem: set of chlorophyll molecules and other pigments in grana that act as a light-collecting unit of a chloroplast

5. a. Materials might include: plants, pots, soil, water, light source, green glass or green filter.

b. Control: plants that are exposed to ordinary white light and that are otherwise treated in the same way as the variable setup; variable: plants exposed to green light;

c. A control and variable setup, as described above; relative behavior and characteristics of the plants would be observed, recorded, and compared.

d. Data on variables such as plant height, color, healthiness, blooming period, longevity, etc., might be collected. The table would be organized to allow easy comparison of the control and variable setups.

e. The plants grown in green light would do poorly, because chlorophyll, which is necessary for photosynthesis, does not absorb green light. Thus, less energy would be available for photosynthesis.

6. a. It is a process in which food molecules are broken down to release energy for work.

b. Glucose is converted to PGAL and then to pyruvate, and energy is released. NADH is formed and ATP is produced.

c. Pyruvate reacts with coenzyme A and NAD^+ to form acetyl-CoA, NADH, and CO_2

d. Acetyl-CoA binds to a 4-carbon compound, producing citric acid, which then is oxidized, releases CO_2, and is restored to the 4-carbon compound. ATP and electrons are produced. NAD^+ is reduced to NADH, and FAD is reduced to $FADH_2$

e. Electrons from NADH and $FADH_2$ collect on the mitochondrial membrane and are accepted by O_2, and water is formed. H^+ is pumped across the membrane through a protein, converting ADP to ATP, and producing energy.

7. a. Anaerobic respiration takes place in the absence of oxygen; aerobic respiration requires oxygen.

b. anaerobic respiration in which ethanol and CO_2 are produced from pyruvate and NADH; unicellular organisms such as yeast;

c. anaerobic respiration in which lactic acid is produced from pyruvate and NADH; animals (especially in muscle cells)

Chapter 7

TEST A

1. c	**10.** d	**19.** a
2. d	**11.** a	**20.** c
3. a	**12.** b	**21.** a
4. c	**13.** a	**22.** a
5. a	**14.** b	**23.** b
6. b	**15.** a	**24.** a
7. a	**16.** c	**25.** a
8. b	**17.** a	
9. b	**18.** b	

TEST B

1. a. Number of organelles and amount of cytoplasm increase.
   b. Chromosomes replicate to produce sister chromatids.
   c. Cell makes organelles and substances it needs for division.
   d. Nucleus divides into two nuclei with identical genetic material.
   e. Cell cytoplasm divides to form daughter cells.
2. a. Prophase: Sister chromatids become thick; nucleus and nuclear envelope disappear; microtubules begin to assemble.
   b. Metaphase: Chromosomes are moved to center of cell by spindle fibers attached to centromeres; sister chromatids of each chromosome are attached to spindle fibers radiating from opposite ends of the cell.
   c. Anaphase: Centromeres of chromosomes are pulled by spindle fibers to ends of the cell, separating sister chromatids.
   d. Telophase: New nuclei begin to form around chromosomes at ends of cell; cell membrane begins to pinch cell in two.
3. a. budding
   b. cancer
   c. vegetative reproduction
   d. regeneration
   e. benign-tumor development
   f. fragmentation
   g. differentiation
4. a. diploid, mitosis
   b. 30, $2N$
   c. 15, haploid
   d. meiosis
   e. 15, N
   f. 30, diploid
5. a. Chromosomes become thick; chromosomes of each homologous pair are tangled together, and each pair has 4 chromatids; nucleoli and nuclear envelope disappear; spindle fibers form.
   b. Homologous chromosomes are still together; chromosome pairs are arranged in middle of cell.
   c. Homologous chromosome pairs separate as spindle fibers pull one member from each pair to end of cell.
   d. New nuclear envelope may form; cytokinesis produces haploid daughter cells.
   e. Each daughter cell divides again, and sister chromatids are divided.
   f. Genes are exchanged between pairs of homologous chromosomes.
6. The trout population contains variations developed during its evolution and each time reproduction occurs. During its sexual reproduction, genes from parents are reshuffled in meiosis and fertilization, producing new combinations. The variation in traits in different members of the trout population makes it likely that some individuals are adapted to survive the change. The amebas were produced asexually and are likely to be virtually identical. Thus, a change in environment is likely to endanger all the individuals in the ameba population.

Unit 1A

1. b	**18.** b	**35.** c
2. a	**19.** c	**36.** a
3. b	**20.** a	**37.** c
4. c	**21.** b	**38.** d
5. c	**22.** d	**39.** b
6. b	**23.** b	**40.** a
7. d	**24.** a	**41.** b
8. a	**25.** b	**42.** a
9. a	**26.** d	**43.** c
10. b	**27.** b	**44.** a
11. b	**28.** a	**45.** b
12. a	**29.** d	**46.** a
13. a	**30.** a	**47.** b
14. c	**31.** b	**48.** c
15. b	**32.** a	**49.** a
16. c	**33.** c	**50.** b
17. a	**34.** a	

Chapter 8

TEST A

1. b	10. c	19. b
2. a	11. d	20. c
3. d	12. a	21. b
4. a	13. d	22. c
5. b	14. a	23. a
6. c	15. b	24. b
7. d	16. c	25. b
8. a	17. c	
9. a	18. a	

TEST B

1. a. pure bred, because, when allowed to self-fertilize, each produced only offspring with the parental trait;

   b. all hybrid, because all received from parents different genetic information for a trait;

   c. white: recessive, because it did not show up in the hybrids; blue: dominant, because it alone showed up in the hybrids;

   d. $\frac{3}{4}$ blue, $\frac{1}{4}$ white, because $\frac{3}{4}$ of the genotypes include a dominant gene for blueness, and $\frac{1}{4}$ contain only recessive genes for whiteness.

2. a. Law of dominance: When two copies of a gene pair are different, one allele can control the trait and the other can be hidden.

   b. Law of independent assortment: Gene pairs segregate into gametes randomly and independently.

   c. Law of segregation: Each pair of alleles segregates during meiosis.

3. a. homozygous, white

   b. homozygous, gray

   c. heterozygous, gray

4. a. $P = \frac{1}{2} \times \frac{1}{2} = \frac{1}{4}$

   b. $P = \frac{1}{2} \times \frac{1}{2} = \frac{1}{4}$

   c. $P = \frac{1}{2} \times \frac{1}{2} \times \frac{1}{2} \times \frac{1}{2} \times \frac{1}{2} = \frac{1}{32}$

5. a. dihybrid, because inheritance of two traits at a time is being studied

   b. Gametes of each parent: TR, Tr, tR, tr; line 1 of square: TTRR, TTRr, TtRR, TtRr; line 2: TTRr, TTrr, TtRr, Ttrr; line 3: TtRR, TtRr, ttRR, ttRr; line 4: TtRr, Ttrr, ttRr, ttrr;

   c. 9 tall and red, 3 tall and yellow, 3 short and red, 1 short and yellow; 9:3:3:1

6. a. codominance

   b. multiple alleles

   c. incomplete dominance

   d. polygenic traits

Chapter 9

TEST A

1. b	10. c	19. b
2. a	11. a	20. b
3. d	12. b	21. a
4. a	13. c	22. b
5. b	14. b	23. b
6. a	15. a	24. a
7. b	16. b	25. b
8. c	17. a	
9. b	18. a	

TEST B

1. The theory that the material of inheritance is carried by chromosomes; Mendel's factors occur in pairs, which separate in gamete production and assort independently. Chromosomes have analogous properties.

2. a. all fringed/orange

   b. 9 fringed/orange : 3 fringed/yellow : 3 unfringed/orange : 1 unfringed/yellow; pairs of chromosomes that assort independently produce this ratio.

   c. 3 fringed/orange : 1 unfringed/yellow; in the absence of crossover, linked genes would remain together.

3. a. sex-linked genes

   b. $X^C Y$; $X^C X^C$

   c. Gametes of male: X^C, Y; gametes of female: X^C, X^c; line 1: $X^C X^c$, $X^C Y$; line 2: $X^C X^c$, $X^c Y$; phenotype ratio: 2 curved females : 1 curved male : 1 flat male

4. a. sex-influenced

   b. sex-limited

   c. sex-linked

5. a. duplication

   b. inversion

   c. normal crossover

   d. translocation

   e. deletion

6. a. nondisjunction

   b. normal meiosis

   c. polyploidy

   d. monosomy

   e. normal fertilization

   f. trisomy

Chapter 10

TEST A

1. a	**10.** b	**19.** a
2. b	**11.** a	**20.** b
3. d	**12.** c	**21.** a
4. c	**13.** d	**22.** c
5. a	**14.** a	**23.** a
6. d	**15.** b	**24.** c
7. a	**16.** a	**25.** a
8. c	**17.** d	
9. a	**18.** c	

TEST B

1. a. He showed that either DNA or protein can be absorbed by bacteria and can transform them; observed that a mixture of harmless bacteria and heat-killed bacteria of a different strain could cause effects of the heat-killed strain to show up in mice injected with the mixture.

b. They proved that DNA makes up genes; they found that radioactively marked DNA, and not radioactively marked viral protein, passed from phages into cells.

2. Check drawings for accuracy.

3. Each gene on a strand of DNA contains instructions for the manufacture of one particular polypeptide chain, or one protein.

4. DNA is double strand and contains the purines adenine and guanine, the pyrimidines cytosine and thymine, and the sugar deoxyribose. RNA is single strand and contains the purines adenine and guanine, the pyrimidines cytosine and uracil, and the sugar ribose.

5. a. U, C, C, G, U, A

b. transcription; messenger RNA (mRNA)

c. Transfer RNA (tRNA) brings amino acids to ribosomes in correct order for protein building. Ribosomal RNA (rRNA) makes up much of the structure of ribosomes.

6. a. exon

b. intron

c. regulator

d. promoter gene

e. operon

f. methyl group

g. repressor protein

h. regulatory protein

i. operator

j. structural gene

7. a. frameshift mutation

b. mutagen

c. carcinogen

d. oncogene

e. base-pair substitution

f. deletion

g. gene mutation

h. base analog

i. point mutation

j. addition

Chapter 11

TEST A

1. d	**10.** a	**19.** c
2. a	**11.** c	**20.** d
3. b	**12.** a	**21.** d
4. b	**13.** a	**22.** a
5. c	**14.** b	**23.** a
6. a	**15.** b	**24.** c
7. c	**16.** a	**25.** a
8. a	**17.** b	
9. b	**18.** c	

TEST B

1. a. eugenics

b. gene mapping

c. biotechnology

d. genetic engineering

e. gene transfer

2. a. outbreeding

b. selective breeding

c. induced polyploidy

d. inbreeding

3. a. DNA that has components from different organisms

b. a carrier of genetic material

c. a small circular piece of DNA within a bacterium

d. protein that can cut DNA at a specific series of base pairs.

4. Obtain DNA from a bacterial plasmid and from a person able to make the enzyme. Use restriction enzymes to cut from the human DNA a sequence containing the gene that makes the enzyme. Also use a restriction enzyme to cut the plasmid DNA. Use DNA ligase enzyme to join the "sticky ends" (complementary base-pair matched ends) of the plasmid DNA and the human gene. Insert the altered plasmid into a bacterium. Grow a large number of these bacteria and harvest the desired digestive enzyme as they produce it.

5. a. Answers will vary. Students may, for example discuss the use of new bacteria to increase crop production, to help plants resist frost, to help plants or animals resist disease, or to improve the size, yield, or other qualities of livestock.

b. Answers will vary. Students may discuss modifying microorganisms that are involved in breadmaking, cheesemaking, etc., to make the organisms more efficient, or engineering bacteria to help in cleaning up oil spills or in processing sewage.

c. Answers will vary. Students may discuss the engineering of bacteria to produce human insulin, vaccines, growth hormone, blood-clot dissolvers, proteins that will bind to specific kinds of cells, etc. They may also discuss the use of genetic engineering to study and map DNA and detect defective genes.

6. a. Answers will vary. Students may point out the possible usefulness of such a virus in killing bacteria that are harmful to people, in sterilizing particular areas, as antiseptics, etc.

b. Answers will vary. Students may point out the danger of producing a virus that will be directly harmful to people, of allowing a virus to escape from the laboratory, of producing a virus that will have unpredicted negative effects on the food chain, etc.

c. Answers will vary. Students may point out the importance of testing such viruses thoroughly before use on people, of using procedures and equipment that will prevent escape of the viruses, and of the thorough study of possible wider effects.

d. Some danger is likely to remain because of failure of technological systems, unpredictability and complexity of changes in nature, etc.

Chapter 12

TEST A

1. b	**10.** a	**19.** a
2. a	**11.** d	**20.** a
3. b	**12.** b	**21.** b
4. d	**13.** b	**22.** b
5. c	**14.** a	**23.** c
6. a	**15.** b	**24.** a
7. c	**16.** d	**25.** d
8. c	**17.** a	
9. b	**18.** b	

TEST B

1. a. females; males

   b. marriages; parent-child relationships

   c. individuals who have the genetic disorder trait; individuals who do not have it

   d. yes; no

   e. Dominant; all of the II generation has the trait even though the mother does not.

   f. homozygous, because he has passed it on to all his offspring (subsequent ratios support this also); heterozygous, because she did not pass on this dominant trait to all her offspring

2. Karyotyping involves cell collection and growth, photography of chromosomes, with subsequent analysis as to length, pairing, etc. It reveals visible chromosomal abnormalities.

3. A project to map all genes in human chromosomes; answers on possible benefits, drawbacks, and abuses will vary but should refer to value of information for various purposes and to the limitations or the danger of misuse of the resulting knowledge.

4. a. Huntington's, dominant single

   b. hemophilia, sex-linked

   c. sickle-cell, codominant

   d. cri-du-chat, defective chromosome

   e. Down, trisomy

   f. Tay-Sach's, recessive single

   g. Klinefelter, trisomy

   h. cystic fibrosis, recessive single

   i. color blindness, sex-linked

   j. Turner, monosomy

5. a. counseling by medical specialist to provide prospective parents with information on probability of passing on genetic disorders

   b. pedigree tracing, molecular tests

   c. amniocentesis (removal of fluid from womb to test for fetal genetic defects); ultrasound (passage of high-frequency sound through body, with reflection used to construct image of fetus); CVS (removal of bits of membranes around fetus to test for defects)

   d. in making decisions as to whether to have children, in knowing whether there are abnormalities in the fetus

Unit 2A

1. b	**18.** d	**35.** c
2. c	**19.** d	**36.** d
3. b	**20.** d	**37.** a
4. d	**21.** a	**38.** b
5. b	**22.** b	**39.** c
6. c	**23.** c	**40.** a
7. a	**24.** a	**41.** b
8. b	**25.** a	**42.** a
9. d	**26.** b	**43.** b
10. a	**27.** c	**44.** a
11. b	**28.** d	**45.** d
12. a	**29.** a	**46.** a
13. d	**30.** b	**47.** c
14. a	**31.** a	**48.** a
15. b	**32.** c	**49.** b
16. c	**33.** d	**50.** c
17. a	**34.** a	

Chapter 13

TEST A

1. c	**10.** b	**19.** a
2. a	**11.** a	**20.** d
3. b	**12.** d	**21.** d
4. c	**13.** a	**22.** a
5. a	**14.** c	**23.** b
6. b	**15.** c	**24.** a
7. a	**16.** a	**25.** b
8. d	**17.** b	
9. a	**18.** d	

TEST B

1. a. Life can come from nonliving matter; no longer accepted.

   b. Life comes only from life. Students may give evidence on the development of maggots in uncovered vs. covered meat, on the growth of bacteria in boiled broth to which dust has access, etc.

   c. Mitochondria evolved from engulfed free-living aerobic prokaryotes, and chloroplasts evolved from engulfed photosynthetic prokaryotes. Both look like prokaryotes, contain their own circular DNA, make their own proteins, reproduce on their own, and have ribosomes like those of bacteria.

2. a. Primitive: more carbon dioxide, methane, ammonia, sulfur-containing substances; Modern: more oxygen, nitrogen

   b. Early cells were heterotrophic anaerobic prokaryotes that thrived because there was no oxygen. Photosynthetic one-celled organisms evolved to give off oxygen into the atmosphere. The oxygen killed the exposed anaerobes. Some surviving anaerobes were able to tolerate oxygen, and some of these evolved into organisms that were highly successful in the new oxygen-rich environment.

3. a. Conditions on ancient Earth, including energy from UV radiation and lightning, caused reactions that produced organic molecules essential to life.

   b. Experiments will vary. Students may suggest placing gas mixtures like those of the early atmosphere into 2 containers. One sample, the control, will be subjected to ordinary light and energy conditions; the other will be exposed to light from UV sources and electricity from sparking devices. Data on energy and on final composition of the mixture might be collected. The formation of organic substances, such as amino acids, only in the energized containers would support the hypothesis.

4. a. Paleozoic, 570; Mesozoic, 225; Cenozoic, 65

   b. Cenozoic

   c. Mesozoic

   d. Paleozoic

   e. Mesozoic

   f. Paleozoic

5. $\frac{1}{8} = \frac{1}{2} \times \frac{1}{2} \times \frac{1}{2}$, which indicates that 3 half-life periods have elapsed; 3 x 5600 years = 16,800 years

6. a. homologous

   b. analogous

   c. vestigial

   d. analogous

   e. vestigial

   f. homologous

7. a. Discovery of homologous and vestigial structures gives evidence of common ancestry. Lack of common ancestry gives evidence of evolutionary branching.

   b. Discovery of similarities between developing embryos reveals evolutionary relationships and common ancestry.

   c. Analysis of similarities and differences of biochemcial processes and substances, especially the basic structure of DNA, gives evidence on ancestry, evolution, and proximity of relationship.

Chapter 14

TEST A

1. c	**10.** d	**19.** c
2. a	**11.** a	**20.** b
3. d	**12.** c	**21.** a
4. a	**13.** a	**22.** b
5. b	**14.** c	**23.** a
6. b	**15.** a	**24.** d
7. a	**16.** c	**25.** b
8. c	**17.** d	
9. a	**18.** a	

TEST B

1. a. Organisms strive to improve themselves; this effort causes used body structures to develop and unused ones to waste away; acquired modifications in structure are inherited by offspring.

   b. Organisms do evolve over time and become better adapted to their environment; used and unused body structures in an individual do behave this way; in many cases, the offspring of organisms do develop in the way that their parents did.

   c. He cut off the tails of 20 generations of mice, and mice with tails continued to be produced, showing that acquired characteristics are not inherited.

2. a. Geological changes are very slow, uniform processes.

   b. When a population exceeds its resources, disasters limit further growth of the population.

3. a. Within populations, there is variation that can be inherited, and some variations are favorable.

   b. More offspring are produced than can survive.

   c. They have favorable variations.

   d. Small changes occur gradually, over enormous spans of time.

4. a. Stabilizing; no change is produced.

   b. Disruptive; the medium-green ones will be eaten more and the light and dark ones will blend in better and be eaten less, causing them to increase in relative numbers.

   c. Directional; the chipmunks of light color will stand out less than medium- and dark-colored ones, will be eaten less, and will increase in relative number.

5. a. Does; there must be no selective advantage and no natural selection.

   b. Does not; there must be no migration into or out of the population, but movement within the area is not ruled out.

   c. Does; there must be no migration at all into or out of the population.

   d. Does; mating must be random, even within population.

6. a. divergent evolution by isolation

   b. convergent evolution

   c. adaptive radiation

   d. convergent evolution

Chapter 15

TEST A

1. c	10. b	19. b
2. a	11. a	20. b
3. a	12. a	21. a
4. d	13. c	22. d
5. a	14. c	23. c
6. b	15. b	24. b
7. c	16. a	25. a
8. a	17. b	
9. c	18. b	

TEST B

1. **a.** humans only
   b. all primates
   c. all primates
   d. humans only
   e. all primates
   f. all primates
2. **a.** Old World monkeys; baboon, rhesus monkey;
   b. apes; chimpanzees, gorillas, orangutans, gibbons
   c. New World monkeys; spider monkey
   d. prosimians; lemur, loris, potto, tarsier
3. *Australopithecus:* walked upright, long-armed, brains only slightly larger than those of modern apes, lived about 4 million to 1 million years ago, no evidence of special skills or tool use; "southern ape," from apelike appearance and discovery in southern Africa; *Homo habilis:* walked upright, larger brain than that of Australopithecus, lived about 2.5 million to 1.5 million years ago, made and used tools; "handy man," because of toolmaking; *Homo erectus:* walked upright, larger brain than that of *H. habilis,* lived about 1.5 million to 500,00 years ago, lived in shelters, wore clothing, may have used fire; "upright man," because of posture
4. **a.** human appearance, with heavier brows and smaller chin, brain as large as that of modern humans
   b. probably had language, made, used, and decorated tools, performed ritual burial, probably had religion and complex social structure
   c. Homo sapiens
   d. Neander Valley, Germany
   e. competition with Cro-Magnons, who may have been better hunters and had better language ability; possible (but unlikely) interbreeding with Cro-Magnons
5. **a.** Identical to those of modern humans
   b. like that of modern humans, known to have done decorative painting
   c. Homo sapiens
   d. French town of Cro-Magnon
6. The fossil record is scattered and incomplete; hominid fossils are found in forest soil, which does not preserve them well; there are only very small differences between many fossils; soft tissue is not preserved; injury or disease may have changed bone structures. Various errors in classification (as to species vs. sexes; normal vs. accidentally acquired features; etc.) could result.

Chapter 16

TEST A

1. d	10. a	19. a
2. c	11. a	20. c
3. a	12. b	21. d
4. c	13. a	22. a
5. a	14. b	23. c
6. d	15. d	24. b
7. a	16. a	25. c
8. d	17. c	
9. a	18. d	

TEST B

1. **a.** field of biology that deals with classifying organisms
   b. hierarchy based on structural similarities; two kingdoms divided into classes, orders, genera, and species; two Latin names assigned to each species
   c. based on a universal language that was unlikely to change; brief names for organisms; logically based on similarities
   d. did not take evolution into account; not enough taxa
2. **a.** two names used
   b. *Canis,* genus; *lupus,* species
   c. The genus name is common to the dog and wolf but not to the fox, which shows that dogs and wolves are more closely related to each other than to foxes.
3. kingdom, phylum, class, order, family, genus, species
4. **a.** prokaryotic, unicellular, either
   b. eukaryotic, either (mostly unicellular), either
   c. eukaryotic, either (mostly multicellular), heterotrophic
   d. eukaryotic, multicellular, autotrophic
   e. eukaryotic, multicellular, heterotrophic
5. X is closer to Y. Despite the external similarity of leglessness in X and Z, and the internal similarity of a four-chambered heart, X and Y have in common a more fundamental similarity, coldbloodedness, that Z does not. More tellingly, X and Y are more similar biochemically, in terms of protein (and therefore DNA).
6. **a.** Lagomorpha (share most-recent common ancestry, nearest separation by branching)
   b. Carnivora, Primates (least-recent common ancestry)
   c. Primates (branched highest on the tree)
   d. Insectivora (branched lowest on the tree)
7. Look at first pair of dichotomous choices, decide which fits the plant, follow directions to next pair, decide which fits the plant, etc., until you reach the point in the key that states the identity of the plant.

Unit 3A

1. c	**18.** c	**35.** a
2. b	**19.** a	**36.** d
3. a	**20.** a	**37.** d
4. c	**21.** c	**38.** c
5. b	**22.** a	**39.** b
6. a	**23.** c	**40.** d
7. c	**24.** b	**41.** b
8. a	**25.** a	**42.** d
9. d	**26.** c	**43.** a
10. a	**27.** d	**44.** b
11. b	**28.** c	**45.** a
12. c	**29.** d	**46.** d
13. c	**30.** a	**47.** d
14. d	**31.** c	**48.** a
15. a	**32.** c	**49.** d
16. a	**33.** a	**50.** c
17. a	**34.** d	

Chapter 17

TEST A

1. d	10. a	19. a
2. a	11. b	20. c
3. c	12. a	21. c
4. b	13. b	22. a
5. a	14. a	23. c
6. c	15. c	24. a
7. d	16. c	25. c
8. b	17. a	
9. a	18. b	

TEST B

1. By transferring sap from diseased plants, Mayer discovered that the disease was contagious and that the agent was smaller than a typical bacterium. Ivanovsky found that the agent was too small even to be filtered. Beijerinck discovered that it could reproduce within cells, and hypothesized that it was not bacterial, but a virus. From the juice of infected plants, Stanley grew crystals that could cause the disease, demonstrating that the virus was a chemical particle.

2. Viruses are noncellular particles, lack organelles and nuclei, and have a core of nucleic acid surrounded by a capsid protein coat and sometimes an envelope. They vary in shape and are much smaller than bacteria. Each type can attack only bacteria, only plants, or only animals.

3. Living: They reproduce themselves and contain nucleic acid and proteins. Nonliving: Outside of cells, they cannot reproduce, grow, move, or respire.

4. They were fragments of chromosomes in organisms. They escaped, occupied other cells, replicated there, and evolved the ability to make their host cells produce capsids. This allowed the viruses to move from cell to cell. Evidence includes the complete dependence of viruses on living hosts, the specificity of viruses, and the greater degree of similarity between viral and host genes than between the genes of different families of viruses.

5. **a.** Virus (phage) attaches to bacterial cell wall, injects its DNA into host. DNA takes control of cell and makes it produce new phage DNA and proteins, which assemble into new viruses and release an enzyme that opens the cell wall and releases viruses.

   b. Virus (phage) attaches to bacterial cell wall, and injects its DNA, which forms a circle, attaches to a bacterial chromosome, and becomes an inactive prophage. Host cell reproduces itself and prophage DNA.

6. Standard: contains DNA, which then makes cell produce proteins and copies of itself, which are reassembled to make new viruses. Retrovirus: contains RNA, releases enzyme to cause cell to make viral DNA from RNA. DNA makes RNA, which can be used directly to assemble viruses.

7. **a.** either; either; yes

   b. plants; RNA; no

   c. animals; neither; yes

Chapter 18

TEST A

1. b	10. b	19. a
2. a	11. c	20. b
3. b	12. a	21. a
4. a	13. c	22. b
5. c	14. a	23. d
6. a	15. b	24. c
7. d	16. d	25. a
8. c	17. a	
9. a	18. c	

TEST B

1. They are prokaryotes, having no nucleus or membrane-bound organelles. Their cells are smaller, their ribosomes are different, and they are mostly single-celled.

2. **a.** chemosynthesizer
   b. extreme halophile
   c. thermoacidophile
   d. methanogen

3. **a.** group of monerans that are true bacteria and do not normally live in unusually harsh environments
   b. Gram-positive, Gram-negative, cyanobacteria
   c. Gram-positive: purple after Gram staining, no extra lipid layer outside cell wall; Gram-negative: pink after Gram staining, extra lipid layer outside cell wall; cyanobacteria: pink after Gram staining, perform photosynthesis, release oxygen

4. spherical (cocci), rod-shaped (bacilli), spiral (spirilla)

5. **a.** sunlight and inorganic molecules
   b. inorganic molecules only
   c. organic molecules (produced by other organisms) only
   d. sunlight and organic molecules

6. **a.** facultative anaerobe, intestinal bacterium *Escherichia coli*
   b. obligate aerobe, tuberculosis bacterium *Mycobacterium tuberculosis*
   c. obligate anaerobe, tetanus bacterium *Clostridium tetani*

7. **a.** binary fission, asexual cell reproduction
   b. endospore formation, survival strategy
   c. transformation, genetic exchange
   d. transduction, genetic exchange
   e. conjugation, genetic exchange

8. Answers will vary but may refer to decomposer action (recycling of nutrients), forms of mutualism (such as within intestines), use in tanning leather, in making yogurt, in biotechnology (making hormones, interferon, insulin), and in nonpolluting insecticides.

Chapter 19

TEST A

1. b	10. a	19. b
2. a	11. b	20. c
3. b	12. d	21. a
4. c	13. c	22. c
5. d	14. c	23. a
6. d	15. d	24. c
7. c	16. d	25. d
8. a	17. c	
9. b	18. a	

TEST B

1. a. They are eukaryotes.
   b. They are unicellular.
   c. They have little in common, and include a great variety of organisms that are classified as protists simply because they do not belong in any other kingdom.
2. a. animals, heterotrophic
   b. plants, autotrophic
   c. fungi, decomposers
3. sarcodinians, by extending cytoplasm, ameba; zooflagellates, by moving flagella, *Trichonympha;* ciliaphorans, by moving cilia, *Paramecium;* sporozoans, no movement on their own, *Plasmodium*
4. a. oral groove
   b. cilia
   c. food vacuole
   d. micronucleus
   e. macronucleus
   f. anal pore
   g. contractile vacuole
   h. pellicle
   i. trichocysts
5. Malaria; uninfected mosquito bites a person who has malaria, and takes in sporozoans, and bites a healthy person. Sporozoans enter the person's bloodstream, are carried to the liver, reproduce mitotically there, reenter the blood stream, invade red blood cells. Blood cells burst, releasing the sporozoans, which then invade other blood cells.
6. a. euglenoid
   b. Rhodophyta
   c. diatom
   d. Phaeophyta
   e. dinoflagellate
   f. Chlorophyta
7. a. shiny, wet-looking, texture like gelatin, resemble fungi
   b. plasmodial slime molds, cellular slime molds, water molds
   c. Plasmodial: live on land, have different forms at different stages in life cycle, form a plasmodium during feeding stage, in which they function as a single cell with many nuclei and can creep along the ground, are decomposers; when food is scarce, forms fruiting bodies and produce spores that release haploid cells that form a zygote. Cellular: live in water, have different forms at different stages, ameboid cell during feeding stage; when food is scarce, clump into haploid pseudoplasmodium of individual cells, produce fruiting bodies that release spores, are decomposers; water molds: are decomposers or parasites, undergo asexual reproduction to produce spores with flagella, grow in fresh water on decaying or live plants or animals, or on land as plant parasites.

Chapter 20

TEST A

1. b	10. c	19. a
2. a	11. a	20. c
3. c	12. c	21. a
4. d	13. c	22. c
5. c	14. d	23. d
6. a	15. a	24. c
7. c	16. c	25. a
8. b	17. b	
9. a	18. d	

TEST B

1. eukaryotic, have nuclei and mitochondria, heterotrophs (depend on other organisms for nutrition), generally multicellular, have chitin in cell walls, cannot move on their own, are generally saprophytes
2. a. rhizoid
   b. septum
   c. ascus
   d. fruiting body
   e. hypha
   f. basidium
   g. mycelium
   h. stolon
3. a. sac fungi, asexual and sexual, yeast
   b. imperfect fungi, asexual, *Penicillium*
   c. common molds, asexual and sexual, bread mold
   d. club fungi, sexual, mushrooms
4. Spores are formed in basidia, which line the gills. In fertilization, a (+) haploid nucleus and a (−) haploid nucleus in each basidium fuse to form a diploid nucleus, which then undergoes meiosis. Four basidiospores, some (+) and some (−), are produced, and they can later form (+) and (−) hyphae. The spores are released and germinate to form new mycelia.
5. Beneficial: Decompose decaying materials for recycling of nutrients in ecosystem, support the growth of tree roots, can be used to make drugs such as penicillin, and to make cheese and soy sauce, can be used directly as food, are used in making bread and fermenting wine, can be used in genetic engineering; Harmful: Can be parasitic and destroy crops, cause Dutch elm disease, cause athlete's foot, ringworm, and yeast infections, damage wood, cause food to spoil.
6. a. Fungus and photosynthetic alga or cyanobacteria grow together, the fungus obtaining food through the photosynthesis by the other organism; probably parasitism, because only the fungus benefits (although traditionally it was seen as mutualism, as the other organism was thought to benefit also).
   b. Fungus and roots of tree grow together, hyphae of fungus act as root extensions, increase water absorption, and help break down organic matter for use by the plant; mutualism, because both organisms benefit

Unit 4A

1. c	**18.** a	**35.** a
2. a	**19.** c	**36.** d
3. b	**20.** d	**37.** c
4. c	**21.** b	**38.** a
5. d	**22.** a	**39.** b
6. b	**23.** c	**40.** a
7. a	**24.** d	**41.** d
8. a	**25.** b	**42.** b
9. b	**26.** a	**43.** a
10. a	**27.** b	**44.** c
11. c	**28.** d	**45.** c
12. a	**29.** a	**46.** a
13. d	**30.** b	**47.** b
14. d	**31.** d	**48.** c
15. b	**32.** b	**49.** a
16. c	**33.** a	**50.** c
17. b	**34.** c	

Chapter 21

TEST A

1. b	**10.** a	**19.** a
2. d	**11.** a	**20.** c
3. a	**12.** c	**21.** b
4. c	**13.** a	**22.** c
5. d	**14.** d	**23.** a
6. a	**15.** a	**24.** b
7. b	**16.** d	**25.** c
8. a	**17.** a	
9. c	**18.** c	

TEST B

1. They perform photosynthesis, are multicellular, reproduce sexually, and their cells are eukaryotic (have a nucleus and organelles) and have a cell wall made of cellulose.

2. a. Plants are thought to have evolved millions of years ago from a green alga.

b. Plants and green algae contain the same photosynthetic pigment, have cell walls that contain cellulose, develop a cell plate during cell division, and store food as starch.

c. Plants evolved alternation of generations, adaptations that require less water, such as a cuticle, guard cells, and seeds, and lignin in cell walls for support.

3. Nonvascular plants do not have tissue specialized for long-distance transport of water and solutes through the plants, and lack true roots, stems, and leaves. Vascular plants do have the specialized tissue for transport, and have true roots, stems, and leaves.

4. a. nonvascular, neither, no, mosses
b. vascular, neither, yes, ferns
c. vascular, seeds in cones, yes, pines
d. vascular, seeds in fruit, yes, apple

5. Monocot would have one cotyledon, narrow leaves with parallel veins, flower parts in multiples of 3, and vascular tissue in bundles. Dicot would have two cotyledons, broad leaves with branching veins, flower parts in multiples of 4 or 5, and vascular tissue in rings.

6. a. They perform photosynthesis, providing oxygen most organisms must have to survive and removing carbon dioxide; they are at the start of the food chain, as producers and food sources; they make inorganic elements available to other organisms; they provide shelter to other organisms.

b. Answers will vary but may include: various food items from plants, wood for building and fuel, fibers for clothing, dyes, medicines.

c. Answer will vary but may include: producing poisons, causing allergies, robbing other plants of nutrients, and damaging houses, septic systems, and water lines.

Chapter 22

TEST A

1. b	**10.** a	**19.** c
2. c	**11.** a	**20.** b
3. a	**12.** c	**21.** a
4. a	**13.** a	**22.** d
5. b	**14.** b	**23.** a
6. c	**15.** d	**24.** c
7. a	**16.** a	**25.** a
8. b	**17.** b	
9. d	**18.** c	

TEST B

1. a. Bryophyta;
b. There is no specialized vascular tissue; transport is from cell to cell by osmosis.

2. a. sporophyte
b. spore
c. capsule
d. stalk
e. gametophyte
f. rhizoid
g. antheridium
h. sperm
i. egg
j. archegonium

3. Diploid sporophyte releases haploid spores, which then develop into gametophyte. On gametophyte, sperm swim from the antheridium to the archegonium, where the egg is. Fertilization occurs and the resulting zygote undergoes mitosis and produces the sporophyte.

4. Both are nonmoss bryophytes. A liverwort is liver-shaped, has small umbrella-shaped antheridia and archegonia, and grows along the ground, producing newer branches that survive the older ones. A hornwort gametophyte can look somewhat similar to a liverwort, but its antheridia and archegonia are internal; also, hornworts develop long, hornlike sporophytes that can perform photosynthesis.

5. a. They have specialized vascular tissue, true roots, stems, and leaves, produce gametophytes that tend to be smaller than their sporophytes, and produce spores rather than seeds.

b. whisk ferns, club mosses, horsetails, true ferns

6. a. frond
b. blade
c. sorus
d. spore
e. petiole
f. rhizome
g. root
h. sporophyte
i. gametophyte
j. archegonium
k. egg
l. sperm
m. antheridium

7. Large diploid sporophyte releases haploid spores from sori. Spores develop into small gametophytes. On gametophyte, sperm swim from the antheridium to the archegonium, where the egg is. Fertilization occurs and the resulting zygote produces the sporophyte.

Chapter 23

TEST A

1. c	10. a	19. d
2. a	11. d	20. c
3. c	12. a	21. a
4. a	13. c	22. d
5. b	14. b	23. a
6. a	15. c	24. c
7. d	16. d	25. a
8. a	17. b	
9. b	18. a	

TEST B

1. **a.** collenchyma
   b. sclerenchyma
   c. fibers
   d. sclereids
   e. parenchyma
2. As transpiration, or evaporation of water from a plant, occurs, a negative pressure is created in the xylem, and water is pulled upward. Cohesion of water molecules also causes the molecules to stick together and pull each other up.
3. **a.** would be carrying water and dissolved minerals
   b. would carry water and minerals and would be made up of long, narrow cells with thin separations between them
   c. would carry water and minerals and would be made up of short, wide cells with no end walls
   d. would carry sugar sap
   e. would carry sugar sap, would be stacked to form tubes that would have holes in their end walls
   f. would control movement of substances through sieve tubes, allowing sieve tube elements to function
4. **a.** to absorb water and minerals, to anchor a plant, and sometimes to store food
   b. to hold leaves up to the light, to transport water and food between roots and leaves, and sometimes to store food
   c. to trap light, to perform photosynthesis, and sometimes to store food
5. **a.** epidermis
   b. root hair
   c. cortex
   d. endodermis
   e. vascular cylinder
   f. epidermis
   g. cortex
   h. vascular bundle
   i. phloem
   j. xylem
   k. pith
   l. node
   m. cuticle
   n. upper epidermis
   o. mesophyll
   p. guard cell
   q. stoma
   r. vein (vascular bundle)
   s. bundle sheath
   t. lower epidermis
6. **a.** pinnately compound
   b. palmate
   c. monocot
   d. pinnate
   e. palmately compound

Chapter 24

TEST A

1. c	10. b	19. a
2. b	11. d	20. b
3. a	12. c	21. d
4. a	13. d	22. b
5. c	14. a	23. a
6. a	15. d	24. b
7. c	16. c	25. d
8. a	17. b	
9. b	18. b	

TEST B

1. **a.** plant embryo, stored food, and protective seed coat
   b. gymnosperms: develop on scales of cones, not in fruit; monocots: develop in fruit, have one cotyledon, contain an endosperm that takes up most of the space have a coleoptile that protects the young plant; dicots: develop in fruit, have two cotyledons, which contain the endosperm
2. Male and female gametes are made by separate male and female cones on the same tree. Male cones release pollen containing sperm. Pollen is carried to female cones, sticks to resin, and grows a pollen tube down to the ovule, which contains the egg. Fertilization occurs, a zygote forms and grows into an embryo in a seed. Seed is released when the cone enlarges and its scales separate. Seed can then germinate and produce a new plant.
3. **a.** petal
   b. corolla
   c. anther
   d. filament
   e. stamen
   f. stigma
   g. style
   h. ovary
   i. pistil
   j. sepal
   k. calyx
4. There is alternation of generations. The sporophyte undergoes meiosis. A megaspore is formed in each ovule and from it an egg, or female gametophyte, and two polar nuclei are formed. Microspores are formed in anthers through meiosis, and become pollen grains, or male gametophytes. Pollen lands on the stigma, sends out a pollen tube to the ovule, and releases two sperm nuclei. One sperm nucleus fertilizes the egg and forms a zygote. Another sperm joins with the two polar nuclei in the ovule, to form endosperm. The zygote develops into an embryo and the ovule becomes a seed. The ovary forms a fruit around the seed. When the seed is released and sprouts, a new sporophyte develops.
5. **a.** Make changes in the environment of the plant, reduce fertilizer and water.
   b. Sexual reproduction, unlike asexual reproduction, produces offspring with new combinations of characteristics, increasing the likelihood that some of them may may able to survive and reproduce well under the new conditions.
6. Cutting: removal and planting of piece of stem or leaf; grafting: fusing of cut ends of two different plants, to make them grow as one; tissue culturing: growth of an entire plant from individual cells or small pieces of leaf, stem, or root

Chapter 25

TEST A

1. d	**10.** a	**19.** c
2. c	**11.** c	**20.** a
3. c	**12.** a	**21.** a
4. b	**13.** a	**22.** c
5. a	**14.** c	**23.** a
6. a	**15.** a	**24.** a
7. b	**16.** d	**25.** b
8. a	**17.** b	
9. d	**18.** a	

TEST B

1. a. Embryo in seed uses energy from food stored in cotyledons or endosperm and grows, splitting seed coat and forming root and shoot.

   b. Water is needed to activate enzymes for growth. Temperature must be high enough to promote germination.

   c. Monocot shoots grow straight up, through a protective coleoptile. Dicot shoots often break surface in hooked shape and pull cotyledons out as the hook straightens.

2. a. embryo, primary, root

   b. between xylem and phloem, secondary, secondary xylem and phloem

   c. between phloem and epidermis, secondary, cork

   d. tip of stem, primary, stem or leaf

   e. base of leaf, primary, branch or flower

3. a. recently formed secondary xylem, light-colored, in outer part

   b. clogged secondary xylem, dark-colored, in center

   c. large, wide secondary xylem cells, in alternating rings with summer wood

   d. thick-walled, narrow secondary xylem cells, in alternating rings with spring wood

4. a. Hardwoods contain tough fibers and are difficult to drive nails into. Softwoods do not contain such fibers and are relatively easy to drive nails into.

   b. hardwoods: dicots; softwoods: gymnosperms

5. a. cytokinin

   b. abscisic acid

   c. auxin

   d. gibberellin

   e. ethylene

6. a. photoperiodism

   b. nastic movement

   c. gravitropism

   d. thigmotropism

   e. phototropism

7. Experiments will vary. Students may suggest using a glass container lighted from below to see whether the roots continue to grow downward; in the control setup the lighting would be from above. An alternative approach would be to wrap the soil so that it does not fall out, hang a plant upside down, so that its roots are above its stem, and light the plant from below, to see whether the roots turn downward. A control would be hung and lighted normally. All other factors, such as water and temperature, should be kept the same. Data on position or angling of roots could be collected.

Unit 5A

1. c	**18.** a	**35.** c
2. a	**19.** c	**36.** c
3. d	**20.** d	**37.** b
4. c	**21.** a	**38.** a
5. a	**22.** c	**39.** d
6. c	**23.** b	**40.** a
7. b	**24.** d	**41.** c
8. b	**25.** c	**42.** d
9. a	**26.** c	**43.** c
10. c	**27.** a	**44.** a
11. d	**28.** b	**45.** c
12. a	**29.** d	**46.** c
13. d	**30.** a	**47.** a
14. a	**31.** a	**48.** c
15. c	**32.** d	**49.** c
16. a	**33.** a	**50.** a
17. b	**34.** b	

Chapter 26

TEST A

1. d	10. c	19. c
2. a	11. b	20. b
3. a	12. a	21. a
4. b	13. c	22. b
5. d	14. b	23. a
6. b	15. c	24. c
7. c	16. a	25. c
8. a	17. d	
9. a	18. b	

TEST B

1. eukaryotic, multicellular, cells organized into tissues and organs, no cell walls, heterotrophic, store energy as glycogen, locomotion, ability to sense surroundings, system that coordinates responses of body

2. Sample answer: mollusks, clams; echinoderms, sea star; chordates, humans; arthropods, insects; annelids, earthworms

3. **a.** Bilateral; concentration of complex sense organs at anterior end allows for rapid and efficient motion and an ability to sense the environment best in the direction in which animal is moving.

   b. Radial; no motion, so no need for differences in sensing ability at different ends of the body; also, radial arrangement places sensory organs around the body, allowing for sensing of approach from any direction.

4. **a.** anterior
   b. dorsal
   c. posterior
   d. ventral

5. **a.** Embryo becomes a hollow ball, or blastula, as it cleaves into smaller cells. Some cells move inward from the surface of the blastula, to form a two-layered, cup-shaped gastrula.

   b. ectoderm: skin, nerves, sense organs; endoderm: digestive tract, respiratory system; mesoderm, circulatory and reproductive systems, muscles

6. **a.** Coelomates have a fully lined body cavity, with mesoderm lining both ectoderm and endoderm. Animals with no coelom have no body cavity, the mesoderm forming a solid layer of tissue between endoderm and ectoderm. Animals with a pseudocoelom have mesoderm cells that line only the ectoderm side.

   b. Coelom provides a place for development of more complex organ systems and cushions internal organs, allowing freedom of movement of surrounding muscles.

   c. In protostomes, blastopore develops into a mouth; in deuterostomes, blastopore develops into an anus, and a mouth develops later, at the other end.

7. **a.** exoskeleton, hard encasement on surface
   b. endoskeleton, rigid internal framework
   c. hydrostatic skeleton, muscles surround and are supported by a water-filled cavity

8. **a.** tube-within-tube: two openings (mouth and anus), one-way tube, specialized in different parts, no mixing of digested and undigested food; two-way: food enters and wastes leave through single opening, digested and undigested foods mix

   b. nerve net: individual nerve cells in network throughout body, no central control; system with clustered ganglia: network leads to anterior coordinating center, or brain

   c. hermaphrodite: male and female sex organs in each individual, mating between any two individuals; nonhermaphrodite: male and female sex organs in different individuals, reproduction only through mating of individuals of different sexes

Chapter 27

TEST A

1. c	10. b	19. c
2. b	11. d	20. a
3. d	12. c	21. c
4. a	13. c	22. b
5. c	14. b	23. a
6. a	15. a	24. c
7. a	16. c	25. a
8. a	17. a	
9. c	18. b	

TEST B

1. **a.** pores through which water moves, no specialized tissues or organ systems, heterotrophs, sessile, no body symmetry
   b. sponges

2. **a.** opening at top of sponge sac, through which wastes leave
   b. cells that move through body, supply nutrients and remove wastes
   c. network of protein fibers, support
   d. tiny needlelike or starlike structures made of calcium carbonate or silicon dioxide, support
   e. flagellate cells in inside layer of sponge, create current of water flowing into pores

3. **a.** soft-bodied, hollow central cavity with single opening surrounded by tentacles, radial symmetry, polyp and medusa body plans
   b. When the prey brushes against the hydra, a cnidocyte, or stinging cell, launches a filament and poisonous barb that kills or paralyzes the prey and entangles it in the filament. The nerve net of the hydra carries signals to the contractile cells in the hydra's tentacles, which move, grasp the prey, and carry it into the mouth.

4. The medusa form produces gametes by meiosis. Sperm from a male and eggs from a female join in the water to produce a zygote that develops into a blastula and then a planula, or free-swimming ciliated larva. The planula attaches itself to a surface and develops into a polyp, which forms a stack of medusa that bud off and mature.

5. **a.** Platyhelminthes
   b. bilateral symmetry, sensory receptors and ganglia at anterior end, unsegmented, flat, ciliated, water-dwelling, generally scavengers, move over slime track they secrete, incomplete digestive system, excretory flame cells, hermaphroditic but not self-fertilizing, can also reproduce asexually by fragmentation and regeneration

6. **a.** Nematoda
   b. cylindrical, bilateral symmetry, one-way complete digestive system, pseudocoelom, sexual reproduction, nonhermaphroditic, eggs fertilized inside female

7. **a.** Egg-filled tapeworm proglottids on grass are eaten by cow. Eggs develop into larvae in cow's intestine, bore into bloodstream, move to muscles, form cysts containing bladderworms; if undercooked infested beef is eaten by human, cysts release bladder worms in intestine, worms develop into adults, attach to intestine, using hooked scolex, produce proglottids that are shed and are released with feces.

   b. Specialized structures were evolved that allow for continuing host-parasite interactions that are specific to the organisms; such structures include: a scolex with hooks and suckers to allow grasping and feeding, enzymes that dissolve skin to allow penetration of host, tough coverings to prevent digestion by host, loss of unnecessary structures such as digestive systems or sense organs.

Chapter 28

TEST A

1. a	**10.** a	**19.** c
2. d	**11.** c	**20.** c
3. c	**12.** a	**21.** d
4. b	**13.** b	**22.** a
5. a	**14.** c	**23.** c
6. b	**15.** a	**24.** a
7. b	**16.** c	**25.** b
8. c	**17.** b	
9. b	**18.** c	

TEST B

1. Both are protosomes and have a trochophore larval form, a true coelom, and either segments or distinct body regions.

2. Annelids such as earthworms loosen soil and break down organic matter for use by plants, and are therefore an aid in farming. Mollusks are important food sources, clean aquatic environments by filter-feeding, and serve as monitors of water purity.

3. a. coelom
   b. dorsal blood vessel
   c. aortic arch
   d. mouth
   e. brain
   f. ventral blood vessel
   g. crop
   h. nerve cord
   i. gizzard
   j. seta
   k. intestine

4. a. polychaetes: generally marine, usually have feathery tentacles, live in burrows, can bite, have parapodia, setae, distinct head with sense organs and mouthparts, powerful jaws; leeches: generally live in fresh water, no setae or parapodia, often parasitic, jaws with sharp teeth, able to suck blood; earthworms: land-dwelling, have setae but no parapodia, nonparasitic, etc.
   b. segmented bodies, wormlike form, internal similarities

5. distinct body regions, muscular foot, mantle, visceral mass, special organs (gills or lungs) for respiration, complete one-way digestive tract, one or two nephridia, sexual reproduction only

6. a. yes, neither, yes, yes, no, chiton
   b. yes, ganglia, yes, yes, no, snail
   c. no, ganglia, no, yes, no, clam
   d. yes, brain, yes, no, yes, octopus

Chapter 29

TEST A

1. c	**10.** c	**19.** c
2. a	**11.** a	**20.** d
3. b	**12.** b	**21.** c
4. c	**13.** c	**22.** a
5. d	**14.** a	**23.** c
6. d	**15.** c	**24.** d
7. a	**16.** b	**25.** d
8. b	**17.** c	
9. b	**18.** a	

TEST B

1. segmented, invertebrate, paired jointed appendages, chitinous exoskeleton, open circulatory system, dorsal heart

2. a. chelicerate
   b. uniramian
   c. crustacean
   d. uniramian
   e. chelicerate

3. a. antenna
   b. eye
   c. green gland
   d. stomach
   e. cephalothorax
   f. heart
   g. testis or ovary
   h. carapace
   i. abdomen
   j. intestine
   k. telson
   l. anus
   m. swimmeret
   n. nerve cord
   o. walking leg
   p. digestive gland
   q. mandible
   r. mouth
   s. jaw foot
   t. brain

4. a. holding and chewing of food
   b. excretion
   c. gas exchange
   d. making of web

5. a. tracheoles, spiracles, tracheae
   b. brain, ventral nerve cord, ganglia
   c. mouth, esophagus, crop, gizzard, midgut, hindgut, anus
   d. Malpighian tubules

6. a. series of changes during which young insects develop into adults
   b. silverfish
   c. egg, nymph, adult; grasshopper
   d. egg, larva, pupa, adult; butterfly

7. Possible answer: syrphid fly mimicking banding of bees, swallowtail butterfly camouflaged to look like dead leaf, praying mantis mimicking twig

8. Possible answer: Coleoptera, two pairs of hard wings, heavy exoskeleton, biting and chewing mouthparts, beetle; Diptera, one pair of membranous wings, sucking, piercing, or lapping mouthparts, fly; Lepidoptera: two pairs of large wings, hairy body, siphoning mouthparts, butterfly

9. food for many animals and people, essential part of food chain, control of other organism populations, pollination of plants, damaging of crops, transmission of disease

Chapter 30

1. b	**10.** d	**19.** c
2. a	**11.** d	**20.** b
3. c	**12.** a	**21.** b
4. c	**13.** c	**22.** c
5. b	**14.** a	**23.** a
6. a	**15.** b	**24.** c
7. c	**16.** a	**25.** b
8. c	**17.** b	
9. b	**18.** c	

TEST B

1. a. radial

   b. 5

   c. spiny

   d. vascular, with tube feet

   e. deuterostome

   f. endoskeleton

   g. marine

2. a. Star uses tube feet to capture and hold mollusk, wraps arms around it, attaches tube feet to shell, and pulls. When shell opens, star pushes its lower stomach out through its mouth and into the shell, digesting mollusk. Star removes its stomach and food to its body, where digestion is completed. Nutrients pass throughout the body and wastes leave through the anus.

   b. Nerve ring around mouth, radial nerves branch off and extend to tip of each arm. Chemical and touch receptors and sometimes eyespots carry information, and response is coordinated by nerve ring, which sends impulses to muscles and tube feet.

   c. Asexual: regeneration of body parts from parts containing part of central nerve ring; sexual: separate sexes with testes or ovaries in arms, fertilization in water, egg develops into bilaterally symmetrical, free-swimming larva, which settles to bottom and metamorphoses into adult.

3. Sample answer: Sea stars move slowly, have suckers and ampullae, have ventral mouth. Brittle stars move quickly, have suckerless tube feet and no ampullae, have ventral mouth. Sea lilies are sessile, have dorsal mouth, have suckerless tube feet covered with sticky mucus.

4. dorsal hollow nerve cord, notochord, gill slits or pouches, post-anal tail at some point of development

5. a. tunicate

   b. vertebrate

   c. lancelet

   d. tunicate

Unit 6A

1. b	**18.** c	**35.** c
2. a	**19.** b	**36.** c
3. c	**20.** c	**37.** a
4. d	**21.** c	**38.** d
5. c	**22.** b	**39.** b
6. a	**23.** d	**40.** b
7. c	**24.** a	**41.** a
8. b	**25.** c	**42.** a
9. c	**26.** a	**43.** c
10. c	**27.** c	**44.** c
11. a	**28.** b	**45.** d
12. c	**29.** b	**46.** a
13. a	**30.** c	**47.** d
14. c	**31.** d	**48.** a
15. a	**32.** a	**49.** b
16. d	**33.** c	**50.** b
17. a	**34.** a	

Chapter 31

TEST A

1. c	**10.** b	**19.** b
2. c	**11.** a	**20.** a
3. a	**12.** a	**21.** c
4. b	**13.** c	**22.** b
5. d	**14.** c	**23.** c
6. a	**15.** c	**24.** a
7. d	**16.** b	**25.** d
8. a	**17.** c	
9. a	**18.** c	

TEST B

1. dorsal nerve cord, notochord, gill slits or pouches, post-anal tail, backbone made up of bony segments, endoskeleton, generally two pairs of appendages, distinct head at anterior end of vertebral column, well-developed brain and sensory organs, high degree of cephalization, closed circulatory system with multichambered heart

2. sample answer: cartilaginous fishes (Chondrichthyes), shark; bony fishes (Osteichthyes), salmon; amphibians (Amphibia), frog

3. First fish was jawless, bony-plated ostracoderm, which evolved from invertebrates. Jawless fishes without armor evolved from it, and in turn produced modern jawless fishes. Jawed armored fishes called placoderms also evolved from ostracoderms, but eventually these evolved into armorless jawed fishes. Both cartilaginous and bony fishes evolved from these; the cartilaginous evolved in a marine environment, the bony in a freshwater environment that, because of greater variation, encouraged rapid and varied evolution.

4. a. Chondrichthyes
b. Agnatha
c. Chondrichthyes
d. Osteichthyes
e. Agnatha
f. Chondrichthyes

5. Lobe-finned: muscular, paddlelike fins supported by bones attached to girdle, no lungs, coelacanth; lungfish: lungs and gills, long, eel-like body, Australian lungfish; ray-finned: fanlike fins made of thin membranes supported by bony rays, gills, no lungs, tuna

6. a. dorsal fin
b. nerve cord
c. brain
d. gills
e. heart
f. liver
g. stomach
h. pelvic fin
i. intestine
j. ovary or testis
k. swim bladder
l. anus
m. lateral line

7. Female that has swum upstream from sea digs nest, deposits eggs, male deposits sperm onto them, female covers nest. Adults may either die then or move downstream again. Eggs hatch, young hide in gravel and are nourished by attached yolk sac, later feed on plankton. They travel downstream to the sea, remain there for some time, then find their home stream, swim upstream, undergoing various physical changes, and mate again.

Chapter 32

TEST A

1. c	**10.** a	**19.** a
2. a	**11.** c	**20.** d
3. c	**12.** a	**21.** c
4. a	**13.** a	**22.** c
5. d	**14.** a	**23.** c
6. b	**15.** b	**24.** c
7. b	**16.** c	**25.** b
8. c	**17.** a	
9. d	**18.** c	

TEST B

1. Most start life as aquatic larvae and live as adults on land. All require a moist environment for reproduction They produce eggs without shells. As adults, they have no scales and only modified teeth and are smooth-skinned; most have four limbs.

2. Devonian lobe-finned fishes with lungs were able to crawl across land when ponds dried up and to breathe oxygen in air. Some of them evolved into fishlike amphibians that had scales and a lateral line system. These evolved into true amphibians during the Carboniferous period, and thrived until the end of the Paleozoic era.

3. Urodela: usually gills as larvae, often replaced with lungs as adults, long tail throughout life, long body, two pairs of legs as adults; salamander; Anura: tails as larvae, not as adults, gills as larvae, lungs as adults, two pairs of legs as adults; frog; Apoda: no legs, even as adults, blind or nearly blind, smooth skin; caecilian

4. Larvae have feathery external gills for gas exchange in water. Oxygen in the water diffuses into the blood that flows through the gill capillaries. Most adults have lungs, allowing for gas exchange in air. Many also exchange gases by simple diffusion through the moist lining of skin and mouth.

5. Male climbs onto female's back and grasps her under forelimbs. Female picks a moist site and releases her eggs. Male deposits sperm on them. Eggs are fertilized and are not typically guarded by adults. Eggs hatch into aquatic larvae, or tadpoles, which have gills. As tadpoles develop into adults, they lose their gills and develop lungs for terrestrial life, lose their tails, and develop legs. The metamorphosis is triggered by a hormone called thyroxine. Adult teeth and jaws and a short digestive tract also develop. The single-loop, two-chambered-heart circulatory system of the tadpoles changes to a double-loop, three-chambered-heart system characteristic of the adults.

6. a. esophagus
b. liver
c. gall bladder
d. pancreas
e. stomach
f. small intestine
g. large intestine
h. cloaca
i. anus
j. lung
k. atrium
l. ventricle
m. heart
n. fat body
o. ovary or testis
p. kidney
q. bladder

Chapter 33

TEST A

1. a	**10.** b	**19.** c
2. b	**11.** a	**20.** a
3. a	**12.** b	**21.** d
4. d	**13.** a	**22.** d
5. b	**14.** b	**23.** c
6. b	**15.** a	**24.** b
7. a	**16.** c	**25.** b
8. a	**17.** b	
9. c	**18.** a	

TEST B

1. a. evolved either from amphibians or directly from lobe-finned fishes

b. from stem reptiles; along with turtles, were the only reptile survivors of mass extinction at end of Permian period

c. from thecodonts in Triassic period of Mesozoic era

d. crocodiles: from thecodonts

2. a. tuatara, Rhynchocephalia

b. lizard, Squamata

c. alligator, Crocodilia

d. turtle, Chelonia

e. snake, Squamata

f. tortoise, Chelonia

g. crocodile, Crocodilia

h. lizard, Squamata

3. a. scaly, waterproof skin that reduces water loss, bladder that returns water from waste to blood, relatively dry urine, shelled egg that keeps eggs from drying out

b. strong legs tucked close to body

c. flexible jaws, sharp teeth, venom, heat detectors

d. ability to absorb heat from environment and to adjust position relative to sun

e. four-chambered or partially divided three-chambered heart to prevent or reduce mixing of oxygen-rich and oxygen-poor blood, well-developed lungs with large internal surface area

4. a. shell

b. chorion

c. albumin

d. amnion

e. amniotic fluid

f. embryo

g. yolk

h. allantois

5. a. internal, sperm deposited directly into female

b. Many lay eggs, some snakes and lizards hold eggs in body, where the eggs hatch and the young are then born live.

c. in sand, soil, or rotting logs, some nests deeply dug, some in small depressions, eggs laid where they will stay warm

d. Most provide no care; alligator guards eggs, unburies them when young are heard peeping, carries them to water.

Chapter 34

TEST A

1. c	**10.** c	**19.** a
2. b	**11.** b	**20.** b
3. a	**12.** c	**21.** b
4. d	**13.** a	**22.** d
5. d	**14.** b	**23.** d
6. b	**15.** d	**24.** a
7. c	**16.** a	**25.** c
8. d	**17.** c	
9. d	**18.** c	

TEST B

1. Evolved from thecodont reptiles about 225 million years ago, during Triassic period. Early birdlike reptiles had reptilian and avian features and may have originally been leaping animals for which adaptations of gliding and flying were useful. Developed into true birds and evolved rapidly after dinosaurs became extinct. *Protoavis:* chicken-sized animal, lived about 225 million years ago, had reptilian and avian features; *Archaeopteryx:* first known animal with feathers, had reptilian and avian features, lived during late Jurassic period, was probably not direct ancestor of modern birds.

2. sample answer: Galliformes (game birds), chickens; Passeriformes (perching songbirds), robins; Falconiformes (birds of prey), eagles

3. contour: stiff central shaft with many side barbs, each of which has hooked interlocking barbules; to streamline the body, form a smooth flying surface and waterproof the body; down: short shafts, tuft of long fluffy barbs at end; to insulate by trapping layers of air

4. a. strong but light hollow bones, reducing weight, absence of teeth to lighten head, fused bones to reduce heavy ligaments and provide stability for flight

b. large, powerful muscles, especially those that move wings, special arrangements of tendons

c. rapid heartbeat, high blood pressure, four-chambered heart, for efficient gas exchange necessary to power flight

d. highly efficient oxygen intake, one-way air flow through lungs, air sacs to hold large amounts of oxygen

5. Flight requires much energy. Birds maintain heat by keeping body temperature constant. This also allows them to live in cold climates.

6. Birds must eat and rapidly digest large amounts of food to power flight and endothermy. Avian digestive system is compact and fast-acting. Food is swallowed unchewed, mixed with saliva, moves to esophagus and to crop, where it is softened; moves to muscular gizzard, which contains small stones used for grinding; nutrients are absorbed quickly in intestines because of fingerlike villi.

7. Reproductive organs enlarge at nesting season. Sperm produced in testes surrounded by air sacs is transferred directly to females, which have one ovary and oviduct. Fertilization is internal; fertilized egg travels with yolk though oviduct, is coated with albumin and shell, leaves female through cloaca. Egg is amniotic and, because of endothermy, must be incubated.

8. Courtship behaviors include singing of males to establish territory and attract mates, feather-spreading, parading, building of elaborate nests, and courtship dancing. Most species are monogamous, which provides for intensive involvement during nest-building, incubation, and caring for young. Events such as mating and nest-building are triggered by amount of daylight, which affects release of hormones that activate reproductive organs and initiate mating behaviors.

9. Answers might refer to specially shaped beaks that aid various birds in cracking seeds, digging and pecking for worms, etc., and to specially adapted feet for swimming, perching, etc.

Chapter 35

TEST A

1. d	10. d	19. b
2. b	11. b	20. b
3. c	12. a	21. d
4. b	13. b	22. c
5. b	14. d	23. d
6. c	15. d	24. a
7. b	16. d	25. c
8. a	17. c	
9. c	18. b	

TEST B

1. endothermic, vertebrate, has hair, internal fertilization, female produces milk in mammary glands

2. They evolved from therapsids, mammal-like reptiles, during Triassic period, were small insect-eaters; at end of Mesozoic era, as climate and vegetation changed and dinosaurs became extinct, mammals evolved into a great many forms and became the dominant vertebrates of the Cenozoic era.

3. Climate became cooler, endothermy and insulation provided by hair became great advantages.

4. **a.** hatched, yes, no, duck-billed platypus
   b. nourished in pouch, no, yes, kangaroo
   c. nourished by internal structure, no, yes, mouse

5. **a.** Artiodactyla, deer
   b. Cetacea, whale
   c. Proboscidea, elephant
   d. Primates, monkey
   e. Chiroptera, bat
   f. Carnivora, dog
   g. Rodentia, rat
   h. Perissodactyla, horse
   i. Lagomorpha, rabbit

6. incisors: conelike, in front of mouth, stripping and cutting; canines: long, pointed, to sides of mouth, piercing and tearing; molars: broad, flattened, in back of mouth, for grinding and crushing

7. sample answer: deer, large flat molars for grinding leaves and twigs; wolf, sharp canines for cutting flesh; mouse, long, continuously growing incisors for gnawing

8. **a.** diaphragm to cause air to enter and leave lungs efficiently, air sacs to improve gas exchange
   b. double-loop circulatory system, four-chambered heart, improving efficiency of oxygen delivery and removal of waste gases
   c. large brain, well-developed cerebrum for intelligence and rapid learning, echolocation in some mammals, well-developed specialized senses, such as taste, smell, hearing, for reception of information

9. newborn offspring protected and kept warm in mother's pouch, mother free to move from place to place

10. embryo develops more completely inside mother and is nourished by her through placenta

Chapter 36

TEST A

1. d	10. b	19. b
2. a	11. c	20. d
3. c	12. c	21. c
4. d	13. a	22. b
5. a	14. d	23. b
6. b	15. c	24. c
7. c	16. b	25. b
8. d	17. c	
9. d	18. a	

TEST B

1. the way an organism responds to its environment

2. stimulus: something in environment to which an organism can respond; response: the way the organism behaves when the stimulus is applied; example: bright light (stimulus) that causes an insect to hide (response)

3. innate: inborn, or present and complete without need for experience; learned: acquired as result of experience

4. **a.** complex programmed behavior
   b. reflex
   c. fixed-action pattern
   d. reflex

5. **a.** classical conditioning, dog is trained to salivate when a bell rings
   b. reasoning, ape figures out how to use a tool to perform a task
   c. habituation, turtle repeatedly touched without being harmed stops drawing in its head
   d. imprinting, goslings quickly learn to follow a moving object
   e. operant conditioning, a pigeon learns by trial-and-error that pecking at a certain button in its cage causes a food pellet to be released to it

6. **a.** female insect releases a chemical to attract males
   b. parrot puffs out its feathers to appear larger when it sees another parrot
   c. male ducks perform a series of motions in water and air to attract females
   d. dog frightens off other dogs that enter its territory

7. cooperation, division of labor, protection of individuals from predators

8. ranking system in which higher-ranking individuals get better food and have a greater opportunity to mate; pecking order in birds

9. self-sacrifice of an individual for the protection of relatives; worker bees stinging an encroacher despite the fact that they will die as a result

10. Students should design an operant-conditioning experiment in which the monkey might be placed in a room with a piano. When the monkey touches a certain key, the animal might be rewarded with a banana. If it touches that key and a second key, it can be rewarded again, etc., until it learns to touch three particular keys in succession. Students should point out that successful completion of this task would confirm a hypothesis that such learning is possible.

Unit 7A

1. a	**18.** d	**35.** a
2. c	**19.** b	**36.** b
3. a	**20.** a	**37.** c
4. c	**21.** d	**38.** a
5. c	**22.** c	**39.** c
6. a	**23.** c	**40.** b
7. b	**24.** b	**41.** c
8. c	**25.** a	**42.** c
9. a	**26.** d	**43.** d
10. d	**27.** c	**44.** b
11. b	**28.** d	**45.** c
12. a	**29.** a	**46.** a
13. c	**30.** b	**47.** d
14. b	**31.** a	**48.** c
15. c	**32.** c	**49.** a
16. b	**33.** b	**50.** c
17. d	**34.** d	

Chapter 37

TEST A

1. a	**10.** b	**19.** b
2. c	**11.** a	**20.** a
3. d	**12.** a	**21.** c
4. b	**13.** d	**22.** b
5. a	**14.** b	**23.** d
6. c	**15.** a	**24.** c
7. d	**16.** b	**25.** a
8. d	**17.** a	
9. a	**18.** c	

TEST B

1. **a.** ventral side
   b. dorsal side
   c. cranial cavity
   d. thoracic cavity
   e. abdominal cavity
   f. diaphragm
2. **a.** skin, nails
   b. bones, joints
   c. brain, spinal cord
   d. heart, blood vessels
   e. lungs, breathing passages
   f. kidneys, bladder
   g. stomach, intestines
3. **a.** muscle
   b. epithelial
   c. connective
   d. nervous
   e. muscle
   f. connective
4. support, anchors for muscles, protection of internal organs, making of blood cells, storage of minerals
5. **a.** ligament
   b. cartilage
   c. Haversian canal
   d. tendon
   e. red bone marrow
   f. periosteum
6. **a.** skeletal: striated, long fibers with many nuclei per cell, voluntary movement of bone; smooth: unstriated, one nucleus per cell, involuntary regulation and control; cardiac: striated, works without stimulation from nervous system, in heart only, involuntary
   b. Nerve impulse causes contraction or shortening of muscle, which pulls on bone. Muscles are typically paired, alternating contracting and relaxing, to pull bone in different directions.
   c. how skeletal muscles contract and move
7. **a.** epidermis
   b. dermis
   c. sebaceous gland
   d. hair follicle
   e. fat layer
   f. blood vessel
   g. sweat gland
   h. pore
   i. nerve ending

Chapter 38

TEST A

1. d	**10.** c	**19.** c
2. b	**11.** b	**20.** d
3. a	**12.** a	**21.** a
4. d	**13.** c	**22.** a
5. c	**14.** d	**23.** a
6. c	**15.** b	**24.** b
7. b	**16.** c	**25.** d
8. a	**17.** b	
9. b	**18.** d	

TEST B

1. **a.** carbohydrates: energy source, mouth, small intestine
   b. fats: storage of energy and of other nutrients, small intestine
   c. proteins: growth and repair and making of other proteins, stomach, small intestine
   d. vitamins: enzyme helpers and participants in cellular reactions, large intestine
   e. minerals: components of bones, in oxygen transport, in nerve function, large intestine
2. **a.** All are carbohydrates and have roughly a 1:2:1 ratio of carbon, hydrogen, and oxygen. Sugars have one or two sugar units, and are classified as monosaccharides and disaccharides. Starches are polysaccharides, or long chains of sugars. Cellulose is a kind of polysaccharide in the cell walls of plants.
   b. All are made of three fatty acids joined to a glycerol molecule. Saturated fats have no double bonds, monounsaturated fats have one per molecule, and polyunsaturated fats have more than one.
   c. All are involved in body part construction. Essential amino acids are protein-building units that cannot be made by the body. Nonessential amino acids are units that can be made by the body from other food sources. Proteins are made up of amino acid units.
3. more carbohydrates, in the form of breads, grains, and pasta, more sources of B vitamins, such as beans, whole grains, skim milk, fish, and potatoes, more sources of vitamin C, such as green leafy vegetables, strawberries, and citrus fruits; less red meat and whole dairy products
4. **a.** amount of heat needed to raise the temperature of 1 g of water by 1°C; 1000 calories; 1000 calories, or 1 kcal
   b. 4, 9, 4
   c. number of kcal an animal or person must use in a set amount of time to maintain life; 1600–1800, 1300–1500
5. **a.** mouth
   b. salivary gland
   c. pharynx
   d. epiglottis
   e. esophagus
   f. liver
   g. stomach
   h. pancreas
   i. gallbladder
   j. small intestine
   k. large intestine
   l. rectum
   m. anus
6. **a.** conversion of glucose to glycogen, storage of glycogen, fats, vitamins, iron, and other nutrients, making of lipoproteins, filtering of nutrients from blood, detoxification
   b. storage of bile made by liver
   c. secretion of fluids containing enzymes and sodium bicarbonate into intestine, secretion of insulin to control glucose uptake

Chapter 39

TEST A

1. c	10. a	19. c
2. a	11. d	20. a
3. d	12. a	21. b
4. b	13. b	22. c
5. b	14. c	23. a
6. a	15. a	24. c
7. c	16. b	25. b
8. d	17. d	
9. c	18. a	

TEST B

1. a. to deliver oxygen, nutrients, and other substances to the cells and to pick up and remove wastes from cells

b. heart, blood, blood vessels

c. pulmonary: short loop of circulatory system that carries blood between heart and lungs; systemic: loop of system that carries blood between heart and body.

2. a. four chambers, two atria (upper chambers), two ventricles (lower chambers), septum dividing sides of heart, one-way valves

b. Right side receives oxygen-poor blood from the body and pumps it to the lungs; left side receives oxygen-rich blood from the lungs and pumps it to the rest of the body

3. a. Diastole: heart muscle relaxes, allowing blood to flow into atria and ventricles; Systole: ventricles contract, pumping blood to body

b. Sinoatrial node (pacemaker) in right atrium sends out electrical signals that cause atria to contract; the signals travel to atrioventricular node, in septum between atria, which causes ventricles to contract. Rate is also affected by exercise and certain emotions.

4. a. phagocyte

b. erythrocyte

c. platelet

d. lymphocyte

e. erythrocyte

5. Arteries: contain endothelium, smooth muscle, and connective tissue, carry blood away from heart, typically carry oxygen-rich blood. Veins: contain endothelium, smooth muscle, and connective tissue, carry blood toward heart, typically carry oxygen-poor blood. Capillaries: tiny, thin-walled, contain endothelium, carry blood in networks to cells and connect arteries and veins, contain blood that is oxygen-rich but that becomes depleted in oxygen as diffusion takes place through contact with cells.

6. System collects intercellular fluid, cleans it, and returns it to the circulatory system. Lymph capillaries intertwine with blood capillaries, absorb fluid that leaks through them, and merge to form larger lymph vessels. Lymph is filtered through lymph nodes, eventually enters ducts in the neck that empty into large veins. Lymph is directed by one-way valves and is moved by the action of skeletal muscles. Lymphatic system includes the spleen, an organ that removes old blood cells and other particles from blood, stores iron, and serves as a site for increase in number of white blood cells during an infection.

7. a. Narrowing of arteries because of fatty deposits called plaques inside vessel walls; blood flow is reduced and there is an increased chance of clot formation and blockage that may lead to heart attack or stroke.

b. High blood pressure; can damage arteries, overwork heart, and lead to heart attack and stroke.

Chapter 40

TEST A

1. c	10. b	19. c
2. d	11. b	20. a
3. a	12. a	21. d
4. d	13. b	22. c
5. c	14. d	23. a
6. a	15. c	24. a
7. b	16. a	25. b
8. a	17. d	
9. c	18. a	

TEST B

1. a. Within cells; cells get energy from oxidation of glucose.

b. In capillaries; oxygen and carbon dioxide are exchanged between blood and body cells.

c. In lungs; oxygen and carbon dioxide are exchanged between blood and air.

2. a. nostril

b. epiglottis

c. pharynx

d. larynx

e. trachea

f. bronchus

g. lung

h. bronchiole

i. alveolus

j. diaphragm

3. Inhalation: Diaphragm contracts and moves down, and intercostal muscles push ribs out, expanding chest cavity and reducing air pressure in lungs, which causes air to rush in from outside. Exhalation: Diaphragm relaxes and moves up, and intercostal muscles relax, shrinking chest cavity and increasing pressure in lungs, which causes air to be forced to outside.

4. Diffusion occurs in each case, and hemoglobin binds or releases oxygen, depending on oxygen concentration. In alveoli, oxygen is more concentrated than in capillaries and carbon dioxide is less concentrated, so oxygen diffuses from alveoli to capillaries and CO_2 diffuses from capillaries to alveoli. In body tissues, oxygen is less concentrated than in capillaries and carbon dioxide is more concentrated, so oxygen diffuses from capillaries to tissues and CO_2 diffuses from tissues to capillaries.

5. a. to rid the body of nitrogen-containing wastes

b. cortex: outer portion, contain nephrons and blood vessels; medulla: inner part, contains collecting tubules and blood vessels; nephrons: remove wastes from blood and form urine; glomerulus: clump of capillaries in nephron where waste is given up by blood; Bowman's capsule: surrounds glomerulus and is beginning of tube in which urine forms; renal tubule: part of nephron in which urine forms and moves along to collecting tubules, which lead to ureters

c. filtration, reabsorption, secretion

d. Urine coming from ureters is stored there and is expelled to the outside from there, through urethra.

Chapter 41

TEST A

1. c	**10.** b	**19.** c
2. b	**11.** b	**20.** c
3. a	**12.** c	**21.** b
4. a	**13.** b	**22.** a
5. d	**14.** b	**23.** c
6. a	**15.** a	**24.** a
7. c	**16.** d	**25.** b
8. c	**17.** d	
9. a	**18.** b	

TEST B

1. a. to gather information from outside and inside the body, to transmit information to processing areas in the brain and spinal cord, to process the information to determine the best response, and to send information to muscles, glands, and organs so that they can respond

b. central nervous system (CNS; brain and spinal cord): main control center, to process information and send instructions to the rest of the body; peripheral nervous system (PNS; nerves that extend throughout the body): to gather information from and deliver information to CNS.

2. a. a nerve cell, functional unit of nervous system

b. dendrites: receive information and carry it toward cell body; axon: carries nerve impulses away from cell body

c. sensory: to conduct nerve impulses from information-gathering structures to the CNS; motor neurons: to conduct impulses from CNS to effectors; interneurons: to conduct impulses within CNS; d. to protect, mechanically support, and assist neurons; Schwann cells and astrocytes

3. a. (1) Section of neuron is at rest, with positive charge on outside and negative charge on inside surface of cell membrane. (2) Channels in neuron membrane open and positive sodium ions flow into cell, reversing charge on membrane. (3) Charge reversal opens channels in next section of nerve fibers, and so on. (4) Channels open through which positive potassium ions flow out of cell, restoring section of fiber to its resting potential.

b. Impulse reaches end of axon and causes some sacs containing neurotransmitter molecules to fuse with axon's membrane. Fused sacs release neurotransmitters into synapse gap between neurons. Molecules diffuse across synapse and bind to receptors on next neuron, changing membrane potential.

4. a. meninges
b. cerebrum
c. thalamus
d. hypothalamus
e. pons
f. cerebellum
g. medulla oblongata
h. brain stem
i. spinal cord

5. a. Engrams for memory storage are distributed throughout cerebral cortex. Memory involves changes in synapses and amounts of released neurotransmitters along series of neurons. Repeated stimulation of same neurons makes impulse transmission easier.

b. Broca's area, on left side of cerebral cortex, translates thoughts into speech and coordinates muscles used for speaking. Wernicke's area, also on left side of cerebral cortex, stores information needed to understand language. There are many other specialized language-area clusters in the brain that serve different functions.

6. a. somatic: motor nerves that control voluntary responses (involving skeletal muscles); autonomic: control involuntary responses (involving smooth muscles, organs, and glands)

b. sympathetic: motor nerves that control responses of body to stress; parasympathetic: control body functions associated with rest and digestion

Chapter 42

TEST A

1. b	**10.** d	**19.** a
2. c	**11.** d	**20.** c
3. a	**12.** d	**21.** d
4. b	**13.** b	**22.** a
5. c	**14.** a	**23.** c
6. a	**15.** a	**24.** c
7. b	**16.** b	**25.** a
8. c	**17.** d	
9. b	**18.** c	

TEST B

1. a. to control the body by means of chemical messengers

b. Unlike exocrine glands, endocrine glands are ductless and release hormones directly into blood. Check examples for accuracy.

c. Sample answer: Thyroid makes thyrosine, which speeds up metabolism and controls growth and development; pineal makes melatonin, which controls body functions in response to daylight and seasonal changes.

d. Protein: made of peptides, bind to outside of target cell membranes, which brings about changes inside; steroid: made of lipids, enter target cells and cause changes by gene regulation.

2. a. Hypothalamus sends signals to pituitary to speed up or slow down releases of stored hormones from the latter. The hormones stimulate activity of other endocrine glands.

b. When blood glucose level is low, islets of Langerhans in pancreas are stimulated to release glucagon, a hormone that stimulates conversion of stored glycogen to glucose. When blood glucose level is high, islets of Langerhans are stimulated to release insulin, a hormone that stimulates cells to take up sugar from the blood and that causes glucose to be changed to glycogen. This step therefore inhibits the first step (glucose-to-glucagon conversion) and there is a negative feedback mechanism.

3. Testes in scrotum produce sperm cells and testosterone. Mature sperm are stored in epididymus. Penis delivers sperm to female reproductive system. Sperm travel from vas deferens to urethra and then out of the body.

4. a. Fallopian tube
b. uterus
c. ovary
d. ovum
e. follicle
f. oocyte
g. cervix
h. vagina

5. a. If egg not fertilized, endometrium lining of uterus and unfertilized egg are shed and pass out of body through vagina.

b. Hypothalamus stimulates pituitary to relase FSH and LH. FSH stimulates follicle in ovary to develop, oocyte within continues meiotic division, and estrogen is released, which stimulates development of endometrium. More LH is released from pituitary, which causes follicle to release egg.

c. Ruptured follicle becomes corpus luteum, which releases progesterone, causing endometrium to thicken, and also releases estrogen. The two hormones stop hypothalamus from signaling pituitary to release LH and FSH. Egg moves down Fallopian tube, may be fertilized and attach to endometrium. If not, corpus luteum is reabsorbed, levels of estrogen and progesterone drop, and endometrium begins to break down.

6. a. Sperm deposited in female move to Fallopian tubes. Many move through outer membrane and jellylike covering and attach to binding sites on egg surface. One sperm breaks through membrane, and membranes of sperm and egg join. Sperm nucleus enters egg cytoplasm and fuses with egg nucleus, producing zygote.

b. Zygote cleaves repeatedly to become solid-ball morula, which develops into hollow-ball blastocyst. Blastocyst releases enzyme that causes it to become embedded in uterus wall. Cleavage continues and three germ layers form. Outer layer of blastocyst develops into amnion and chorion. Placenta forms from chorion and endometrium.

c. In early weeks, head is about half length of embryo, organ systems develop, heart begins to beat. Then body grows quickly, appearance becomes human, brain and sense organs develop, as do bones, joints, and nervous system. Eyes blink, legs kick, sleeping and thumb-sucking occur. Teeth become covered with enamel, weight increases, fat develops, antibodies are transferred from mother, respiratory system completes development.

d. Fetus is generally upside down. Oxytocin from pituitary of mother starts labor. Uterus contracts rhythmically, amniotic sac breaks, cervix widens. Baby is delivered through vagina. Umbilical cord is cut and placenta is discharged as afterbirth.

Chapter 43

TEST A

1. b	**10.** b	**19.** c
2. a	**11.** b	**20.** b
3. d	**12.** a	**21.** b
4. c	**13.** d	**22.** a
5. a	**14.** b	**23.** b
6. c	**15.** a	**24.** b
7. b	**16.** b	**25.** d
8. b	**17.** a	
9. a	**18.** b	

TEST B

1. a. any illness caused by organisms or viruses that enter and reproduce inside the host

b. an organism or virus that causes an infectious disease

c. sample answer: common cold, virus (rhinovirus); malaria, protist (*Plasmodium*)

2. Examine the blood of some cattle that are sick with X fever and some that are not. The bacterium should be in the blood of the former, but not of the latter. Remove some of the bacterium from infected cattle and grow a pure culture of it in the laboratory. Place some of the laboratory-grown bacteria into healthy cattle and observe that it causes X fever in them. Finally, recover some of the same kind of bacteria from these newly infected cattle.

3. direct contact with an infected person (syphilis), indirect contact with an infected person (common cold), contaminated food or water (amebic dysentery), the bite of an infected animal (rabies)

4. a. mechanisms by which the body protects itself against many different disease-causing agents

b. responses of the immune system to specific pathogens

c. humoral: immune response that occurs in body fluids, antibodies; cell-mediated: immune response in which special cells attack cells dangerous to the body, T lymphocytes

5. a. nonspecific
b. cell-mediated
c. nonspecific
d. nonspecific
e. humoral
f. nonspecific
g. nonspecific

6. a. Immune system reacts to harmless substance in pollen as if substance were an antigen of a dangerous pathogen. Histamine is released by macrophages, causing eyes to tear and nasal passages to secrete mucus.

b. HIV enters body as a result of sexual contact, sharing of needles, or transfusion. First, there may be flulike symptoms and HIV antibodies are produced by body. T4 cells that activate further immune response are attacked and destroyed by HIV. Symptoms such as fever, weight loss, and swollen lymph nodes may begin to appear. Eventually T4 cells may become so

reduced in number that the immune system cannot effectively fight disease. Dangerous opportunistic infections occur, and full-blown AIDS has developed.

Chapter 44

TEST A

1. c	**10.** d	**19.** c
2. d	**11.** b	**20.** c
3. b	**12.** a	**21.** b
4. a	**13.** b	**22.** a
5. b	**14.** a	**23.** c
6. c	**15.** d	**24.** c
7. a	**16.** a	**25.** b
8. b	**17.** a	
9. d	**18.** c	

TEST B

1. a. a nonfood chemical substance that, when taken into the body, changes the way the body behaves

b. misuse: taking of drug for a medical purpose other than its intended purpose; abuse: deliberate taking of drug in excessive quantities or for purposes other than acceptable medical use, or any taking of illegal drugs

2. a. physical or psychological difficulty in functioning normally without a drug

b. physical dependency on a drug

c. period in which the body must adjust to functioning without a drug

3. a. tranquilizer
b. narcotic
c. steroid
d. stimulant
e. barbiturate
f. hallucinogen

4. a. depressant, affects brain and liver functioning, excreted through kidneys, some broken down by stomach enzymes or exhaled from lungs, absorbed into bloodstream, eventually broken down by liver; depending on amount consumed, can induce relaxation, produce loss of coordination, impairment of vision, loss of control over body and mind, loss of consciousness, coma, and death; long-term effects can include cirrhosis

b. alcohol dependency; recognizable in a number of ways—e.g., if there is a need to drink to relax, a need to drink in the morning, or forgetfulness of what occurs during drinking periods

5. a. nicotine: addictive stimulant drug; tar: thick, dark, sticky, carcinogenic substance; carbon monoxide: poisonous gas

b. paralysis and eventual destruction of cilia, accumulation of mucus in lungs, "smoker's cough," respiratory infections, lung cancer, emphysema

c. narrowing of blood vessels, increased blood pressure, reduced circulation, lowered delivery of oxygen to tissues, heart attacks

Unit 8A

1. d	**18.** c	**35.** c
2. c	**19.** b	**36.** c
3. a	**20.** a	**37.** a
4. c	**21.** d	**38.** b
5. b	**22.** a	**39.** a
6. a	**23.** c	**40.** b
7. b	**24.** c	**41.** c
8. c	**25.** a	**42.** b
9. a	**26.** a	**43.** b
10. c	**27.** d	**44.** b
11. d	**28.** c	**45.** d
12. c	**29.** b	**46.** b
13. d	**30.** c	**47.** a
14. a	**31.** a	**48.** b
15. d	**32.** c	**49.** d
16. a	**33.** a	**50.** d
17. d	**34.** d	

Chapter 45

TEST A

1. c	10. d	19. b
2. b	11. c	20. a
3. a	12. b	21. a
4. c	13. b	22. d
5. b	14. a	23. a
6. b	15. b	24. b
7. a	16. c	25. c
8. b	17. a	
9. a	18. c	

TEST B

1. a. biotic: grasses, trees, mice, owls; abiotic: rocks, soil, water, air

b. mice: eat grasses, provide food for owls, drink water, use oxygen given off by plants into air, provide carbon dioxide and nutrients for grasses and trees, nest on soil and grasses return plant nutrients to soil through droppings; owls: eat mice, live in trees, drink water, use oxygen given off by plants into air, provide carbon dioxide and nutrients for grasses and trees; trees: make nutrients from carbon dioxide given off by animals into air, obtain nutrients from animal droppings and remains, produce oxygen that animals use, provide shelter for owls, take in water

2. a. typical weather pattern of an area over time

b. temperature and precipitation

c. latitude, altitude, nearness to bodies of water; as latitude increases, temperature decreases; as altitude increases, temperature decreases; as distance from major bodies of water increases, temperature increases in summer and decreases in winter

3. Primary succession begins as pioneer organisms—the lichens—occupy a previously-lifeless area. The lichens break down the rocks and create soil. In the soil, grasses later germinate from seeds carried into the area, become dense, and cause the lichens to die off. The soil layer thickens, and weeds then germinate, causing grasses to die off. The weeds are the climax community until the fire upsets the community. Afterwards, secondary succession begins. The new shrubs develop, soil becomes thicker, pines grow, and the shrubs tend to die off. Then oaks gradually replace the pines. Finally, beeches replace the oaks. The beeches represent the final climax community.

4. a. temperate forest
b. chaparral
c. tundra
d. tropical rain forest
e. taiga
f. grasslands

5. a. intertidal zone
b. benthic zone
c. photic zone
d. oceanic zone
e. aphotic zone
f. neritic zone

6. a. shallow area where river empties into ocean, fresh and salt water mix (brackish water); freshwater and marine animals present, including crustaceans, fishes, mollusks

b. place where fresh water and land meet, include marshes, swamps, and bogs; reeds, cattails, cypress trees, water lilies, waterfowl, muskrats present

c. streams and rivers; few algae or small plants; insects, trout, and salmon present

d. lakes and ponds; fishes, frogs, insects, turtles, birds, algae present

Chapter 46

TEST A

1. b	10. a	19. c
2. c	11. c	20. d
3. a	12. c	21. d
4. c	13. a	22. a
5. d	14. c	23. b
6. b	15. a	24. c
7. c	16. b	25. a
8. c	17. a	
9. d	18. b	

TEST B

1. a. a community refers only to organisms; ecosystem includes nonliving factors.

b. a step in the transfer of energy and matter in a community

c. producers: autotrophs, which make their own food; consumers: heterotrophs, which cannot make their own food and that eat other organisms; decomposers: heterotrophs, which cannot make their own food and that obtain food from dead organism and organic wastes.

2. A: primary consumer (example: mouse feeding on cabbage); B: producer (cabbage); C: tertiary consumer (wolf feeding on weasel); D: secondary consumer (weasel feeding on mouse)

3. Arrows should point from: grass to rabbit, grass to mouse, grass to deer, mouse to snake, rabbit to fox, mouse to fox, grass to beetle, beetle to toad, rabbit to eagle, snake to eagle, owl to eagle, mouse to owl, toad to owl, deer to cougar.

4. a. total mass of organic matter at a trophic level

b. a representation that shows the relationships between producers and consumers at different trophic levels in an ecosystem

c. becomes lower; becomes lower; becomes lower

5. a. repeated movement of water between Earth's surface and the atmosphere

b. Water evaporates from surface of bodies of water and enters atmosphere as water vapor, where it cools, condenses, and returns to Earth as precipitation. Water is taken up by plants and animals and is returned to the environment through evaporation, transpiration, perspiration, breathing, cellular respiration, etc.

6. Producers make oxygen and carbon-containing glucose from carbon dioxide and water vapor during photosynthesis. In respiration of both producers and consumers, carbon dioxide and water vapor are produced from oxygen and glucose. These two processes therefore cycle oxygen and carbon compounds back and forth.

7. Prehistoric photosynthetic organisms used energy of sun, carbon dioxide, and water vapor to make sugars and other carbon-rich substances. Some of these organisms that were not eaten by consumers were buried and compressed over millions of years and transformed into coal, oil, and natural gas.

8. a. Nitrogen-fixing bacteria in soil and on roots of legumes convert atmospheric nitrogen gas to usable nitrogen compounds, such as ammonium ions.

b. Ammonium ions are changed into nitrites and nitrates by nitrifying bacteria.

c. Decomposers break down nitrogen compounds in the wastes and remains of organisms into ammonia.

d. Denitrifying bacteria convert ammonia, nitrites, and nitrates into free nitrogen gas.

Chapter 47

TEST A

1. d	**10.** a	**19.** c
2. d	**11.** b	**20.** b
3. c	**12.** a	**21.** b
4. a	**13.** a	**22.** b
5. b	**14.** d	**23.** a
6. b	**15.** a	**24.** c
7. a	**16.** d	**25.** a
8. b	**17.** c	
9. b	**18.** b	

TEST B

1. a. group of organisms of the same species that live in a particular area

b. any condition of the environment that limits the size of a population

c. disease, availability of water, climate, predation, competition for food, etc.

2. a. curve (2), exponential growth

b. curve (4), carrying capacity

c. curve (1), boom-and-bust curve

3. Growth rate = Change in no. of individuals/Time period = (40 + 20 − 18 − 6)/3 years = 36/3 years = 12/year

4. a. Density-dependent; effect depends on large size and density of zebra and lion populations

b. Density-independent; effect is not dependent on existence of large numbers of palms.

c. Density-dependent; effect depends on large numbers of roundworms and on density of fish for spreading of parasite.

d. Density-dependent: effect depends on high density and severe competition among squirrels.

e. Density-independent; effect is not dependent on number or density of bees.

5. Population was low and grew slowly when people were hunters and gatherers; starvation and disease kept birth rates low and death rates high. After food storage and agriculture were introduced, death rate from starvation decreased and birth rate increased greatly, so overall growth rate increased greatly. Since the Industrial Revolution, food production increased, and medical care and sanitation increased; death rates dropped and life expectancy increased, so the overall growth rate increased greatly.

Chapter 48

TEST A

1. a	**10.** b	**19.** c
2. c	**11.** d	**20.** d
3. d	**12.** c	**21.** c
4. a	**13.** a	**22.** b
5. c	**14.** c	**23.** a
6. c	**15.** a	**24.** d
7. a	**16.** d	**25.** c
8. c	**17.** c	
9. c	**18.** a	

TEST B

1. a. maintenance of resources needed for survival while ensuring that they will still be available in future

b. in terms of carrying capacity, critical factors such as malnutrition, and negative environmental consequences (e.g., damaging of environment by factors such as pollution and large-scale habitat destruction) resulting from population size

2. a. buildup of pollutants in organisms at higher trophic levels in a food chain

b. DDT pesticide entered groundwater, rivers, and lakes, was taken in by organisms in water, and built up in tissues of fishes through biological magnification. Eagles that ate the fish were not directly harmed, but DDT concentration in their tissues built up greatly. They produced thin-shelled eggs as a result, and many of the eggs broke before hatching, reducing numbers of offspring.

3. Sulfur dioxide can form sulfuric acid in atmosphere and thus lead to production of acid rain, which is destructive to ecosystems and to some structural materials. Carbon dioxide contributes to greenhouse effect and global warming. Hot water causes thermal pollution, raising river temperature to levels unsuitable for some kinds of organisms.

4. a. living space for humans and other terrestrial organisms; soil as a growth medium for plants; useful materials, such as stone, sand, and clay; minerals, such as diamonds, rock salt, and various metals; fossil fuels

b. erosion, or wearing away of land and topsoil by water and wind, caused by overgrazing of animals, allowing land to remain barren, and changing shape of land through building; desertification, or reduction of ability of soil to retain water and nutrients, caused by overgrazing and erosion; deforestation, or removal of large numbers of trees from forest, caused by clearing of land for lumber or building sites; improper or inadequate waste disposal, or removal of materials no longer used by humans, caused when dangerous materials are released, when nuclear wastes are not properly disposed of, etc.

5. a. release of pollutants such as sulfur dioxide and of particulates that can create haze that could reduce the amount of light reaching Earth and cause cooling

b. Such substances are not broken down by natural processes and remain in the environment for very long periods.

c. CFCs react in upper atmosphere and destroy ozone layer that protects Earth from ultraviolet radiation.

6. a. nonrenewable, will be used up, release carbon dioxide, which contributes to greenhouse effect and global warming

b. potential for dangerous nuclear accidents, release of radioactive waste, waste storage problems, long-term dangerous nature of substances used and produced, thermal pollution

c. nonpolluting windmills used to harness energy in moving air to generate electricity, nonpolluting, decentralized solar energy collectors to convert sun's energy to electricity

7. a. extinctions leading to wide-ranging effects on ecosystems because of interdependencies, loss of species of plants valuable for medicine

b. loss of diversification, rendering individuals in community more vulnerable to parasites

c. malnutrition, worsening pollution, disease, destructive unrest, etc.

Unit 9A

1. a	18. c	35. b
2. b	19. c	36. c
3. d	20. b	37. a
4. a	21. b	38. a
5. d	22. b	39. c
6. b	23. d	40. d
7. a	24. d	41. d
8. d	25. c	42. b
9. d	26. d	43. a
10. c	27. d	44. a
11. a	28. c	45. c
12. d	29. d	46. c
13. b	30. c	47. b
14. c	31. d	48. a
15. d	32. b	49. c
16. b	33. a	50. d
17. a	34. b	

Final Exam

1. d	35. b	69. b
2. a	36. a	70. a
3. d	37. c	71. a
4. c	38. a	72. b
5. a	39. d	73. d
6. a	40. c	74. c
7. b	41. d	75. a
8. a	42. a	76. d
9. c	43. d	77. b
10. b	44. c	78. c
11. d	45. b	79. a
12. c	46. a	80. d
13. b	47. c	81. b
14. a	48. d	82. d
15. b	49. c	83. b
16. c	50. b	84. c
17. c	51. a	85. b
18. a	52. d	86. a
19. d	53. a	87. a
20. c	54. b	88. c
21. d	55. b	89. d
22. d	56. b	90. d
23. b	57. d	91. c
24. a	58. c	92. a
25. c	59. b	93. d
26. b	60. c	94. b
27. a	61. d	95. d
28. d	62. c	96. c
29. b	63. c	97. d
30. a	64. b	98. b
31. c	65. a	99. c
32. d	66. c	100. d
33. d	67. c	
34. c	68. a	